Selected Titles in This Series

Fourier
Analysis

Fourier Analysis

Javier Duoandikoetxea

Translated and revised by
David Cruz-Uribe, SFO

Graduate Studies
in Mathematics

Volume 29

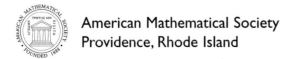

American Mathematical Society
Providence, Rhode Island

ANÁLISIS DE FOURIER

by Javier Duoandikoetxea Zuazo

Published in Spanish by Addison-Wesley and Universidad Autónoma de Madrid in 1995

Translated from the Spanish by David Cruz-Uribe, SFO

2000 *Mathematics Subject Classification.* Primary 42B15, 42B20, 42B25.

ABSTRACT. The purpose of this book is to develop Fourier analysis using the real variable methods introduced by A. P. Calderón and A. Zygmund. It begins by reviewing the theory of Fourier series and integrals, and introduces the Hardy-Littlewood maximal function. It then treats the Hilbert transform and its higher dimensional analogues, singular integrals. In subsequent chapters it discusses some more recent topics: H^1 and BMO, weighted norm inequalities, Littlewood-Paley theory, and the $T1$ theorem. At the end of each chapter are extensive references and notes on additional results.

Library of Congress Cataloging-in-Publication Data

Duoandikoetxea, Zuazo, Javier.
  [Análisis de Fourier. English]
  Fourier analysis / Javier Duoandikoetxea ; translated and revised by David Cruz-Uribe.
    p. cm. — (Graduate studies in mathematics ; v. 29)
  Includes bibliographical references and index.
  ISBN 0-8218-2172-5
  1. Fourier analysis. I. Title. II. Series.
QA403.5 .D8313   2000
515′.2433—dc21   00-064301

Dedicated to the memory of
José Luis Rubio de Francia, my teacher and friend,
who would have written a much better book than I have

Contents

Preface

Fourier Analysis is a large branch of mathematics whose point of departure is the study of Fourier series and integrals. However, it encompasses a variety of perspectives and techniques, and so many different introductions with that title are possible. The goal of this book is to study the real variable methods introduced into Fourier analysis by A. P. Calderón and A. Zygmund in the 1950's.

We begin in Chapter 1 with a review of Fourier series and integrals, and then in Chapters 2 and 3 we introduce two operators which are basic to the field: the Hardy-Littlewood maximal function and the Hilbert transform. Even though they appeared before the techniques of Calderón and Zygmund, we treat these operators from their point of view. The goal of these techniques is to enable the study of analogs of the Hilbert transform in higher dimensions; these are of great interest in applications. Such operators are known as singular integrals and are discussed in Chapters 4 and 5 along with their modern generalizations. We next consider two of the many contributions to the field which appeared in the 1970's. In Chapter 6 we study the relationship between H^1, BMO and singular integrals, and in Chapter 7 we present the elementary theory of weighted norm inequalities. In Chapter 8 we discuss Littlewood-Paley theory; its origins date back to the 1930's, but it has had extensive later development which includes a number of applications. Those presented in this chapter are useful in the study of Fourier multipliers, which also uses the theory of weighted inequalities. We end the book with an important result of the 80's, the so-called $T1$ theorem, which has been of crucial importance to the field.

At the end of each chapter there is a section in which we try to give some idea of further results which are not discussed in the text, and give references for the interested reader. A number of books and all the articles cited appear only in these notes; the bibliography at the end of the text is reserved for books which treat in depth the ideas we have presented.

The material in this book comes from a graduate course taught at the Universidad Autónoma de Madrid during the academic year 1988-89. Part of it is based on notes I took as a student in a course taught by José Luis Rubio de Francia at the same university in the fall of 1985. It seemed to have been his intention to write up his course, but he was prevented from doing so by his untimely death. Therefore, I have taken the liberty of using his ideas, which I learned both in his class and in many pleasant conversations in the hallway and at the blackboard, to write this book. Although it is dedicated to his memory, I almost regard it as a joint work. Also, I would like to thank my friends at the Universidad Autónoma de Madrid who encouraged me to teach this course and to write this book.

The book was first published in Spanish in the *Colección de Estudios* of the Universidad Autónoma de Madrid (1991), and then was republished with only some minor typographical corrections in a joint edition of Addison-Wesley/Universidad Autónoma de Madrid (1995). From the very beginning some colleagues suggested that there would be interest in an English translation which I never did. But when Professor David Cruz-Uribe offered to translate the book I immediately accepted. I realized at once that the text could not remain the same because some of the many developments of the last decade had to be included in the informative sections closing each chapter together with a few topics omitted from the first edition. As a consequence, although only minor changes have been introduced to the core of the book, the sections named "Notes and further results" have been considerably expanded to incorporate new topics, results and references.

The task of updating the book would have not been accomplished as it has been without the invaluable contribution of Professor Cruz-Uribe. Apart from reading the text, suggesting changes and clarifying obscure points, he did a great work on expanding the above mentioned notes, finding references and proposing new results to be included. The improvements of this book with respect to the original have certainly been the fruit of our joint work, and I am very grateful to him for sharing with me his knowledge of the subject much beyond the duties of a mere translator.

Javier Duoandikoetxea

Bilbao, June 2000

Acknowledgment: The translator would like to thank the Ford Foundation and the Dean of Faculty at Trinity College for their generous support during the academic year 1998–99. It was during this year-long sabbatical that this project was conceived and the first draft of the translation produced.

Preliminaries

Here we review some notation and basic results, but we assume that they are mostly well known to the reader. For more information, see, for example, Rudin [14].

In general we will work in $\mathbb{R}^n$. The Euclidean norm will be denoted by $|\cdot|$. If $x \in \mathbb{R}^n$ and $r > 0$,

$$B(x,r) = \{y \in \mathbb{R}^n : |x - y| < r\}$$

is the ball with center x and radius r. Lebesgue measure in $\mathbb{R}^n$ is denoted by dx and on the unit sphere S^{n-1} in $\mathbb{R}^n$ by $d\sigma$. If E is a subset of $\mathbb{R}^n$, $|E|$ denotes its Lebesgue measure and χ_E its characteristic function: $\chi_E(x) = 1$ if $x \in E$ and 0 if $x \notin E$. The expressions *almost everywhere* or *for almost every* x refer to properties which hold except on a set of measure 0; they are abbreviated by "a.e." and "a.e. x."

If $a = (a_1, \ldots, a_n) \in \mathbb{N}^n$ is a multi-index and $f : \mathbb{R}^n \to \mathbb{C}$, then

$$D^a f = \frac{\partial^{|a|} f}{\partial x_1^{a_1} \cdots \partial x_n^{a_n}},$$

where $|a| = a_1 + \cdots + a_n$ and $x^a = x_1^{a_1} \cdots x_n^{a_n}$.

Let (X, μ) be a measure space. $L^p(X, \mu)$, $1 \le p < \infty$, denotes the Banach space of functions from X to $\mathbb{C}$ whose p-th powers are integrable; the norm of $f \in L^p(X, \mu)$ is

$$\|f\|_p = \left(\int_X |f|^p \, d\mu \right)^{1/p}.$$

$L^\infty(X, \mu)$ denotes the Banach space of essentially bounded functions from X to $\mathbb{C}$; more precisely, functions f such that for some $C > 0$,

$$\mu(\{x \in X : |f(x)| > C\}) = 0.$$

The norm of f, $\|f\|_\infty$, is the infimum of the constants with this property. In general X will be $\mathbb{R}^n$ (or a subset of $\mathbb{R}^n$) and $d\mu = dx$; in this case we often do not give the measure or the space but instead simply write L^p. For general measure spaces we will frequently write $L^p(X)$ instead of $L^p(X, \mu)$; if μ is absolutely continuous and $d\mu = w\,dx$ we will write $L^p(w)$. The conjugate exponent of p is always denoted by p':

$$\frac{1}{p} + \frac{1}{p'} = 1.$$

The triangle inequality on L^p has an integral version which we refer to as Minkowski's integral inequality and which we will use repeatedly. Given measure spaces (X, μ) and (Y, ν) with σ-finite measures, the inequality is

$$\left(\int_X \left| \int_Y f(x, y)\, d\nu(y) \right|^p d\mu(x) \right)^{1/p} \le \int_Y \left(\int_X |f(x, y)|^p\, d\mu(x) \right)^{1/p} d\nu(y).$$

The convolution of two functions f and g defined on $\mathbb{R}^n$ is given by

$$f * g(x) = \int_{\mathbb{R}^n} f(y)g(x - y)\, dy = \int_{\mathbb{R}^n} f(x - y)g(y)\, dy$$

whenever this expression makes sense.

The spaces of test functions are $C_c^\infty(\mathbb{R}^n)$, the space of infinitely differentiable functions of compact support, and $\mathcal{S}(\mathbb{R}^n)$, the so-called Schwartz functions. A Schwartz function is an infinitely differentiable function which decreases rapidly at infinity (more precisely, the function and all its derivatives decrease more rapidly than any polynomial increases). Given the appropriate topologies, their duals are the spaces of distributions and tempered distributions. It makes sense to define the convolution of a distribution and a test function as follows: if $T \in C_c^\infty(\mathbb{R}^n)'$ and $f \in C_c^\infty(\mathbb{R}^n)$, then

$$T * f(x) = \langle T, \tau_x \tilde{f} \rangle,$$

where $\tilde{f}(y) = f(-y)$ and $\tau_x f(y) = f(x + y)$. Note that this definition coincides with the previous one if T is a locally integrable function. Similarly, we can take $T \in \mathcal{S}(\mathbb{R}^n)'$ and $f \in \mathcal{S}(\mathbb{R}^n)$. We denote the duality by either $\langle T, f \rangle$ or $T(f)$ without distinction.

References in square brackets are to items in the bibliography at the end of the book.

Finally, we remark that C will denote a positive constant which may be different even in a single chain of inequalities.

Chapter 1

Fourier Series and Integrals

1. Fourier coefficients and series

The problem of representing a function f, defined on (an interval of) $\mathbb{R}$, by a trigonometric series of the form

$$(1.1) \qquad f(x) = \sum_{k=0}^{\infty} a_k \cos(kx) + b_k \sin(kx)$$

arises naturally when using the method of separation of variables to solve partial differential equations. This is how J. Fourier arrived at the problem, and he devoted the better part of his *Théorie Analytique de la Chaleur* (1822, results first presented to the Institute de France in 1807) to it. Even earlier, in the middle of the 18th century, Daniel Bernoulli had stated it while trying to solve the problem of a vibrating string, and the formula for the coefficients appeared in an article by L. Euler in 1777.

The right-hand side of (1.1) is a periodic function with period 2π, so f must also have this property. Therefore it will suffice to consider f on an interval of length 2π. Using Euler's identity, $e^{ikx} = \cos(kx) + i\sin(kx)$, we can replace the functions $\sin(kx)$ and $\cos(kx)$ in (1.1) by $\{e^{ikx} : k \in \mathbb{Z}\}$; we will do so from now on. Moreover, we will consider functions with period 1 instead of 2π, so we will modify the system of functions to $\{e^{2\pi ikx} : k \in \mathbb{Z}\}$. Our problem is thus transformed into studying the representation of f by

$$(1.2) \qquad f(x) = \sum_{k=-\infty}^{\infty} c_k e^{2\pi ikx}.$$

If we assume, for example, that the series converges uniformly, then by multiplying by $e^{-2\pi i m x}$ and integrating term-by-term on $(0,1)$ we get

$$c_m = \int_0^1 f(x) e^{-2\pi i m x}\, dx$$

because of the orthogonality relationship

(1.3)
$$\int_0^1 e^{2\pi i k x} e^{-2\pi i m x}\, dx = \begin{cases} 0 & \text{if } k \neq m \\ 1 & \text{if } k = m. \end{cases}$$

Denote the additive group of the reals modulo 1 (that is $\mathbb{R}/\mathbb{Z}$) by $\mathbb{T}$, the one-dimensional torus. This can also be identified with the unit circle, S^1. Saying that a function is defined on $\mathbb{T}$ is equivalent to saying that it is defined on $\mathbb{R}$ and has period 1. To each function $f \in L^1(\mathbb{T})$ we associate the sequence $\{\hat{f}(k)\}$ of Fourier coefficients of f, defined by

(1.4)
$$\hat{f}(k) = \int_0^1 f(x) e^{-2\pi i k x}\, dx.$$

The trigonometric series with these coefficients,

(1.5)
$$\sum_{k=-\infty}^{\infty} \hat{f}(k) e^{2\pi i k x},$$

is called the Fourier series of f.

Our problem now consists in determining when and in what sense the series (1.5) represents the function f.

2. Criteria for pointwise convergence

Denote the N-th symmetric partial sum of the series (1.5) by $S_N f(x)$; that is,

$$S_N f(x) = \sum_{k=-N}^{N} \hat{f}(k) e^{2\pi i k x}.$$

Note that this is also the N-th partial sum of the series when it is written in the form of (1.1).

Our first approach to the problem of representing f by its Fourier series is to determine whether $\lim S_N f(x)$ exists for each x, and if so, whether it is equal to $f(x)$. The first positive result is due to P. G. L. Dirichlet (1829), who proved the following convergence criterion: if f is bounded, piecewise continuous, and has a finite number of maxima and minima, then $\lim S_N f(x)$ exists and is equal to $\frac{1}{2}[f(x+) + f(x-)]$. Jordan's criterion, which we prove below, includes this result as a special case.

In order to study $S_N f(x)$ we need a more manageable expression. Dirichlet wrote the partial sums as follows:

$$S_N f(x) = \sum_{k=-N}^{N} \int_0^1 f(t)e^{-2\pi i k t}\,dt \cdot e^{2\pi i k x}$$

$$= \int_0^1 f(t)D_N(x-t)\,dt$$

$$= \int_0^1 f(x-t)D_N(t)\,dt,$$

where D_N is the Dirichlet kernel,

$$D_N(t) = \sum_{k=-N}^{N} e^{2\pi i k t}.$$

If we sum this geometric series we get

(1.6) $$D_N(t) = \frac{\sin(\pi(2N+1)t)}{\sin(\pi t)}.$$

This satisfies

$$\int_0^1 D_N(t)\,dt = 1 \quad \text{and} \quad |D_N(t)| \le \frac{1}{\sin(\pi\delta)}, \quad \delta \le |t| \le 1/2.$$

We will prove two criteria for pointwise convergence.

Theorem 1.1 (Dini's Criterion). *If for some x there exists $\delta > 0$ such that*

$$\int_{|t|<\delta} \left| \frac{f(x+t) - f(x)}{t} \right| dt < \infty,$$

then

$$\lim_{N\to\infty} S_N f(x) = f(x).$$

Theorem 1.2 (Jordan's Criterion). *If f is a function of bounded variation in a neighborhood of x, then*

$$\lim_{N\to\infty} S_N f(x) = \frac{1}{2}[f(x+) + f(x-)].$$

At first it may seem surprising that these results are local, since if we modify the function slightly, the Fourier coefficients of f change. Nevertheless, the convergence of a Fourier series is effectively a local property, and if the modifications are made outside of a neighborhood of x, then the behavior of the series at x does not change. This is made precise by the following result.

Theorem 1.3 (Riemann Localization Principle). *If f is zero in a neighborhood of x, then*

$$\lim_{N \to \infty} S_N f(x) = 0.$$

An equivalent formulation of this result is to say that if two functions agree in a neighborhood of x, then their Fourier series behave in the same way at x.

From the definition of Fourier coefficients (1.4) it follows immediately that

$$|\hat{f}(k)| \le \|f\|_1,$$

but a sharper estimate is true which we will use to prove the preceding results.

Lemma 1.4 (Riemann-Lebesgue). *If $f \in L^1(\mathbb{T})$ then*

$$\lim_{|k| \to \infty} \hat{f}(k) = 0.$$

Proof. Since $e^{2\pi i x}$ has period 1,

$$\hat{f}(k) = \int_0^1 f(x) e^{-2\pi i k x}\, dx$$

$$= -\int_0^1 f(x) e^{-2\pi i k(x+1/2k)}\, dx$$

$$= -\int_0^1 f(x - 1/2k) e^{-2\pi i k x}\, dx.$$

Hence,

$$\hat{f}(k) = \frac{1}{2} \int_0^1 [f(x) - f(x - 1/2k)] e^{-2\pi i k x}\, dx.$$

If f is continuous, it follows immediately that

$$\lim_{|k| \to \infty} \hat{f}(k) = 0.$$

For arbitrary $f \in L^1(\mathbb{T})$, given $\epsilon > 0$, choose g continuous such that $\|f - g\|_1 < \epsilon/2$ and choose k sufficiently large that $|\hat{g}(k)| < \epsilon/2$. Then

$$|\hat{f}(k)| \le |(f - g)\widehat{\ }(k)| + |\hat{g}(k)| \le \|f - g\|_1 + |\hat{g}(k)| < \epsilon.$$

$\square$

Proof of Theorem 1.3. Suppose that $f(t) = 0$ on $(x - \delta, x + \delta)$. Then

$$S_N f(x) = \int_{\delta \le |t| < 1/2} f(x - t) \frac{\sin(\pi(2N + 1)t)}{\sin(\pi t)} \, dt$$
$$= (ge^{\pi i \cdot})\widehat{}(N) + (ge^{-\pi i \cdot})\widehat{}(-N),$$

where

$$g(t) = \frac{f(x - t)}{2i \sin(\pi t)} \chi_{\{\delta \le |t| < 1/2\}}(t)$$

is integrable. By the Riemann-Lebesgue lemma we conclude that

$$\lim_{N \to \infty} S_N f(x) = 0.$$

$\square$

Proof of Theorem 1.1. Since the integral of D_N equals 1,

$$S_N f(x) - f(x) = \int_{-1/2}^{1/2} [f(x - t) - f(x)] \frac{\sin(\pi(2N + 1)t)}{\sin(\pi t)} \, dt$$
$$= \int_{|t| < \delta} + \int_{\delta \le |t| < 1/2} .$$

By the Riemann-Lebesgue lemma both of these integrals tend to 0. The second if we argue as in the previous proof, the first since by hypothesis the function

$$\frac{f(x - t) - f(x)}{\sin(\pi t)} \chi_{\{|t| < \delta\}}(t)$$

is integrable. (Recall that if $|t| < \delta$, $\sin(\pi t)$ and πt are equivalent.) $\square$

Proof of Theorem 1.2. Since every function of bounded variation is the difference of two monotonic functions, we may assume that f is monotonic in a neighborhood of x. Since

$$S_N f(x) = \int_{-1/2}^{1/2} f(x - t) D_N(t) \, dt = \int_0^{1/2} [f(x - t) + f(x + t)] D_N(t) \, dt,$$

it will be enough to show that for g monotonic

$$\lim_{N \to \infty} \int_0^{1/2} g(t) D_N(t) \, dt = \frac{1}{2} g(0+).$$

Further, we may assume that $g(0+) = 0$ and that g is increasing to the right of 0. Given $\epsilon > 0$, choose $\delta > 0$ such that $g(t) < \epsilon$ if $0 < t < \delta$. Then

$$\int_0^{1/2} g(t) D_N(t) \, dt = \int_0^{\delta} + \int_{\delta}^{1/2} .$$

Again by the Riemann-Lebesgue lemma, the second integral tends to 0. We
apply the second mean value theorem for integrals[1] to the first integral.
Then for some ν, $0 < \nu < \delta$,

$$\int_0^\delta g(t) D_N(t)\, dt = g(\delta-) \int_\nu^\delta D_N(t)\, dt.$$

Furthermore,

$$\left| \int_\nu^\delta D_N(t)\, dt \right| \leq \left| \int_\nu^\delta \sin(\pi(2N+1)t) \left(\frac{1}{\sin(\pi t)} - \frac{1}{\pi t} \right) dt \right|$$

$$+ \left| \int_\nu^\delta \frac{\sin(\pi(2N+1)t)}{\pi t}\, dt \right|$$

$$\leq \int_\nu^\delta \left| \frac{1}{\sin(\pi t)} - \frac{1}{\pi t} \right| dt + 2 \sup_{M>0} \left| \int_0^M \frac{\sin(\pi t)}{t}\, dt \right|$$

$$\leq C.$$

Hence,

$$\left| \int_0^\delta g(t) D_N(t)\, dt \right| \leq C\epsilon.$$

$\square$

3. Fourier series of continuous functions

If f satisfies a Lipschitz-type condition in a neighborhood of x, that is,
$|f(x+t) - f(x)| \leq C|t|^a$ for some $a > 0$, $|t| < \delta$, then Dini's criterion applies
to it. However, continuous functions need not satisfy this condition or any
other convergence criterion we have seen. This must be the case because of
the following result due to P. du Bois-Reymond (1873).

Theorem 1.5. *There exists a continuous function whose Fourier series diverges at a point.*

Du Bois-Reymond constructed a function with this property, but we will
show that one exists by applying the uniform boundedness principle, also
known as the Banach-Steinhaus theorem.

Lemma 1.6 (Uniform Boundedness Principle). *Let X be a Banach space,
Y a normed vector space, and let $\{T_a\}_{a \in A}$ be a family of bounded linear*

---

[1]If ϕ is continuous and h monotonic on $[a, b]$, then there exists c, $a < c < b$, such that

$$\int_a^b h\phi = h(b-) \int_c^b \phi + h(a+) \int_a^c \phi.$$

operators from X to Y. Then either

$$\sup_a \|T_a\| < \infty$$

or there exists $x \in X$ such that

$$\sup_a \|T_a x\|_Y = \infty.$$

(Recall that the operator norm of T_a is $\|T_a\| = \sup\{\|T_a x\|_Y : \|x\|_X \leq 1\}$.) A proof of this result can be found, for example, in Rudin [**14**, Chapter 5].

Now let $X = C(\mathbb{T})$ with the norm $\|\cdot\|_\infty$ and let $Y = \mathbb{C}$. Define $T_N : X \to Y$ by

$$T_N f = S_N f(0) = \int_{-1/2}^{1/2} f(t) D_N(t)\, dt.$$

Define the Lebesgue numbers L_N by

$$L_N = \int_{-1/2}^{1/2} |D_N(t)|\, dt;$$

it is immediate that $|T_N f| \leq L_N \|f\|_\infty$. $D_N(t)$ has a finite number of zeros so $\operatorname{sgn} D_N(t)$ has a finite number of jump discontinuities. Therefore, by modifying it on a small neighborhood of each discontinuity, we can form a continuous function f such that $\|f\|_\infty = 1$ and $|T_N f| \geq L_N - \epsilon$. Hence, $\|T_N\| = L_N$. Thus if we can prove that $L_N \to \infty$ as $N \to \infty$, then by the uniform boundedness principle there exists a continuous function f such that

$$\limsup_{N \to \infty} |S_N f(0)| = \infty;$$

that is, the Fourier series of f diverges at 0.

Lemma 1.7. $L_N = \dfrac{4}{\pi^2} \log N + O(1)$.

Proof.

$$L_N = 2 \int_0^{1/2} \left| \frac{\sin(\pi(2N+1)t)}{\pi t} \right| dt + O(1)$$

$$= 2 \int_0^{N+1/2} \left| \frac{\sin(\pi t)}{\pi t} \right| dt + O(1)$$

$$= 2 \sum_{k=0}^{N-1} \int_k^{k+1} \left| \frac{\sin(\pi t)}{\pi t} \right| dt + O(1)$$

$$= \frac{2}{\pi} \sum_{k=0}^{N-1} \int_0^1 \frac{|\sin(\pi t)|}{t + k}\, dt + O(1)$$

$$= \frac{2}{\pi} \int_0^1 |\sin(\pi t)| \sum_{k=1}^{N-1} \frac{1}{t+k} \, dt + O(1)$$

$$= \frac{4}{\pi^2} \log N + O(1).$$

$\square$

4. Convergence in norm

The development of measure theory and L^p spaces led to a new approach to the problem of convergence. We can now ask:

(1) Does $\lim_{N \to \infty} \|S_N f - f\|_p = 0$ for $f \in L^p(\mathbb{T})$?

(2) Does $\lim_{N \to \infty} S_N f(x) = f(x)$ almost everywhere if $f \in L^p(\mathbb{T})$?

We can restate the first question by means the following lemma.

Lemma 1.8. $S_N f$ converges to f in L^p norm, $1 \leq p < \infty$, if and only if there exists C_p independent of N such that

(1.7) $$\|S_N f\|_p \leq C_p \|f\|_p.$$

Proof. The necessity of (1.7) follows from the uniform boundedness principle.

To see that it is sufficient, first note that if g is a trigonometric polynomial, then $S_N g = g$ for $N \geq \deg g$. Therefore, since the trigonometric polynomials are dense in L^p (see Corollary 1.11), if $f \in L^p$ we can find a trigonometric polynomial g such that $\|f - g\|_p < \epsilon$, and so for N sufficiently large

$$\|S_N f - f\|_p \leq \|S_N(f-g)\|_p + \|S_N g - g\|_p + \|f - g\|_p \leq (C_p + 1)\epsilon.$$

$\square$

If $1 < p < \infty$, then inequality (1.7) holds, as we will show in Chapter 3. When $p = 1$, the L^1 operator norm of S_N is again L_N, and so by Lemma 1.7 the answer to the first question is no.

When $p = 2$, the functions $\{e^{2\pi i k x}\}$ form an orthonormal system (by (1.3)) which is complete (i.e. an orthonormal basis) by the density of the trigonometric polynomials in L^2. Therefore, we can apply the theory of Hilbert spaces to get the following.

Theorem 1.9. *The mapping $f \mapsto \{\hat{f}(k)\}$ is an isometry from L^2 to ℓ^2, that is,*

$$\|f\|_2^2 = \sum_{k=-\infty}^{\infty} |\hat{f}(k)|^2.$$

Convergence in norm in L^2 follows from this immediately.

The second question is much more difficult. A. Kolmogorov (1926) gave an example of an integrable function whose Fourier series diverges at every point, so the answer is no if $p = 1$. If $f \in L^p$, $1 < p < \infty$, then the Fourier series of f converges almost everywhere. This was shown by L. Carleson (1965, $p = 2$) and R. Hunt (1967, $p > 1$). Until the result by Carleson, the answer was unknown even for f continuous.

5. Summability methods

In order to recover a function f from its Fourier coefficients it would be convenient to find some other method than taking the limit of the partial sums of its Fourier series since, as we have seen, this approach does not always work well.

One such method, Cesàro summability, consists in taking the limit of the arithmetic means of the partial sums. As is well known, if $\lim a_k$ exists then

$$\lim_{k \to \infty} \frac{a_1 + \cdots + a_k}{k}$$

also exists and has the same value.

Define

$$\sigma_N f(x) = \frac{1}{N+1} \sum_{k=0}^{N} S_k f(x)$$

$$= \int_0^1 f(t) \frac{1}{N+1} \sum_{k=0}^{N} D_k(x-t) \, dt$$

$$= \int_0^1 f(t) F_N(x-t) \, dt,$$

where F_N is the Fejér kernel,

$$F_N(t) = \frac{1}{N+1} \sum_{k=0}^{N} D_k(t) = \frac{1}{N+1} \left(\frac{\sin(\pi(N+1)t)}{\sin(\pi t)} \right)^2.$$

F_N has the following properties:

$$F_N(t) \geq 0,$$

(1.8)
$$\|F_N\|_1 = \int_0^1 F_N(t)\,dt = 1,$$

$$\lim_{N \to \infty} \int_{\delta < |t| < 1/2} F_N(t)\,dt = 0 \quad \text{if } \delta > 0.$$

Because F_N is positive, its L^1 norm coincides with its integral and is 1. This is not the case for the Dirichlet kernel: its integral equals 1 because of cancellation between its positive and negative parts while its L^1 norm tends to infinity with N.

Theorem 1.10. *If $f \in L^p$, $1 \le p < \infty$, or if f is continuous and $p = \infty$, then*

$$\lim_{N \to \infty} \|\sigma_N f - f\|_p = 0.$$

Proof. Since $\int F_N = 1$, by Minkowski's inequality we have that

$$\|\sigma_N f - f\|_p = \int_{-1/2}^{1/2} \|f(\cdot - t) - f(\cdot)\|_p F_N(t)\,dt$$

$$\le \int_{|t| < \delta} \|f(\cdot - t) - f(\cdot)\|_p F_N(t)\,dt + 2\|f\|_p \int_{\delta < |t| < 1/2} F_N(t)\,dt.$$

Since for $1 \le p < \infty$,

$$\lim_{t \to 0} \|f(\cdot - t) - f(\cdot)\|_p = 0,$$

and the same limit holds if $p = \infty$ and f is continuous, the first term can be made as small as desired by choosing a suitable δ. And for fixed δ, by (1.8) the second term tends to 0. $\qquad\square$

Corollary 1.11.

(1) *The trigonometric polynomials are dense in L^p, $1 \le p < \infty$.*

(2) *If f is integrable and $\hat{f}(k) = 0$ for all k, then f is identically zero.*

A second summability method is gotten by treating a Fourier series as the formal limit on the unit circle (in the complex plane) of

(1.9)
$$u(z) = \sum_{k=0}^{\infty} \hat{f}(k)z^k + \sum_{k=-\infty}^{-1} \hat{f}(k)\bar{z}^{|k|}, \quad z = re^{2\pi i\theta}.$$

Since $\{\hat{f}(k)\}$ is a bounded sequence, this function is well defined on $|z| < 1$. It can be rewritten as

$$u(re^{2\pi i\theta}) = \sum_{k=-\infty}^{\infty} \hat{f}(k)r^{|k|}e^{2\pi ik\theta} = \int_{-1/2}^{1/2} f(t)P_r(\theta - t)\,dt,$$

where

$$P_r(t) = \sum_{k=-\infty}^{\infty} r^{|k|} e^{2\pi i k t} = \frac{1 - r^2}{1 - 2r\cos(2\pi t) + r^2}$$

is the Poisson kernel. The Poisson kernel has properties analogous to those of the Fejér kernel:

(1.10)

$$P_r(t) \geq 0,$$

$$\int_0^1 P_r(t)\,dt = 1,$$

$$\lim_{r \to 1^-} \int_{\delta < |t| < 1/2} P_r(t)\,dt = 0 \quad \text{if } \delta > 0.$$

Therefore, we can prove a result analogous to Theorem 1.10.

Theorem 1.12. *If $f \in L^p$, $1 \leq p < \infty$, or if f is continuous and $p = \infty$, then*

$$\lim_{r \to 1^-} \|P_r * f - f\|_p = 0.$$

Since the function u is harmonic on $|z| < 1$, it is the solution to the Dirichlet problem:

$$\Delta u = 0 \quad \text{if } |z| < 1,$$
$$u = f \quad \text{if } |z| = 1,$$

where the boundary condition is interpreted in terms of Theorem 1.12.

In Chapter 2 we will study the almost everywhere convergence of $\sigma_N f(x)$ and $P_r * f(x)$.

6. The Fourier transform of L^1 functions

Given a function $f \in L^1(\mathbb{R}^n)$, define its Fourier transform by

(1.11)

$$\hat{f}(\xi) = \int_{\mathbb{R}^n} f(x) e^{-2\pi i x \cdot \xi}\,dx,$$

where $x \cdot \xi = x_1\xi_1 + x_2\xi_2 + \cdots + x_n\xi_n$. The following is a list of properties of the Fourier transform:

(1.12) $(\alpha f + \beta g)\hat{\ } = \alpha\hat{f} + \beta\hat{g}$ (linearity);

(1.13) $\|\hat{f}\|_\infty \leq \|f\|_1$ and $\hat{f}$ is continuous;

(1.14) $\displaystyle\lim_{|\xi| \to \infty} \hat{f}(\xi) = 0$ (Riemann-Lebesgue);

(1.15) $(f * g)\hat{\ } = \hat{f}\hat{g}$;

(1.16) $(\tau_h f)\widehat{\ }(\xi) = \hat{f}(\xi)e^{2\pi i h \cdot \xi}$, where $\tau_h f(x) = f(x + h)$;

              $(fe^{2\pi i h \cdot x})\widehat{\ }(\xi) = \hat{f}(\xi - h)$;

(1.17)   if $\rho \in O_n$ (an orthogonal transformation), then

              $(f(\rho \cdot))\widehat{\ }(\xi) = \hat{f}(\rho \xi)$;

(1.18)   if $g(x) = \lambda^{-n} f(\lambda^{-1} x)$, then $\hat{g}(\xi) = \hat{f}(\lambda \xi)$;

(1.19) $\left(\dfrac{\partial f}{\partial x_j}\right)\widehat{\ }(\xi) = 2\pi i \xi_j \hat{f}(\xi)$;

(1.20) $(-2\pi i x_j f)\widehat{\ }(\xi) = \dfrac{\partial \hat{f}}{\partial \xi_j}(\xi)$.

The continuity of $\hat{f}$ follows from the dominated convergence theorem; (1.14) can be proved like Lemma 1.4; the rest follow from a change of variables, Fubini's theorem and integration by parts. In (1.19) we assume that $\partial f/\partial x_j \in L^1$ and in (1.20) that $x_j f \in L^1$.

Unlike on the torus, $L^1(\mathbb{R}^n)$ does not contain $L^p(\mathbb{R}^n)$, $p > 1$, so (1.11) does not define the Fourier transform of functions in those spaces. For the same reason, the formula which should allow us to recover f from $\hat{f}$,

$$\int_{\mathbb{R}^n} \hat{f}(\xi)e^{2\pi i x \cdot \xi}\, d\xi,$$

may not make sense since (1.13) and (1.14) are all that we know about $\hat{f}$, and they do not imply that $\hat{f}$ is integrable. (In fact, $\hat{f}$ is generally not integrable.)

7. The Schwartz class and tempered distributions

A function f is in the Schwartz class, $\mathcal{S}(\mathbb{R}^n)$, if it is infinitely differentiable and if all of its derivatives decrease rapidly at infinity; that is, if for all $\alpha, \beta \in \mathbb{N}^n$,

$$\sup_x |x^\alpha D^\beta f(x)| = p_{\alpha,\beta}(f) < \infty.$$

Functions in C_c^∞ are in $\mathcal{S}$, but so are functions like $e^{-|x|^2}$ which do not have compact support. The collection $\{p_{\alpha,\beta}\}$ is a countable family of seminorms on $\mathcal{S}$, and we can use it to define a topology on $\mathcal{S}$: a sequence $\{\phi_k\}$ converges to 0 if and only if for all $\alpha, \beta \in \mathbb{N}^n$,

$$\lim_{k \to \infty} p_{\alpha,\beta}(\phi_k) = 0.$$

With this topology $\mathcal{S}$ is a Fréchet space (complete and metrizable) and is dense in $L^p(\mathbb{R}^n)$, $1 \leq p < \infty$. In particular, $\mathcal{S} \subset L^1$ and (1.11) defines the Fourier transform of a function in $\mathcal{S}$.

The space of bounded linear functionals on $\mathcal{S}$, $\mathcal{S}'$, is called the space of tempered distributions. A linear map T from $\mathcal{S}$ to $\mathbb{C}$ is in $\mathcal{S}'$ if

$$\lim_{k\to\infty} T(\phi_k) = 0 \quad \text{whenever} \quad \lim_{k\to\infty} \phi_k = 0 \quad \text{in } \mathcal{S}.$$

Theorem 1.13. *The Fourier transform is a continuous map from $\mathcal{S}$ to $\mathcal{S}$ such that*

$$(1.21) \qquad \int_{\mathbb{R}^n} f\hat{g} = \int_{\mathbb{R}^n} \hat{f}g$$

and

$$(1.22) \qquad f(x) = \int_{\mathbb{R}^n} \hat{f}(\xi)e^{2\pi i x\cdot\xi}\, d\xi.$$

Equality (1.22) is referred to as the inversion formula.

To prove Theorem 1.13 we need to compute the Fourier transform of a particular function.

Lemma 1.14. *If $f(x) = e^{-\pi|x|^2}$ then $\hat{f}(\xi) = e^{-\pi|\xi|^2}$.*

Proof. We could prove this result directly by integrating in $\mathbb{C}$, but we will give a different proof here. It is enough to prove this in one dimension, since in $\mathbb{R}^n$ $\hat{f}$ is the product of n identical integrals.

The function $f(x) = e^{-\pi x^2}$ is the solution of the differential equation

$$u' + 2\pi x u = 0,$$
$$u(0) = 1.$$

By (1.19) and (1.20) we see that $\hat{u}$ satisfies the same differential equation with the initial value

$$\hat{u}(0) = \int_{\mathbb{R}} u(x)\, dx = \int_{\mathbb{R}} e^{-\pi x^2}\, dx = 1.$$

Therefore, by uniqueness, $\hat{f} = f$. $\qquad\square$

Proof of Theorem 1.13. By (1.19) and (1.20) we have

$$\xi^\alpha D^\beta \hat{f}(\xi) = C(D^\alpha x^\beta f)\hat{\ }(\xi),$$

so

$$|\xi^\alpha D^\beta \hat{f}(\xi)| \leq C\|D^\alpha x^\beta f\|_1.$$

The L^1 norm can be bounded by a finite linear combination of seminorms of f, which implies that the Fourier transform is a continuous map from $\mathcal{S}$ to itself.

Equality (1.21) is an immediate consequence of Fubini's theorem since $f(x)g(y)$ is integrable on $\mathbb{R}^n \times \mathbb{R}^n$.

From (1.18) and (1.21) we get

$$\int f(x)\hat{g}(\lambda x)\, dx = \int \hat{f}(x)\lambda^{-n}g(\lambda^{-1}x)\, dx.$$

If we make the change of variables $\lambda x = y$ in the first integral, this becomes

$$\int f(\lambda^{-1}x)\hat{g}(x)\, dx = \int \hat{f}(x)g(\lambda^{-1}x)\, dx;$$

if we then take the limit as $\lambda \to \infty$, we get

$$f(0)\int \hat{g}(x)\, dx = g(0)\int \hat{f}(x)\, dx.$$

Let $g(x) = e^{-\pi|x|^2}$; then by Lemma 1.14,

$$f(0) = \int \hat{f}(\xi)\, d\xi,$$

which is (1.22) for $x = 0$. If we replace f by $\tau_x f$, then by (1.16),

$$f(x) = (\tau_x f)(0) = \int (\tau_x f)\hat{}(\xi)\, d\xi = \int \hat{f}(\xi)e^{2\pi i x \cdot \xi}\, d\xi.$$

$\square$

If we let $\tilde{f}(x) = f(-x)$, we get the following corollary.

Corollary 1.15. *For $f \in \mathcal{S}$, $(\hat{f})\hat{} = \tilde{f}$, and so the Fourier transform has period 4 (i.e. if we apply it four times, we get the identity operator).*

Definition 1.16. The Fourier transform of $T \in \mathcal{S}'$ is the tempered distribution $\hat{T}$ given by

$$\hat{T}(f) = T(\hat{f}), \qquad f \in \mathcal{S}.$$

By Theorem 1.13, $\hat{T}$ is a tempered distribution, and in particular, if T is an integrable function, then $\hat{T}$ coincides with the Fourier transform defined by equation (1.11). Likewise, if μ is a finite Borel measure (i.e. a bounded linear functional on $C_0(\mathbb{R}^n)$, the space of continuous functions which vanish at infinity), then $\hat{\mu}$ is the bounded continuous function given by

$$\hat{\mu}(\xi) = \int_{\mathbb{R}^n} e^{-2\pi i x \cdot \xi}\, d\mu(x).$$

For δ, the Dirac measure at the origin, this gives us $\hat{\delta} = 1$.

Theorem 1.17. *The Fourier transform is a bounded linear bijection from $\mathcal{S}'$ to $\mathcal{S}'$ whose inverse is also bounded.*

Proof. If $T_n \to T$ in $\mathcal{S}'$, then for any $f \in \mathcal{S}$,

$$\hat{T}_n(f) = T_n(\hat{f}) \to T(\hat{f}) = \hat{T}(f).$$

Furthermore, the Fourier transform has period 4, so its inverse is equivalent to applying it 3 times; therefore, its inverse is also continuous.   □

If we define $\tilde{T}$ by $\tilde{T}(f) = T(\tilde{f})$, then it follows from Corollary 1.15 that $(\hat{\tilde{T}})^{\widehat{}} = T$. And if $\hat{T} \in L^1$ then by the inversion formula we get that

$$T(x) = \int_{\mathbb{R}^n} \hat{T}(\xi) e^{2\pi i x \cdot \xi} \, d\xi;$$

in particular, T is a bounded, continuous function.

8. The Fourier transform on L^p, $1 < p \le 2$

If $f \in L^p$, $1 \le p \le \infty$, then f can be identified with a tempered distribution: for $\phi \in \mathcal{S}$ define

$$T_f(\phi) = \int_{\mathbb{R}^n} f\phi.$$

Clearly this integral is finite. To see that T_f is continuous, suppose that $\phi_k \to 0$ in $\mathcal{S}$ as $k \to \infty$. Then by Hölder's inequality,

$$|T_f(\phi_k)| \le \|f\|_p \|\phi_k\|_{p'}.$$

Then $\|\phi_k\|_{p'}$ is dominated by the L^∞ norm of functions of the form $x^a \phi_k$, and so by a finite linear combination of seminorms of ϕ_k; hence, the left-hand side tends to 0 as $k \to \infty$.

Moreover, when $1 \le p \le 2$ we have that $\hat{f}$ is a function.

Theorem 1.18. *The Fourier transform is an isometry on L^2; that is, $\hat{f} \in L^2$ and $\|\hat{f}\|_2 = \|f\|_2$. Furthermore,*

$$\hat{f}(\xi) = \lim_{R \to \infty} \int_{|x| < R} f(x) e^{-2\pi i x \cdot \xi} \, dx$$

and

$$f(x) = \lim_{R \to \infty} \int_{|\xi| < R} \hat{f}(\xi) e^{2\pi i x \cdot \xi} \, d\xi,$$

where the limits are in L^2.

The identity $\|\hat{f}\|_2 = \|f\|_2$ is referred to as the Plancherel theorem.

Proof. Given $f, h \in \mathcal{S}$, let $g = \bar{\hat{h}}$, so that $\hat{g} = \bar{h}$. Then by (1.21) we have that

$$(1.23) \qquad \int_{\mathbb{R}^n} f\bar{h} = \int_{\mathbb{R}^n} \hat{f}\bar{\hat{h}}.$$

If we let $h = f$ then we get $\|f\|_2 = \|\hat{f}\|_2$ for $f \in \mathcal{S}$. Since $\mathcal{S}$ is dense in L^2, the Fourier transform extends to all f in L^2 with equality of norms.

Finally, the continuity of the Fourier transform implies the given formulas for f and $\hat{f}$ as limits in L^2, since $f\chi_{B(0,R)}$ and $\hat{f}\chi_{B(0,R)}$ converge to f and $\hat{f}$ in L^2. $\qquad \square$

If $f \in L^p$, $1 < p < 2$, then it can be decomposed as $f = f_1 + f_2$, where $f_1 \in L^1$ and $f_2 \in L^2$. (For example, let $f_1 = f\chi_{\{x:|f(x)|>1\}}$ and $f_2 = f - f_1$.) Therefore, $\hat{f} = \hat{f_1} + \hat{f_2} \in L^\infty + L^2$. However, by applying an interpolation theorem we can get a sharper result.

Theorem 1.19 (Riesz-Thorin Interpolation). *Let* $1 \leq p_0, p_1, q_0, q_1 \leq \infty$, *and for* $0 < \theta < 1$ *define* p *and* q *by*

$$\frac{1}{p} = \frac{1-\theta}{p_0} + \frac{\theta}{p_1}, \quad \frac{1}{q} = \frac{1-\theta}{q_0} + \frac{\theta}{q_1}.$$

If T *is a linear operator from* $L^{p_0} + L^{p_1}$ *to* $L^{q_0} + L^{q_1}$ *such that*

$$\|Tf\|_{q_0} \leq M_0 \|f\|_{p_0} \quad \text{for } f \in L^{p_0}$$

and

$$\|Tf\|_{q_1} \leq M_1 \|f\|_{p_1} \quad \text{for } f \in L^{p_1},$$

then

$$\|Tf\|_q \leq M_0^{1-\theta} M_1^\theta \|f\|_p \quad \text{for } f \in L^p.$$

The proof of this result uses the so-called "three-lines" theorem for analytic functions; it can be found, for example, in Stein and Weiss [**18**, Chapter 5] or Katznelson [**10**, Chapter 4].

Corollary 1.20 (Hausdorff-Young Inequality). *If* $f \in L^p$, $1 \leq p \leq 2$, *then* $\hat{f} \in L^{p'}$ *and*

$$\|\hat{f}\|_{p'} \leq \|f\|_p.$$

Proof. Apply Theorem 1.19 using inequality (1.13), $\|\hat{f}\|_\infty \leq \|f\|_1$, and the Plancherel theorem, $\|\hat{f}\|_2 = \|f\|_2$. $\qquad \square$

We digress to give another corollary of Riesz-Thorin interpolation which is not directly related to the Fourier transform but which will be useful in later chapters.

Corollary 1.21 (Young's Inequality). *If $f \in L^p$ and $g \in L^q$, then $f * g \in L^r$, where $1/r + 1 = 1/p + 1/q$, and*

$$\|f * g\|_r \leq \|f\|_p \|g\|_q.$$

Proof. If we fix $f \in L^p$ we immediately get the inequalities

$$\|f * g\|_p \leq \|f\|_p \|g\|_1$$

and

$$\|f * g\|_\infty \leq \|f\|_p \|g\|_{p'}.$$

The desired result follows by Riesz-Thorin interpolation. □

9. The convergence and summability of Fourier integrals

The problem of recovering a function from its Fourier transform is similar to the same problem for Fourier series. We need to determine if and when

$$\lim_{R \to \infty} \int_{B_R} \hat{f}(\xi) e^{2\pi i x \cdot \xi} \, d\xi = f(x),$$

where $B_R = \{Rx : x \in B\}$, B is an open convex neighborhood of the origin, and the limit is understood either as in L^p or as pointwise almost everywhere. If we define the partial sum operator S_R by

$$(S_R f)\hat{} = \chi_{B_R} \hat{f},$$

then this problem is equivalent to determining if

$$\lim_{R \to \infty} S_R f = f.$$

Analogous to Lemma 1.8, a necessary and sufficient condition for convergence in norm is that

$$\|S_R f\|_p \leq C_p \|f\|_p,$$

where C_p is independent of R. When $n = 1$ this is the case; we will prove this in Chapter 3. We will also prove several partial results when $n > 1$, but in general there is no convergence in norm when $p \neq 2$. We will discuss this in Chapter 8.

In the case $n = 1$, if $B = (-1, 1)$ then

$$S_R f(x) = D_R * f(x),$$

where D_R is the Dirichlet kernel,

$$D_R(x) = \int_{-R}^{R} e^{2\pi i x \xi} \, d\xi = \frac{\sin(2\pi R x)}{\pi x}.$$

This is clearly not integrable, but it is in $L^q(\mathbb{R})$ for any $q > 1$, so $D_R * f$ is well defined if $f \in L^p$, $1 < p < \infty$.

Almost everywhere convergence depends on the bound

$$\|\sup_R |S_R f|\|_p \le C_p \|f\|_p.$$

This holds if $1 < p < \infty$ (the Carleson-Hunt theorem) but we cannot prove it here.

For the Fourier transform, the method of Cesàro summability consists in taking integral averages of the partial sum operators,

$$\sigma_R f(x) = \frac{1}{R} \int_0^R S_t f(x) \, dt,$$

and determining if $\lim \sigma_R f(x) = f(x)$. When $n = 1$ and $B = (-1, 1)$,

$$\sigma_R f(x) = F_R * f(x),$$

where F_R is the Fejér kernel,

$$(1.24) \qquad F_R(x) = \frac{1}{R} \int_0^R D_t(x) \, dt = \frac{\sin^2(\pi R x)}{R(\pi x)^2}.$$

Unlike the Dirichlet kernel, the Fejér kernel is integrable. Since it has properties analogous to (1.8), one can prove that in L^p, $1 \le p < \infty$,

$$\lim_{R \to \infty} \sigma_R f = f.$$

The proof is similar to that of Theorem 1.10. In Chapter 2 we will prove two general results from which we can deduce convergence in L^p and pointwise almost everywhere for this and the following summability methods.

The method of Abel-Poisson summability consists in introducing the factor $e^{-2\pi t |\xi|}$ into the inversion formula. Then for any $t > 0$ the integral converges, and we take the limit as t tends to 0. If we instead introduce the factor $e^{-\pi t^2 |\xi|^2}$, we get the method of Gauss-Weierstrass summability. More precisely, we define the functions

$$(1.25) \qquad u(x, t) = \int_{\mathbb{R}^n} e^{-2\pi t |\xi|} \hat{f}(\xi) e^{2\pi i x \cdot \xi} \, d\xi,$$

$$(1.26) \qquad w(x, t) = \int_{\mathbb{R}^n} e^{-\pi t^2 |\xi|^2} \hat{f}(\xi) e^{2\pi i x \cdot \xi} \, d\xi,$$

and then try to determine if

$$(1.27) \qquad \lim_{t \to 0^+} u(x, t) = f(x),$$

(1.28)
$$\lim_{t \to 0^+} w(x,t) = f(x)$$

in L^p or pointwise almost everywhere.

One can show that $u(x,t)$ is harmonic in the half-space $\mathbb{R}^{n+1}_+ = \mathbb{R}^n \times (0,\infty)$. When $n = 1$ we have an equivalent formula analogous to (1.9):

(1.29)
$$u(z) = \int_0^\infty \hat{f}(\xi) e^{2\pi i z \xi}\, d\xi + \int_{-\infty}^0 \hat{f}(\xi) e^{2\pi i \bar{z}\xi}\, d\xi, \quad z = x + it,$$

which immediately implies that u is harmonic. The limit (1.27) can be interpreted as the boundary condition of the Dirichlet problem,

$$\Delta u = 0 \quad \text{on } \mathbb{R}^{n+1}_+,$$
$$u(x,0) = f(x), \quad x \in \mathbb{R}^n.$$

It follows from (1.25) that

$$u(x,t) = P_t * f(x),$$

where $\hat{P}_t(\xi) = e^{-2\pi t|\xi|}$. One can prove by a simple calculation if $n = 1$, and a more difficult one when $n > 1$ (see Stein and Weiss [**18**, p. 6]), that

(1.30)
$$P_t(x) = \frac{\Gamma\left(\frac{n+1}{2}\right)}{\pi^{\frac{n+1}{2}}} \frac{t}{(t^2 + |x|^2)^{\frac{n+1}{2}}}.$$

This is called the Poisson kernel.

In the case of Gauss-Weierstrass summability, one can show that the function $\tilde{w}(x,t) = w(x,\sqrt{4\pi t})$ is the solution of the heat equation

$$\frac{\partial \tilde{w}}{\partial t} - \Delta \tilde{w} = 0 \quad \text{on } \mathbb{R}^{n+1}_+,$$
$$\tilde{w}(x,0) = f(x) \quad x \in \mathbb{R}^n,$$

and (1.28) can be interpreted as the initial condition for the problem. We also have the formula

$$w(x,t) = W_t * f(x),$$

where W_t is the Gauss-Weierstrass kernel,

(1.31)
$$W_t(x) = t^{-n} e^{-\pi|x|^2/t^2}.$$

This formula can be proved using Lemma 1.14 and (1.18).

10. Notes and further results

10.1. References.

The classic reference on trigonometric series is the book by Zygmund [**21**], which will also be a useful reference for results in the next few chapters. However, this work can be difficult to consult at times. Another comprehensive reference on trigonometric series is the book by Bary [**1**].

There are excellent discussions of Fourier series and integrals in Katznelson [10] and Dym and McKean [4]. The book by R. E. Edwards [5] is an exhaustive study of Fourier series from a more modern perspective. The article by Weiss [20] and the book by Körner [12] are also recommended. An excellent historical account by J. P. Kahane on Fourier series and their influence on the development of mathematical concepts is found in the first half of [9]. The book *Fourier Analysis and Boundary Value Problems*, by E. González-Velasco (Academic Press, New York, 1995), contains many applications of Fourier's method of separation of variables to partial differential equations and also contains historical information. (Also see by the same author, *Connections in mathematical analysis: the case of Fourier series*, Amer. Math. Monthly **99** (1992), 427–441.) The book by O. G. Jørsboe and L. Melbro (*The Carleson-Hunt Theorem on Fourier Series*, Lecture Notes in Math. **911**, Springer-Verlag, Berlin, 1982) is devoted to the proof of this theorem. The original references for this are the articles by L. Carleson (*On convergence and growth of partial sums of Fourier series*, Acta Math. **116** (1966), 135–157) and R. Hunt (*On the convergence of Fourier series*, Orthogonal Expansions and their Continuous Analogues (Proc. Conf., Edwardsville, Ill., 1967), pp. 235–255, Southern Illinois Univ. Press, Carbondale, 1968). Kolmogorov's example of an L^1 function whose Fourier series diverges everywhere appeared in *Une série de Fourier-Lebesgue divergente partout* (C. R. Acad. Sci. Paris **183** (1926), 1327–1328).

10.2. Multiple Fourier series.

Let $\mathbb{T}^n$ be the n-dimensional torus (which we can identify with the quotient group $\mathbb{R}^n/\mathbb{Z}^n$). A function defined on $\mathbb{T}^n$ is equivalent to a function on $\mathbb{R}^n$ which has period 1 in each variable. If $f \in L^1(\mathbb{R}^n)$ then we can define its Fourier coefficients by

$$\hat{f}(\nu) = \int f(x)e^{-2\pi i x \cdot \nu}\, dx, \quad \nu \in \mathbb{Z}^n,$$

and construct the Fourier series of f with these coefficients,

$$\sum_{\nu \in \mathbb{Z}^n} \hat{f}(\nu)e^{2\pi i x \cdot \nu}.$$

One can prove several results similar to those for Fourier series in one variable, but one needs increasingly restrictive regularity conditions as n increases. See Stein and Weiss [18, Chapter 7].

10.3. The Poisson summation formula.

Let f be a function such that for some $\delta > 0$,

$$|f(x)| \leq A(1 + |x|)^{-n-\delta} \quad \text{and} \quad |\hat{f}(\xi)| \leq A(1 + |\xi|)^{-n-\delta}.$$

(In particular, f and $\hat{f}$ are both continuous.) Then

$$\sum_{\nu \in \mathbb{Z}^n} f(x + \nu) = \sum_{\nu \in \mathbb{Z}^n} \hat{f}(\nu) e^{2\pi i x \cdot \nu}.$$

This equality (or more precisely, the case when $x = 0$) is known as the Poisson summation formula and is nothing more than the inversion formula. The left-hand side defines a function on $\mathbb{T}^n$ whose Fourier coefficients are precisely $\hat{f}(\nu)$.

10.4. Gibbs phenomenon.

Let $f(x) = \text{sgn}(x)$ on $(-1/2, 1/2)$. By Dirichlet's criterion, for example, we know that $S_N f(x)$ converges to $f(x)$ for all x. To the right of 0 the partial sums oscillate around 1 but, contrary to what one might expect, the amount by which they overstep 1 does not tend to 0 as N increases. One can show that

$$\lim_{N \to \infty} \sup_x S_N f(x) = \frac{2}{\pi} \int_0^\pi \frac{\sin(y)}{y} \, dy \approx 1.17898\ldots .$$

This phenomenon occurs whenever a function has a jump discontinuity. It is named after J. Gibbs, who announced it in Nature **59** (1899), although it had already been discovered by H. Wilbraham in 1848. See Dym and McKean [**4**, Chapter 1] and the paper by E. Hewitt and R. E. Hewitt (*The Gibbs-Wilbraham phenomenon: an episode in Fourier analysis*, Arch. Hist. Exact Sci. **21** (1979/80), 129–160).

Gibbs phenomenon is eliminated by replacing pointwise convergence by Cesàro summability. For if $m \le f(x) \le M$, then by the first two properties of Féjer kernels in (1.8), $m \le \sigma_N f(x) \le M$. In fact, it can be shown that if $m \le f(x) \le M$ on an interval (a, b), then for any $\epsilon > 0$, $m - \epsilon \le \sigma_N f(x) \le M + \epsilon$ on $(a + \epsilon, b - \epsilon)$ for N sufficiently large.

10.5. The Hausdorff-Young inequality.

Corollary 1.20 was gotten by an immediate application of Riesz-Thorin interpolation. But in fact a stronger inequality is true: if $1 \le p \le 2$ then

$$\|\hat{f}\|_{p'} \le \left(\frac{p^{1/p}}{(p')^{1/p'}} \right)^{n/2} \|f\|_p.$$

This inequality is sharp since equality holds for $f(x) = e^{-\pi|x|^2}$. This result was proved by W. Beckner (*Inequalities in Fourier analysis*, Ann. of Math. **102** (1975), 159–182); the special case when p is even was proved earlier by K. I. Babenko (*An inequality in the theory of Fourier integrals* (Russian), Izv. Akad. Nauk SSSR Ser. Mat. **25** (1961), 531–542).

In the same article, Beckner also proved a sharp version of Young's inequality (Corollary 1.21).

10.6. Eigenfunctions for the Fourier transform in $L^2(\mathbb{R})$.

Since the Fourier transform has period 4, if f is a function such that $\hat{f} = \lambda f$, we must have that $\lambda^4 = 1$. Hence, $\lambda = \pm 1, \pm i$ are the only possible eigenvalues of the Fourier transform. Lemma 1.14 shows that $\exp(-\pi x^2)$ is an eigenfunction associated with the eigenvalue 1. The Hermite functions give the remaining eigenfunctions: for $n \geq 0$,

$$h_n(x) = \frac{(-1)^n}{n!} \exp(\pi x^2) \frac{d^n}{dx^n} \exp(-\pi x^2)$$

satisfies $\hat{h}_n = (-i)^n h_n$. If we normalize these functions,

$$e_n = \frac{h_n}{\|h_n\|_2} = [(4\pi)^{-n}\sqrt{2n!}]^{1/2} h_n,$$

we get an orthonormal basis of $L^2(\mathbb{R})$ such that

$$\hat{f} = \sum_{n=0}^{\infty} (-i)^n \langle f, e_n \rangle e_n.$$

Thus $L^2(\mathbb{R})$ decomposes into the direct sum $H_0 \oplus H_1 \oplus H_2 \oplus H_3$, where on the subspace H_j, $0 \leq j \leq 3$, the Fourier transform acts by multiplying functions by i^j.

This approach to defining the Fourier transform in $L^2(\mathbb{R})$ is due to N. Wiener and can be found in his book (*The Fourier Integral and Certain of its Applications*, original edition, 1933; Cambridge Univ. Press, Cambridge, 1988). Also see Dym and McKean [**4**, Chapter 2].

In higher dimensions, the eigenfunctions of the Fourier transform are products of Hermite functions, one in each coordinate variable. Also see Chapter 4, Section 7.2.

10.7. Interpolation of analytic families of operators.

The Riesz-Thorin interpolation theorem has a powerful generalization due to E. M. Stein. (See Stein and Weiss [**18**, Chapter 5].) Let $S = \{z \in \mathbb{C} : 0 \leq \operatorname{Re} z \leq 1\}$ and let $\{T_z\}_{z \in S}$ be a family of operators. This family is said to be admissible if given two functions $f, g \in L^1(\mathbb{R}^n)$, the mapping

$$z \mapsto \int_{\mathbb{R}^n} T_z(f) g \, dx$$

is analytic on the interior of S and continuous on the boundary, and if there exists a constant $a < \pi$ such that

$$e^{-a|\operatorname{Im} z|} \log \left| \int_{\mathbb{R}^n} T_z(f) g \, dx \right|$$

is uniformly bounded for all $z \in S$.

Theorem 1.22. *Let $\{T_z\}$ be an admissible family of operators, and suppose that for $1 \le p_0, p_1, q_0, q_1 \le \infty$ and $y \in \mathbb{R}$,*

$$\|T_{iy}f\|_{q_0} \le M_0(y)\|f\|_{p_0} \quad and \quad \|T_{1+iy}f\|_{q_1} \le M_1(y)\|f\|_{p_1},$$

where for some $b < \pi$

$$\sup_{y \in \mathbb{R}} e^{-b|y|} \log M_j(y) < \infty, \quad j = 1, 2.$$

Then for $0 < \theta < 1$, $\operatorname{Re} z = \theta$ and p, q defined as in Theorem 1.19, there exists a constant M_θ such that

$$\|T_z f\|_q \le M_\theta \|f\|_p.$$

10.8. Fourier transforms of finite measures.

As we noted above, if μ is a finite Borel measure then $\hat{\mu}$ is a bounded, continuous function. The collection of all such functions obtained in this way is characterized by the following result.

Theorem 1.23. *If h is a bounded, continuous function, then the following are equivalent:*

(1) $h = \hat{\mu}$ *for some positive, finite Borel measure μ;*

(2) h *is positive definite: given any $f \in L^1(\mathbb{R}^n)$,*

$$\int_{\mathbb{R}^n} \int_{\mathbb{R}^n} h(x - y) f(x) \bar{f}(y) \, dx dy \ge 0.$$

This theorem is due to S. Bochner (*Lectures on Fourier Integrals*, Princeton Univ. Press, Princeton, 1959; translated from *Vorlesungen über Fouriersche Integrale*, Akad. Verlag, Leipzig, 1932). Also see Katznelson [**10**, Chapter 6].

Chapter 2

The Hardy-Littlewood Maximal Function

1. Approximations of the identity

Let ϕ be an integrable function on $\mathbb{R}^n$ such that $\int \phi = 1$, and for $t > 0$ define $\phi_t(x) = t^{-n}\phi(t^{-1}x)$. As $t \to 0$, ϕ_t converges in $\mathcal{S}'$ to δ, the Dirac measure at the origin: if $g \in \mathcal{S}$ then

$$\phi_t(g) = \int_{\mathbb{R}^n} t^{-n}\phi(t^{-1}x)g(x)\,dx = \int_{\mathbb{R}^n} \phi(x)g(tx)\,dx,$$

and so by the dominated convergence theorem,

$$\lim_{t\to 0} \phi_t(g) = g(0) = \delta(g).$$

Since $\delta * g = g$, for $g \in \mathcal{S}$ we have the pointwise limit

$$\lim_{t\to 0} \phi_t * g(x) = g(x).$$

Because of this we say that $\{\phi_t : t > 0\}$ is an approximation of the identity.

The summability methods in the previous chapter can be thought of as approximations of the identity. For Cesàro summability, $\phi = F_1$ and $F_R = \phi_{1/R}$. (See (1.24).) For Abel-Poisson summability, $\phi = P_1$ (see (1.30)) and for Gauss-Weierstrass summability, $\phi = W_1$ (see (1.31)). We see from the following result that these summability methods converge in L^p norm.

Theorem 2.1. *Let $\{\phi_t : t > 0\}$ be an approximation of the identity. Then*

$$\lim_{t\to 0} \|\phi_t * f - f\|_p = 0$$

if $f \in L^p$, $1 \le p < \infty$, and uniformly (i.e. when $p = \infty$) if $f \in C_0(\mathbb{R}^n)$.

Proof. Because ϕ has integral 1,

$$\phi_t * f(x) - f(x) = \int_{\mathbb{R}^n} \phi(y)[f(x - ty) - f(x)]\,dy.$$

Given $\epsilon > 0$, choose $\delta > 0$ such that if $|h| < \delta$,

$$\|f(\cdot + h) - f(\cdot)\|_p < \frac{\epsilon}{2\|\phi\|_1}.$$

(Note that δ depends on f.) For fixed δ, if t is sufficiently small then

$$\int_{|y| \geq \delta/t} |\phi(y)|\,dy \leq \frac{\epsilon}{4\|f\|_p}.$$

Therefore, by Minkowski's inequality

$$\|\phi_t * f - f\|_p \leq \int_{|y| < \delta/t} |\phi(y)|\|f(\cdot + ty) - f(\cdot)\|_p\,dy$$

$$+ 2\|f\|_p \int_{|y| \geq \delta/t} |\phi(y)|\,dy$$

$$< \epsilon.$$

$\square$

As a consequence of this theorem, we know that there exists a sequence $\{t_k\}$, depending on f, such that $t_k \to 0$ and

$$\lim_{k \to \infty} \phi_{t_k} * f(x) = f(x) \quad \text{a.e.}$$

Hence, if $\lim \phi_t * f(x)$ exists then it must equal $f(x)$ almost everywhere. In Section 4 we will study the existence of this limit.

2. Weak-type inequalities and almost everywhere convergence

Let (X, μ) and (Y, ν) be measure spaces, and let T be an operator from $L^p(X, \mu)$ into the space of measurable functions from Y to $\mathbb{C}$. We say that T is weak (p, q), $q < \infty$, if

$$\nu(\{y \in Y : |Tf(y)| > \lambda\}) \leq \left(\frac{C\|f\|_p}{\lambda}\right)^q,$$

and we say that it is weak (p, ∞) if it is a bounded operator from $L^p(X, \mu)$ to $L^\infty(Y, \nu)$. We say that T is strong (p, q) if it is bounded from $L^p(X, \mu)$ to $L^q(Y, \nu)$.

If T is strong (p, q) then it is weak (p, q): if we let $E_\lambda = \{y \in Y : |Tf(y)| > \lambda\}$, then

$$\nu(E_\lambda) = \int_{E_\lambda} d\nu \leq \int_{E_\lambda} \left|\frac{Tf(x)}{\lambda}\right|^q\,d\nu \leq \frac{\|Tf\|_q^q}{\lambda^q} \leq \left(\frac{C\|f\|_p}{\lambda}\right)^q.$$

When $(X, \mu) = (Y, \nu)$ and T is the identity, the weak (p, p) inequality is the classical Chebyshev inequality.

The relationship between weak (p, q) inequalities and almost everywhere convergence is given by the following result. In it we assume that $(X, \mu) = (Y, \nu)$.

Theorem 2.2. *Let $\{T_t\}$ be a family of linear operators on $L^p(X, \mu)$ and define*

$$T^* f(x) = \sup_t |T_t f(x)|.$$

If T^* is weak (p, q) then the set

$$\{f \in L^p(X, \mu) : \lim_{t \to t_0} T_t f(x) = f(x) \ a.e.\}$$

is closed in $L^p(X, \mu)$.

T^* is called the maximal operator associated with the family $\{T_t\}$.

Proof. Let $\{f_n\}$ be a sequence of functions which converges to f in $L^p(X, \mu)$ norm and such that $T_t f_n(x)$ converges to $f_n(x)$ almost everywhere. Then

$$\mu(\{x \in X : \limsup_{t \to t_0} |T_t f(x) - f(x)| > \lambda\})$$

$$\leq \mu(\{x \in X : \limsup_{t \to t_0} |T_t(f - f_n)(x) - (f - f_n)(x)| > \lambda\})$$

$$\leq \mu(\{x \in X : T^*(f - f_n)(x) > \lambda/2\})$$
$$+ \mu(\{x \in X : |(f - f_n)(x)| > \lambda/2\})$$

$$\leq \left(\frac{2C}{\lambda} \|f - f_n\|_p\right)^q + \left(\frac{2}{\lambda} \|f - f_n\|_p\right)^p,$$

and the last term tends to 0 as $n \to \infty$. Therefore,

$$\mu(\{x \in X : \limsup_{t \to t_0} |T_t f(x) - f(x)| > 0\})$$

$$\leq \sum_{k=1}^{\infty} \mu(\{x \in X : \limsup_{t \to t_0} |T_t f(x) - f(x)| > 1/k\})$$

$$= 0.$$

$\square$

By the same technique we can also prove that the set

$$\{f \in L^p(X, \mu) : \lim_{t \to t_0} T_t f(x) \text{ exists a.e.}\}$$

is closed in $L^p(X, \mu)$. It suffices to show that

$$\mu(\{x \in X : \limsup_{t \to t_0} T_t f(x) - \liminf_{t \to t_0} T_t f(x) > \lambda\}) = 0,$$

and this follows as in the above argument since

$$\limsup_{t \to t_0} T_t f(x) - \liminf_{t \to t_0} T_t f(x) \le 2T^* f(x).$$

(If $T_t f(x)$ is complex, we apply this argument to its real and imaginary parts separately.)

Since for $f \in S$ approximations of the identity converge pointwise to f, we can apply this theorem to show pointwise convergence almost everywhere for $f \in L^p$, $1 \le p < \infty$, or for $f \in C_0$ if we can show that the maximal operator $\sup_{t>0} |\phi_t * f(x)|$ is weakly bounded.

3. The Marcinkiewicz interpolation theorem

Let (X, μ) be a measure space and let $f : X \to \mathbb{C}$ be a measurable function. We call the function $a_f : (0, \infty) \to [0, \infty]$, given by

$$a_f(\lambda) = \mu(\{x \in X : |f(x)| > \lambda\}),$$

the distribution function of f (associated with μ).

Proposition 2.3. *Let* $\phi : [0, \infty) \to [0, \infty)$ *be differentiable, increasing and such that* $\phi(0) = 0$. *Then*

$$\int_X \phi(|f(x)|) \, d\mu = \int_0^\infty \phi'(\lambda) a_f(\lambda) \, d\lambda.$$

To prove this it is enough to observe that the left-hand side is equivalent to

$$\int_X \int_0^{|f(x)|} \phi'(\lambda) \, d\lambda \, d\mu$$

and then change the order of integration. If, in particular, $\phi(\lambda) = \lambda^p$ then

(2.1) $$\|f\|_p^p = p \int_0^\infty \lambda^{p-1} a_f(\lambda) \, d\lambda.$$

Since weak inequalities measure the size of the distribution function, this representation of the L^p norm is ideal for proving the following interpolation theorem, which will let us deduce L^p boundedness from weak inequalities. It applies to a larger class of operators than linear ones (note that maximal operators are not linear): an operator T from a vector space of measurable functions to measurable functions is sublinear if

$$|T(f_0 + f_1)(x)| \le |Tf_0(x)| + |Tf_1(x)|,$$
$$|T(\lambda f)| = |\lambda||Tf|, \quad \lambda \in \mathbb{C}.$$

Theorem 2.4 (Marcinkiewicz Interpolation). *Let (X, μ) and (Y, ν) be measure spaces, $1 \le p_0 < p_1 \le \infty$, and let T be a sublinear operator from $L^{p_0}(X, \mu) + L^{p_1}(X, \mu)$ to the measurable functions on Y that is weak (p_0, p_0) and weak (p_1, p_1). Then T is strong (p, p) for $p_0 < p < p_1$.*

Proof. Given $f \in L^p$, for each $\lambda > 0$ decompose f as $f_0 + f_1$, where

$$f_0 = f \chi_{\{x : |f(x)| > c\lambda\}},$$
$$f_1 = f \chi_{\{x : |f(x)| \le c\lambda\}};$$

the constant c will be fixed below. Then $f_0 \in L^{p_0}(\mu)$ and $f_1 \in L^{p_1}(\mu)$. Furthermore,

$$|Tf(x)| \le |Tf_0(x)| + |Tf_1(x)|,$$

so

$$a_{Tf}(\lambda) \le a_{Tf_0}(\lambda/2) + a_{Tf_1}(\lambda/2).$$

We consider two cases.

Case 1: $p_1 = \infty$. Choose $c = 1/(2A_1)$, where A_1 is such that $\|Tg\|_\infty \le A_1 \|g\|_\infty$. Then $a_{Tf_1}(\lambda/2) = 0$. By the weak (p_0, p_0) inequality,

$$a_{Tf_0}(\lambda/2) \le \left(\frac{2A_0}{\lambda} \|f_0\|_{p_0} \right)^{p_0};$$

hence,

$$\|Tf\|_p^p \le p \int_0^\infty \lambda^{p-1-p_0} (2A_0)^{p_0} \int_{\{x : |f(x)| > c\lambda\}} |f(x)|^{p_0} \, d\mu \, d\lambda$$

$$= p(2A_0)^{p_0} \int_X |f(x)|^{p_0} \int_0^{|f(x)|/c} \lambda^{p-1-p_0} \, d\lambda \, d\mu$$

$$= \frac{p}{p - p_0} (2A_0)^{p_0} (2A_1)^{p-p_0} \|f\|_p^p.$$

Case 2: $p_1 < \infty$. We now have the pair of inequalities

$$a_{Tf_i}(\lambda/2) \le \left(\frac{2A_i}{\lambda} \|f_i\|_{p_i} \right)^{p_i}, \quad i = 0, 1.$$

From these we get (arguing as above) that

$$\|Tf\|_p^p \le p \int_0^\infty \lambda^{p-1-p_0} (2A_0)^{p_0} \int_{\{x : |f(x)| > c\lambda\}} |f(x)|^{p_0} \, d\mu \, d\lambda$$

$$+ p \int_0^\infty \lambda^{p-1-p_1} (2A_1)^{p_1} \int_{\{x : |f(x)| \le c\lambda\}} |f(x)|^{p_1} \, d\mu \, d\lambda$$

$$= \left(\frac{p 2^{p_0}}{p - p_0} \frac{A_0^{p_0}}{c^{p-p_0}} + \frac{p 2^{p_1}}{p_1 - p} \frac{A_1^{p_1}}{c^{p-p_1}} \right) \|f\|_p^p.$$

$\square$

We can write the strong (p,p) norm inequality in this theorem more precisely as

$$(2.2) \qquad \|Tf\|_p \leq 2p^{1/p} \left(\frac{1}{p - p_0} + \frac{1}{p_1 - p} \right)^{1/p} A_0^{1-\theta} A_1^{\theta} \|f\|_p,$$

where

$$\frac{1}{p} = \frac{\theta}{p_1} + \frac{1 - \theta}{p_0}, \quad 0 < \theta < 1.$$

When $p_1 = \infty$ this is the constant which appears in the proof; when $p_1 < \infty$ it is enough to take c such that $(2A_0 c)^{p_0} = (2A_1 c)^{p_1}$ and then simplify.

4. The Hardy-Littlewood maximal function

Let $B_r = B(0, r)$ be the Euclidean ball of radius r centered at the origin. The Hardy-Littlewood maximal function of a locally integrable function f on $\mathbb{R}^n$ is defined by

$$(2.3) \qquad Mf(x) = \sup_{r > 0} \frac{1}{|B_r|} \int_{B_r} |f(x - y)| \, dy.$$

(This can equal $+\infty$.) If we let $\phi = |B_1|^{-1} \chi_{B_1}$, then (2.3) coincides for non-negative f with the maximal operator associated with the approximation of the identity $\{\phi_t\}$ as in Theorem 2.2.

Sometimes we will define the maximal function with cubes in place of balls. If Q_r is the cube $[-r, r]^n$, define

$$(2.4) \qquad M'f(x) = \sup_{r > 0} \frac{1}{(2r)^n} \int_{Q_r} |f(x - y)| \, dy.$$

When $n = 1$, M and M' coincide; if $n > 1$ then there exist constants c_n and C_n, depending only on n, such that

$$(2.5) \qquad c_n M'f(x) \leq Mf(x) \leq C_n M'f(x).$$

Because of inequality (2.5), the two operators M and M' are essentially interchangeable, and we will use whichever is more appropriate, depending on the circumstances. In fact, we can define a more general maximal function

$$(2.6) \qquad M''f(x) = \sup_{Q \ni x} \frac{1}{|Q|} \int_Q |f(y)| \, dy,$$

where the supremum is taken over all cubes containing x. Again, M'' is pointwise equivalent to M. One sometimes distinguishes between M' and M'' by referring to the former as the centered and the latter as the non-centered maximal operator. Alternatively, we could define the non-centered maximal function with balls instead of cubes.

Theorem 2.5. *The operator M is weak $(1,1)$ and strong (p,p), $1 < p \leq \infty$.*

We remark that by inequality (2.5), the same result is true for M' (and also for M'').

It is immediate from the definition that

$$(2.7) \qquad \|Mf\|_\infty \leq \|f\|_\infty,$$

so by the Marcinkiewicz interpolation theorem, to prove Theorem 2.5 it will be enough to prove that M is weak $(1,1)$. Here we will prove this when $n = 1$; we will prove the general case in Section 6. In the one-dimensional case we need the following covering lemma whose simple proof we leave to the reader.

Lemma 2.6. *Let $\{I_\alpha\}_{\alpha \in A}$ be a collection of intervals in $\mathbb{R}$ and let K be a compact set contained in their union. Then there exists a finite subcollection $\{I_j\}$ such that*

$$K \subset \bigcup_j I_j, \quad \text{and} \quad \sum_j \chi_{I_j}(x) \leq 2, \quad x \in \mathbb{R}.$$

Proof of Theorem 2.5 for $n = 1$. Let $E_\lambda = \{x \in \mathbb{R} : Mf(x) > \lambda\}$. If $x \in E_\lambda$ then there exists an interval I_x centered at x such that

$$(2.8) \qquad \frac{1}{|I_x|} \int_{I_x} |f| > \lambda.$$

Let $K \subset E_\lambda$ be compact. Then $K \subset \bigcup I_x$, so by Lemma 2.6 there exists a finite collection $\{I_j\}$ of intervals such that $K \subset \bigcup_j I_j$ and $\sum_j \chi_{I_j} \leq 2$. Hence,

$$|K| \leq \sum_j |I_j| \leq \sum_j \frac{1}{\lambda} \int_{I_j} |f| \leq \frac{1}{\lambda} \int_{\mathbb{R}} \sum_j \chi_{I_j} |f| \leq \frac{2}{\lambda} \|f\|_1;$$

the second inequality follows from (2.8). Since this inequality holds for every compact $K \subset E_\lambda$, the weak $(1,1)$ inequality for M follows immediately. $\square$

Lemma 2.6 is not valid in dimensions greater than 1, and though one could replace it with similar results, this is not the approach we are going to take here. (For such a proof, see Section 8.6.)

The importance of the maximal function in the study of approximations of the identity comes from the following result.

Proposition 2.7. *Let ϕ be a function which is positive, radial, decreasing (as a function on $(0, \infty)$) and integrable. Then*

$$\sup_{t>0} |\phi_t * f(x)| \leq \|\phi\|_1 Mf(x).$$

Proof. If we assume in addition to the given hypotheses that ϕ is a simple function, that is, it can be written as

$$\phi(x) = \sum_j a_j \chi_{B_{r_j}}(x)$$

with $a_j > 0$, then

$$\phi * f(x) = \sum_j a_j |B_{r_j}| \frac{1}{|B_{r_j}|} \chi_{B_{r_j}} * f(x) \le \|\phi\|_1 M f(x)$$

since $\|\phi\|_1 = \sum a_j |B_{r_j}|$.

An arbitrary function ϕ satisfying the hypotheses can be approximated by a sequence of simple functions which increase to it monotonically. Any dilation ϕ_t is another positive, radial, decreasing function with the same integral, and it will satisfy the same inequality. The desired conclusion follows at once. $\qquad\square$

Corollary 2.8. *If $|\phi(x)| \le \psi(x)$ almost everywhere, where ψ is positive, radial, decreasing and integrable, then the maximal function $\sup_t |\phi_t * f(x)|$ is weak $(1,1)$ and strong (p,p), $1 < p \le \infty$.*

This is an immediate consequence of Proposition 2.7 and Theorem 2.5. If we combine this corollary with Theorem 2.2 we get the following result.

Corollary 2.9. *Under the hypotheses of the previous corollary, if $f \in L^p$, $1 \le p < \infty$, or if $f \in C_0$, then*

$$\lim_{t \to 0} \phi_t * f(x) = \left(\int \phi \right) \cdot f(x) \ a.e.$$

In particular, the summability methods discussed in Chapter 1, Section 9 (Cesàro, Abel-Poisson and Gauss-Weierstrass summability), each converge to $f(x)$ almost everywhere if f is in one of the given spaces.

Proof. Since we have convergence for $f \in \mathcal{S}$, by Theorem 2.2 we have convergence for $f \in \overline{\mathcal{S}} = L^p$ (or $f \in C_0$ if $p = \infty$). The Poisson kernel (1.30) and the Gauss-Weierstrass kernel (1.31) are decreasing; the Féjer kernel (1.24) is not but $F_1(x) \le \min(1, (\pi x)^{-2})$. $\qquad\square$

5. The dyadic maximal function

In $\mathbb{R}^n$ we define the unit cube, open on the right, to be the set $[0,1)^n$, and we let $\mathcal{Q}_0$ be the collection of cubes in $\mathbb{R}^n$ which are congruent to $[0,1)^n$ and whose vertices lie on the lattice $\mathbb{Z}^n$. If we dilate this family of cubes by a factor of 2^{-k} we get the collection $\mathcal{Q}_k$, $k \in \mathbb{Z}$; that is, $\mathcal{Q}_k$ is the family of cubes, open on the right, whose vertices are adjacent points of the lattice $(2^{-k}\mathbb{Z})^n$. The cubes in $\bigcup_k \mathcal{Q}_k$ are called dyadic cubes.

From this construction we immediately get the following properties:

(1) given $x \in \mathbb{R}^n$ there is a unique cube in each family $\mathcal{Q}_k$ which contains it;

(2) any two dyadic cubes are either disjoint or one is wholly contained in the other;

(3) a dyadic cube in $\mathcal{Q}_k$ is contained in a unique cube of each family $\mathcal{Q}_j$, $j < k$, and contains 2^n dyadic cubes of $\mathcal{Q}_{k+1}$.

Given a function $f \in L^1_{\text{loc}}(\mathbb{R}^n)$, define

$$E_k f(x) = \sum_{Q \in \mathcal{Q}_k} \left(\frac{1}{|Q|} \int_Q f \right) \chi_Q(x);$$

$E_k f$ is the conditional expectation of f with respect to the σ-algebra generated by $\mathcal{Q}_k$. It satisfies the following fundamental identity: if Ω is the union of cubes in $\mathcal{Q}_k$, then

$$\int_\Omega E_k f = \int_\Omega f.$$

$E_k f$ is a discrete analog of an approximation of the identity. The following theorem makes this precise; first, define the dyadic maximal function by

(2.9) $$M_d f(x) = \sup_k |E_k f(x)|.$$

Theorem 2.10.

(1) *The dyadic maximal function is weak $(1,1)$.*

(2) *If $f \in L^1_{\text{loc}}$, $\lim\limits_{k \to \infty} E_k f(x) = f(x)$ a.e.*

Proof. (1) Fix $f \in L^1$; we may assume that f is non-negative: if f is real, it can be decomposed into its positive and negative parts, and if it is complex, into its real and imaginary parts.

Now let

$$\{x \in \mathbb{R}^n : M_d f(x) > \lambda\} = \bigcup_k \Omega_k,$$

where

$$\Omega_k = \{x \in \mathbb{R}^n : E_k f(x) > \lambda \text{ and } E_j f(x) \le \lambda \text{ if } j < k\};$$

that is, $x \in \Omega_k$ if $E_k f(x)$ is the first conditional expectation of f which is greater than λ. (Since $f \in L^1$, $E_k f(x) \to 0$ as $k \to -\infty$, so such a k exists.)

The sets Ω_k are clearly disjoint, and each one can be written as the union of cubes in $\mathcal{Q}_k$. Hence,

$$\begin{aligned}
|\{x \in \mathbb{R}^n : M_d f(x) > \lambda\}| &= \sum_k |\Omega_k| \\
&\leq \sum_k \frac{1}{\lambda} \int_{\Omega_k} E_k f \\
&= \frac{1}{\lambda} \sum_k \int_{\Omega_k} f \\
&\leq \frac{1}{\lambda} \|f\|_1.
\end{aligned}$$

(2) This limit is clearly true if f is continuous, and so by Theorem 2.2 it holds for $f \in L^1$. To complete the proof, note that if $f \in L^1_{\text{loc}}$ then $f\chi_Q \in L^1$ for any $Q \in \mathcal{Q}_0$. Hence, (2) holds for almost every $x \in Q$, and so for almost every $x \in \mathbb{R}^n$. $\square$

This proof uses a decomposition of $\mathbb{R}^n$ which has proved to be extremely useful. It is called the Calderón-Zygmund decomposition and we state it precisely as follows.

Theorem 2.11. *Given a function f which is integrable and non-negative, and given a positive number λ, there exists a sequence $\{Q_j\}$ of disjoint dyadic cubes such that*

(1)   *$f(x) \leq \lambda$ for almost every $x \notin \bigcup_j Q_j$;*

(2)   *$\left| \bigcup_j Q_j \right| \leq \frac{1}{\lambda} \|f\|_1$;*

(3)   *$\lambda < \frac{1}{|Q_j|} \int_{Q_j} f \leq 2^n \lambda$.*

Proof. As in the proof of Theorem 2.10, form the sets Ω_k and decompose each into disjoint dyadic cubes contained in $\mathcal{Q}_k$; together, all of these cubes form the family $\{Q_j\}$.

Part (2) of the theorem is then just the weak $(1,1)$ inequality of Theorem 2.10.

If $x \notin \bigcup_j Q_j$ then for every k, $E_k f(x) \leq \lambda$, and so by part (2) of Theorem 2.10, $f(x) \leq \lambda$ at almost every such point.

Finally, by the definition of the sets Ω_k, the average of f over Q_j is greater than λ; this is the first inequality in (3). Furthermore, if $\tilde{Q}_j$ is the dyadic cube containing Q_j whose sides are twice as long, then the average of f over $\tilde{Q}_j$ is at most λ. Therefore,

$$\frac{1}{|Q_j|}\int_{Q_j}f \leq \frac{|\tilde{Q}_j|}{|Q_j|}\frac{1}{|\tilde{Q}_j|}\int_{\tilde{Q}_j}f \leq 2^n\lambda.$$

$\square$

6. The weak $(1,1)$ inequality for the maximal function

We are now going to use Theorem 2.10 to prove Theorem 2.5. In fact, it is an immediate consequence of the following lemma and inequality (2.5). (Recall that M' is the maximal operator on cubes defined by (2.4).)

Lemma 2.12. *If f is a non-negative function, then*

$$|\{x \in \mathbb{R}^n : M'f(x) > 4^n\lambda\}| \leq 2^n|\{x \in \mathbb{R}^n : M_df(x) > \lambda\}|.$$

Given this lemma, by the weak $(1,1)$ inequality for M_d proved in Theorem 2.10,

$$|\{x \in \mathbb{R}^n : M'f(x) > \lambda\}| \leq 2^n|\{x \in \mathbb{R}^n : M_df(x) > 4^{-n}\lambda\}| \leq \frac{8^n}{\lambda}\|f\|_1.$$

(Since $M'f = M'(|f|)$, we may assume that f is non-negative.)

Proof of Lemma 2.12. As before, we form the decomposition

$$\{x \in \mathbb{R}^n : M_df(x) > \lambda\} = \bigcup_j Q_j.$$

Let $2Q_j$ be the cube with the same center as Q_j and whose sides are twice as long. To complete the proof it will suffice to show that

$$\{x \in \mathbb{R}^n : M'f(x) > 4^n\lambda\} \subset \bigcup_j 2Q_j.$$

Fix $x \notin \bigcup_j 2Q_j$ and let Q be any cube centered at x. Let $l(Q)$ denote the side length of Q, and choose $k \in \mathbb{Z}$ such that $2^{k-1} \leq l(Q) < 2^k$. Then Q intersects $m \leq 2^n$ dyadic cubes in $\mathcal{Q}_k$; call them $R_1, R_2, \ldots, R_m$. None of these cubes is contained in any of the Q_j's, for otherwise we would have $x \in \bigcup_j 2Q_j$. Hence, the average of f on each R_i is at most λ, and so

$$\frac{1}{|Q|}\int_Q f = \frac{1}{|Q|}\sum_{i=1}^m \int_{Q\cap R_i}f \leq \sum_{i=1}^m \frac{2^{kn}}{|Q|}\frac{1}{|R_i|}\int_{R_i}f \leq 2^n m\lambda \leq 4^n\lambda.$$

$\square$

As a consequence of the weak $(1,1)$ inequality and Theorem 2.2 we get a continuous analog of the second half of Theorem 2.10.

Corollary 2.13 (Lebesgue Differentiation Theorem). *If $f \in L^1_{\text{loc}}(\mathbb{R}^n)$ then*

$$\lim_{r \to 0^+} \frac{1}{|B_r|} \int_{B_r} f(x-y)\, dy = f(x) \quad a.e.$$

From this we see that $|f(x)| \le Mf(x)$ almost everywhere. The same is true if we replace M by M' or M''.

We can make the conclusion of Corollary 2.13 sharper:

$$(2.10) \qquad \lim_{r \to 0^+} \frac{1}{|B_r|} \int_{B_r} |f(x-y) - f(x)|\, dy = 0 \text{ a.e.}$$

This follows immediately from the fact that

$$\frac{1}{|B_r|} \int_{B_r} |f(x-y) - f(x)|\, dy \le Mf(x) + |f(x)|.$$

The points in $\mathbb{R}^n$ for which limit (2.10) equals 0 are called the Lebesgue points of f. If x is a Lebesgue point and if $\{B_j\}$ is a sequence of balls such that $B_1 \supset B_2 \supset \cdots$ and $\bigcap_j B_j = \{x\}$ (note that the balls need not be centered at x), then

$$\lim_{j \to \infty} \frac{1}{|B_j|} \int_{B_j} f = f(x).$$

This follows immediately from the inclusion $B_j \subset B(x, 2r_j)$, where r_j is the radius of B_j. A similar argument shows that the set of Lebesgue points of f does not change if we take cubes instead of balls.

The weak $(1,1)$ inequality for M is a substitute for the strong $(1,1)$ inequality, which is false. In fact, it never holds, as the following result shows.

Proposition 2.14. *If $f \in L^1$ and is not identically 0, then $Mf \notin L^1$.*

The proof is simple: since f is not identically 0, there exists $R > 0$ such that

$$\int_{B_R} |f| \ge \epsilon > 0.$$

Now if $|x| > R$, $B_R \subset B(x, 2|x|)$, so

$$Mf(x) \ge \frac{1}{(2|x|)^n} \int_{B_R} |f| \ge \frac{\epsilon}{2^n |x|^n}.$$

Nevertheless, we do have the following.

Theorem 2.15. *If B is a bounded subset of $\mathbb{R}^n$, then*

$$\int_B Mf \leq 2|B| + C \int_{\mathbb{R}^n} |f| \log^+ |f|,$$

where $\log^+ t = \max(\log t, 0)$.

Proof.

$$\int_B Mf \leq 2 \int_0^\infty |\{x \in B : Mf(x) > 2\lambda\}| \, d\lambda$$

$$\leq 2|B| + 2 \int_1^\infty |\{x \in B : Mf(x) > 2\lambda\}| \, d\lambda.$$

Decompose f as $f_1 + f_2$, where $f_1 = f\chi_{\{x:|f(x)|>\lambda\}}$ and $f_2 = f - f_1$. Then

$$\{x \in B : Mf(x) > 2\lambda\} \subset \{x \in B : Mf_1(x) > \lambda\}.$$

Hence,

$$\int_1^\infty |\{x \in B : Mf(x) > 2\lambda\}| \, d\lambda \leq \int_1^\infty \frac{C}{\lambda} \int_{\{x:|f(x)|>\lambda\}} |f(x)| \, dx \, d\lambda$$

$$\leq C \int_{\mathbb{R}^n} |f(x)| \int_1^{\max(|f(x)|,1)} \frac{d\lambda}{\lambda} \, dx$$

$$= C \int_{\mathbb{R}^n} |f(x)| \log^+ |f(x)| \, dx.$$

$\square$

7. A weighted norm inequality

Theorem 2.16. *If w is a non-negative, measurable function and $1 < p < \infty$, then there exists a constant C_p such that*

$$\int_{\mathbb{R}^n} Mf(x)^p w(x) \, dx \leq C_p \int_{\mathbb{R}^n} |f(x)|^p Mw(x) \, dx.$$

Furthermore,

$$(2.11) \qquad \int_{\{x:Mf(x)>\lambda\}} w(x) \, dx \leq \frac{C_1}{\lambda} \int_{\mathbb{R}^n} |f(x)| Mw(x) \, dx.$$

Proof. It will suffice to show that $\|Mf\|_{L^\infty(w)} \leq \|f\|_{L^\infty(Mw)}$ and that the weak $(1,1)$ inequality holds; the strong (p,p) inequality then follows from the Marcinkiewicz interpolation theorem. If $Mw(x) = 0$ for any x, then

$w(x) = 0$ almost everywhere and there is nothing to prove. Therefore, we may assume that for every x, $Mw(x) > 0$. If $a > \|f\|_{L^\infty(Mw)}$ then

$$\int_{\{x:|f(x)|>a\}} Mw(x)\,dx = 0,$$

and so $|\{x \in \mathbb{R}^n : |f(x)| > a\}| = 0$; that is, $|f(x)| \leq a$ almost everywhere. From this it follows that $Mf(x) \leq a$ a.e., so $\|Mf\|_{L^\infty(w)} \leq a$. Hence, $\|Mf\|_{L^\infty(w)} \leq \|f\|_{L^\infty(Mw)}$.

To prove the weak $(1,1)$ inequality we may assume that f is non-negative and $f \in L^1(\mathbb{R}^n)$. (If $f \in L^1(Mw)$ then $f_j = f\chi_{B(0,j)}$ is a sequence of integrable functions which increase pointwise to f.) If $\{Q_j\}$ is the Calderón-Zygmund decomposition of f at height $\lambda > 0$, then as we showed in the proof of Lemma 2.12,

$$\{x \in \mathbb{R}^n : M'f(x) > 4^n\lambda\} \subset \bigcup_j 2Q_j;$$

hence,

$$\int_{\{x:M'f(x)>4^n\lambda\}} w(x)\,dx \leq \sum_j \int_{2Q_j} w(x)\,dx$$

$$= \sum_j 2^n|Q_j|\frac{1}{|2Q_j|}\int_{2Q_j} w(x)\,dx$$

$$\leq \frac{2^n}{\lambda}\sum_j \int_{Q_j} f(y)\left(\frac{1}{|2Q_j|}\int_{2Q_j} w(x)\,dx\right)dy$$

$$\leq \frac{2^nC}{\lambda}\int_{\mathbb{R}^n} f(y)M''w(y)\,dy.$$

Since $M''w(y) \leq C_n Mw(y)$, we get the desired inequality. $\qquad\square$

If w is such that $Mw(x) \leq w(x)$ a.e., then these inequalities hold with the same weight w on both sides. Functions which satisfy this condition are called A_1 weights, and we will consider them in greater detail in Chapter 7.

8. Notes and further results

8.1. References.

The maximal function for $n = 1$ was introduced by G. H. Hardy and J. E. Littlewood (*A maximal theorem with function-theoretic applications*, Acta Math. **54** (1930), 81–116), and for $n > 1$ by N. Wiener (*The ergodic theorem*, Duke Math. J. **5** (1939), 1–18). In their article, Hardy and Littlewood first consider the discrete case, about which they say: "The problem is most easily grasped when stated in the language of cricket, or any other game in which a player compiles a series of scores of which an average is recorded." Their proof, which uses decreasing rearrangements (see 8.2 below) can be found in Zygmund [**21**]. Our proof follows the ideas of Calderón and Zygmund (*On the existence of certain singular integrals*, Acta Math. **88** (1952), 85–139). The decomposition which bears their name also first appeared in this paper. The method of rotations, discussed in Chapter 4, lets us deduce the strong (p, p) inequality for $n > 1$ from the one-dimensional result. For a discussion of questions related to Theorem 2.2, and in particular the necessity of the condition in that theorem, see de Guzmán [**7**]. The Marcinkiewicz interpolation theorem was announced by J. Marcinkiewicz (*Sur l'interpolation d'opérations*, C. R. Acad. Sci. Paris **208** (1939), 1272–1273). However, he died in World War II and a complete proof was finally given by A. Zygmund (*On a theorem of Marcinkiewicz concerning interpolation of operations*, J. Math. Pures Appl. **34** (1956), 223–248). Both Marcinkiewicz interpolation and Riesz-Thorin interpolation in Chapter 1 have been generalized considerably; see, for example the book by C. Bennett and R. Sharpley (*Interpolation of Operators*, Academic Press, New York, 1988). The weighted norm inequality for the maximal operator is due to C. Fefferman and E. M. Stein (*Some maximal inequalities*, Amer. J. Math. **93** (1971), 107–115).

8.2. The Hardy operator, one-sided maximal functions, and decreasing rearrangements of functions.

Given a function g on $\mathbb{R}^+ = (0, \infty)$ the Hardy operator acting on g is defined by

$$Tg(t) = \frac{1}{t} \int_0^t g(s)\, ds, \quad t \in \mathbb{R}^+.$$

If $g \in L^1(\mathbb{R}^+)$ is non-negative, then, since Tg is continuous, one can show that

$$(2.12) \qquad E(\lambda) = \frac{1}{\lambda} \int_{E(\lambda)} g(t)\, dt,$$

where $E(\lambda) = \{t \in \mathbb{R}^+ : Tg(t) > \lambda\}$. From this and (2.1) we get $\|Tg\|_p \leq p'\|g\|_p$, $1 < p \leq \infty$. Other proofs of this result and generalizations of the operator can be found in the classical book by G. H. Hardy, J. E. Littlewood and G. Pólya (*Inequalities*, Cambridge Univ. Press, Cambridge, 1987, first edition in 1932), or in Chapter 2 of the book by Bennett and Sharpley cited above.

For a function f on $\mathbb{R}$, the one-sided Hardy-Littlewood maximal functions are defined by

$$M^+ f(t) = \sup_{h>0} \frac{1}{h} \int_t^{t+h} |f(s)|\, ds \quad \text{and} \quad M^- f(t) = \sup_{h>0} \frac{1}{h} \int_{t-h}^t |f(s)|\, ds.$$

The maximal function as defined by Hardy and Littlewood corresponds to M^- for functions on $\mathbb{R}^+$ (with $0 < h < t$ in the definition). When $|f|$ is decreasing this maximal function coincides with the Hardy operator acting on $|f|$.

If f is a measurable function on $\mathbb{R}^n$, we can define a decreasing function f^* on $(0, \infty)$, called the decreasing rearrangement of f, that has the same distribution function as f:

$$f^*(t) = \inf\{\lambda : a_f(\lambda) \leq t\}.$$

Because f and f^* have the same distribution function, by (2.1) their L^p norms are equal, as well as any other quantity which depends only on their distribution function. (Cf. Section 8.3 below.) The action of the Hardy operator on f^* is usually denoted by f^{**}.

Hardy and Littlewood showed that for functions on $\mathbb{R}^+$,

(2.13) $|\{x : M^- f(x) > \lambda\}| \leq |\{x : f^{**}(x) > \lambda\}|,$

so the weak $(1,1)$ and strong (p,p) inequalities for M^- follow from the corresponding ones for T.

A beautiful proof of the weak $(1,1)$ inequality for M^+ was given by F. Riesz as an application of his "rising sun lemma" (*Sur un théorème du maximum de MM. Hardy et Littlewood*, J. London Math. Soc. **7** (1932), 10–13). Given a function F on $\mathbb{R}$, a point x is a shadow point of F if there exists $y > x$ such that $F(y) > F(x)$. The set of shadow points of F is denoted by $S(F)$.

Lemma 2.17. *Let F be a continuous function such that*

$$\lim_{x \to +\infty} F(x) = -\infty \quad \text{and} \quad \lim_{x \to -\infty} F(x) = +\infty.$$

Then $S(F)$ is open and can be written as the disjoint union $\bigcup_j (a_j, b_j)$ of finite open intervals such that $F(a_j) = F(b_j)$.

Given $f \in L^1(\mathbb{R})$ and $\lambda > 0$, define $F(x) = \int_0^x |f(t)|\, dt - \lambda x$. Then $E(\lambda) = \{x : M^+ f(x) > \lambda\}$ equals $S(F)$. Using Lemma 2.17 one can deduce that

$$E(\lambda) = \frac{1}{\lambda} \int_{E(\lambda)} |f(x)|\, dx,$$

which is similar to (2.12) for the Hardy operator. The strong (p,p) inequality now follows as before with constant p' (which is sharp). We leave the details of the proof of this and of Lemma 2.17 to the reader.

An inequality similar to (2.13) holds for the maximal operator acting on functions on $\mathbb{R}^n$; in fact, we have the following pointwise inequality: there exist positive constants c_n and C_n such that

$$c_n(Mf)^*(t) \le f^{**}(t) \le C_n(Mf)^*(t), \quad t \in \mathbb{R}^+.$$

The left-hand inequality is due to F. Riesz; the right-hand inequality is due to C. Herz $(n = 1)$ and C. Bennet and R. Sharpley $(n > 1)$. See Chapter 3 of the above-cited book by these authors for a proof and further references.

8.3. The Lorentz spaces $L^{p,q}$.

Let (X, μ) be a measure space. $L^{p,q}(X)$ denotes the space of measurable functions f which satisfy

$$\|f\|_{p,q} = \left(\frac{q}{p} \int_0^\infty [t^{1/p} f^*(t)]^q \, \frac{dt}{t} \right)^{1/q} < \infty$$

when $1 \le p < \infty$, $1 \le q < \infty$, and

$$\|f\|_{p,\infty} = \sup_{t>0} t^{1/p} f^*(t) < \infty$$

when $1 \le p \le \infty$. When $p = q$,

$$\|f\|_{p,p} = \|f^*\|_p = \|f\|_p$$

and we recover L^p. In general, however, $\| \cdot \|_{p,q}$ is not a norm since the triangle inequality only holds when $1 \le q \le p < \infty$ or $p = q = \infty$. But when $1 < p \le \infty$ and $1 \le q \le \infty$, if we replace f^* in the definition of $\|f\|_{p,q}$ with f^{**}, we get a quantity which is equivalent to $\|f\|_{p,q}$ and which defines a norm.

If $q_1 \le q_2$ then $\|f\|_{p,q_2} \le \|f\|_{p,q_1}$, so $L^{p,q_1} \subset L^{p,q_2}$.

An operator T is weak (p,p) precisely when

$$\|Tf\|_{p,\infty} \le C\|f\|_p.$$

The Marcinkiewicz interpolation theorem can be generalized to these spaces; this lets us, for example, give a version of the Hausdorff-Young inequality which is stronger than Corollary 1.20: if $f \in L^p(\mathbb{R}^n)$, $1 < p \le 2$, then $\hat{f} \in L^{p',p}$ and there exists a constant B_p such that

$$\|\hat{f}\|_{p',p} \le B_p\|f\|_p.$$

For more information on decreasing rearrangements and the $L^{p,q}$ spaces, see Stein and Weiss [**18**, Chapter 5] and the book by Bennett and Sharpley cited above. Also see this latter book for more on interpolation theorems, particularly the so-called real method of interpolation which is well suited to Lorentz spaces. These spaces were introduced by G. G. Lorentz in two papers (*Some new functional spaces*, Ann. of Math. **51** (1950), 37–55, and *On the theory of spaces Λ*, Pacific J. Math. **1** (1951), 411–429).

8.4. $L \log L$.

In the proof of Proposition 2.14, the integrability of Mf failed at infinity, and did not exclude local integrability. However, the example $f(x) = x^{-1}(\log x)^{-2}\chi_{(0,1/2]}$ shows that even local integrability can fail. A partial converse of Theorem 2.15 is true and characterizes when Mf is locally integrable.

Theorem 2.18. *If f is an integrable function supported on a compact set B, then $Mf \in L^1(B)$ if and only if $f \log^+ f \in L^1(B)$.*

This is due to E. M. Stein (*Note on the class $L \log L$*, Studia Math. **32** (1969), 305–310); a proof can also be found in García-Cuerva and Rubio de Francia [**6**, p. 146].

At the heart of the proof is a stronger version of the weak $(1,1)$ inequality and a "reverse" weak $(1,1)$ inequality for the maximal function:

$$(2.14) \qquad |\{x \in \mathbb{R}^n : Mf(x) > \lambda\}| \leq \frac{C}{\lambda} \int_{\{x:|f(x)|>\lambda/2\}} |f(x)|\,dx,$$

$$(2.15) \qquad |\{x \in \mathbb{R}^n : Mf(x) > \lambda\}| \geq \frac{c}{\lambda} \int_{\{x:|f(x)|>\lambda\}} |f(x)|\,dx.$$

Inequality (2.14) follows from the weak $(1,1)$ inequality applied to $f_1 = f\chi_{\{x:|f(x)|>\lambda/2\}}$; inequality (2.15) follows from the Calderón-Zygmund decomposition if we replace M by M''.

In this and related problems it would be useful to consider functions f such that $f \log^+ f \in L^1$ as members of a Banach space. Unfortunately, the expression $\int f \log^+ f$ does not define a norm. One way around this is to introduce the Luxemburg norm: given a set $\Omega \subseteq \mathbb{R}^n$, define

$$(2.16) \qquad \|f\|_{L \log L(\Omega)} = \inf\left\{\lambda > 0 : \int_\Omega \frac{|f(x)|}{\lambda} \log^+\left(\frac{|f(x)|}{\lambda}\right)\,dx \leq 1\right\}.$$

By using this we can strengthen the conclusion of Theorem 2.18 to the following inequality: $\|Mf\|_{L^1(B)} \leq C\|f\|_{L \log L(B)}$. (See Zygmund [**21**, Chapter 4].)

By replacing the function $t \log^+ t$ in (2.16) by any convex, increasing function Φ, we get a class of Banach function spaces, $L^\Phi(\Omega)$, which generalize the L^p spaces and are referred to as Orlicz spaces. These have a rich theory; for further information, consult the books by M. A. Krasnosel'skiĭ and Ya. B. Rutickiĭ, (*Convex functions and Orlicz spaces*, P. Noordhoff,

Groningen, 1961), and M. M. Rao and Z. D. Ren, (*Theory of Orlicz Spaces*, Marcel Dekker, New York, 1991).

8.5. The size of constants.

In the proofs in this chapter, the constants which appear in the weak $(1,1)$ and strong (p,p) inequalities, $1 < p < \infty$, for M and M' are of exponential type with exponent n. For the strong (p,p) inequality, the method of rotations (see Corollary 4.7) gives a better constant of the form $C_p n$ for M. Furthermore, one can show that there exist constants C_p, independent of n, such that

$$\|Mf\|_p \le C_p \|f\|_p, \qquad 1 < p < \infty.$$

This result is due to E. M. Stein, and the proof appeared in an article by E. M. Stein and J.-O. Strömberg (*Behavior of maximal functions in $\mathbb{R}^n$ for large n*, Ark. Mat. **21** (1983), 259–269); also see E. M. Stein, *Three variations on the theme of maximal functions* (Recent Progress in Fourier Analysis, I. Peral and J. L. Rubio de Francia, eds., pp. 229–244, North-Holland, Amsterdam, 1985). A partial generalization of this result is possible: let B be a convex set which is symmetric about the origin and define

$$M_B f(x) = \sup_{r>0} \frac{1}{|rB|} \int_{rB} |f(x-y)| \, dy.$$

Then if $p > 3/2$ there exists a constant C_p independent of B and n such that

$$\|M_B f\|_p \le C_p \|f\|_p.$$

For the weak $(1,1)$ inequality, the best constant known for M is of order n. (See the article by Stein and Strömberg cited above.)

For the non-centered maximal function defined by (2.6) (but with balls instead of cubes), the best constant in the strong (p,p) inequality must grow exponentially in n. See L. Grafakos and S. Montgomery-Smith (*Best constants for uncentered maximal functions*, Bull. London Math. Soc. **29** (1997), 60–64).

We note that when $n = 1$ the best constants are known for the one-sided and for the non-centered maximal operator M'' but not for M. In the case of the weak $(1,1)$ inequality for M'', one can use Lemma 2.6 to get $C = 2$, and the function $f(t) = \chi_{[0,1]}$ shows this is the best possible. For the strong (p,p) inequality for M'', see the article by Grafakos and Montgomery-Smith cited above. For lower and upper bounds on the weak $(1,1)$ constants for M, see the article by J. M. Aldaz (*Remarks on the Hardy-Littlewood maximal function*, Proc. Roy. Soc. Edinburgh Sect. A **128** (1998), 1–9).

8.6. Covering lemmas.

A standard approach to proving that the maximal function in $\mathbb{R}^n$ is weak $(1,1)$ is to use covering lemmas. Here we give two; the first is a Vitali-type lemma due to N. Wiener (in the paper cited above). If $B = B(x,r)$ and $t > 0$, then we let $tB = B(x,tr)$.

Theorem 2.19. *Let $\{B_j\}_{j \in \mathcal{J}}$ be a collection of balls in $\mathbb{R}^n$. Then there exists an at most countable subcollection of disjoint balls $\{B_k\}$ such that*

$$\bigcup_{j \in \mathcal{J}} B_j \subset \bigcup_k 5B_k.$$

The second is due independently to A. Besicovitch and A. P. Morse; for a proof and further references, see the book by M. de Guzmán (*Differentiation of Integrals in $\mathbb{R}^n$*, Lecture Notes in Math. **481**, Springer-Verlag, Berlin, 1985).

Theorem 2.20. *Let A be a bounded set in $\mathbb{R}^n$, and suppose that $\{B_x\}_{x \in A}$ is a collection of balls such that $B_x = B(x, r_x)$, $r_x > 0$. Then there exists an at most countable subcollection of balls $\{B_j\}$ and a constant C_n, depending only on the dimension, such that*

$$A \subset \bigcup_j B_j \quad and \quad \sum_j \chi_{B_j}(x) \leq C_n.$$

The same result holds if balls are replaced by cubes; more generally, the point x need not be the center of the ball or cube but must be uniformly close to the center.

Using the Besicovitch-Morse lemma, we can extend our results for the maximal function to L^p spaces with respect to other measures. Given a non-negative Borel measure μ, define the maximal function

$$M_\mu f(x) = \sup_{r>0} \frac{1}{\mu(B_r)} \int_{B_r} |f(x-y)| \, d\mu(y).$$

(If $\mu(B_r) = 0$, define the μ-average of f on B_r to be zero.) Then one can show that M_μ is weak $(1,1)$ with respect to μ; hence, by interpolation it is bounded on $L^p(\mu)$, $1 < p < \infty$.

Note that if we define M'_μ as the maximal operator with respect to cubes, then M_μ and M'_μ need not be pointwise equivalent unless μ satisfies an additional doubling condition: there exists C such that for any ball B, $\mu(2B) \leq C\mu(B)$. Furthermore, if we define the non-centered maximal operator M''_μ, then this need not be weak $(1,1)$ if $n > 1$ unless μ satisfies a doubling condition. In this case the weak $(1,1)$ inequality follows from

Wiener's lemma; when $n = 1$, Lemma 2.6 can be applied even to non-doubling measures. An example of μ such that M_μ'' is not weak $(1,1)$ is due to P. Sjögren (*A remark on the maximal function for measures on* $\mathbb{R}^n$, Amer. J. Math. **105** (1983), 1231–1233). For certain kinds of measures a weaker hypothesis than doubling implies that M_μ'' is weak $(1,1)$; see, for example, the paper by A. Vargas (*On the maximal function for rotation invariant measures in* $\mathbb{R}^n$, Studia Math. **110** (1994), 9–17).

8.7. The non-tangential Poisson maximal function.

Given $f \in L^p(\mathbb{R}^n)$, $u(x,t) = P_t * f(x)$ defines the harmonic extension of f to the upper half-space $\mathbb{R}_+^{n+1} = \mathbb{R}^n \times (0,\infty)$, and $\lim_{t \to 0} P_t * f(x)$ is the limit of this function on the boundary as we approach x "vertically", that is, along the line perpendicular to $\mathbb{R}^n$. More generally, one can consider a non-tangential approach: fix $a > 0$ and let

$$\Gamma_a(x) = \{(y,t) : |y - x| < at\}$$

be the cone with vertex x and aperture a. We can then ask whether

$$\lim_{\substack{(y,t) \to (x,0) \\ (y,t) \in \Gamma_a(x)}} u(y,t) = f(x) \qquad \text{a.e. } x \in \mathbb{R}^n.$$

Since this limit holds for all x if f is continuous and has compact support, it suffices to consider the maximal function

$$u_a^*(x) = \sup_{(y,t) \in \Gamma_a(x)} |u(y,t)|,$$

so as to apply Theorem 2.2. But one can show that there exists a constant C_a, depending on a, such that

$$u_a^*(x) \leq C_a M f(x),$$

and so u_a is weak $(1,1)$ and strong (p,p), $1 < p \leq \infty$.

These results can be generalized to "tangential" approach regions, provided the associated maximal function is weakly bounded. For results in this direction, see, for example, the articles by A. Nagel and E. M. Stein (*On certain maximal functions and approach regions*, Adv. in Math. **54** (1984), 83–106) and D. Cruz-Uribe, C. J. Neugebauer and V. Olesen (*Norm inequalities for the minimal and maximal operator, and differentiation of the integral*, Publ. Mat. **41** (1997), 577–604).

8.8. The strong maximal function.

Let $R(h_1, \ldots, h_n) = [-h_1, h_1] \times \cdots \times [-h_n, h_n]$. If $f \in L^1_{\text{loc}}$, define the strong maximal function of f by

$$M_s f(x) = \sup_{h_1, \ldots, h_n > 0} \frac{1}{|R(h_1, \ldots, h_n)|} \int_{R(h_1, \ldots, h_n)} |f(x - y)| \, dy.$$

Then M_s is bounded on $L^p(\mathbb{R}^n)$, $p > 1$; this is a consequence of the one-dimensional result. However, M_s is not weak $(1,1)$: the best possible inequality is

$$|\{x \in \mathbb{R}^n : M_s f(x) > \lambda\}| \le C \int \frac{|f(x)|}{\lambda} \left(1 + \log^+ \frac{|f(x)|}{\lambda}\right)^{n-1} dx.$$

This result is due to B. Jessen, J. Marcinkiewicz and A. Zygmund (*Note on the differentiability of multiple integrals*, Fund. Math. **25** (1935), 217–234). A geometric proof was given by A. Córdoba and R. Fefferman (*A geometric proof of the strong maximal theorem*, Ann. of Math. **102** (1975), 95–100); also see the article by R. J. Bagby (*Maximal functions and rearrangements: some new proofs*, Indiana Univ. Math. J. **32** (1983), 879–891).

The analog of the Lebesgue differentiation theorem,

$$\lim_{\max(h_i) \to 0} \frac{1}{|R(h_1, \ldots, h_n)|} \int_{R(h_1, \ldots, h_n)} f(x - y)\, dy = f(x) \ \text{a.e.}$$

is false for some $f \in L^1$, but is true if $f(1 + \log^+ |f|)^{n-1}$ is locally integrable, and in particular if $f \in L^p_{\text{loc}}$ for some $p > 1$.

If in the definition of M_s we allow rectangles (that is, parallelepipeds) with arbitrary orientation (and not just with edges parallel to the coordinate axes), then the resulting operator is not bounded on any L^p, $p < \infty$, and the associated differentiation theorem does not hold even for f bounded.

For these and other problems related to differentiation of the integral see de Guzmán [7], the book by the same author cited above, and the monograph by A. M. Bruckner (*Differentiation of integrals*, Amer. Math. Monthly **78** (1971), Slaught Memorial Papers, 12).

8.9. The Kakeya maximal function.

Given $N > 1$, let $\mathcal{R}_N$ be the set of all rectangles in $\mathbb{R}^n$ with $n - 1$ sides of length h and one side of length Nh, $h > 0$. The Kakeya maximal function is defined by

$$\mathcal{K}_N f(x) = \sup_{x \in R \in \mathcal{R}_N} \frac{1}{|R|} \int_R |f|.$$

Since each rectangle in $\mathcal{R}_N$ is contained in a ball of radius $c_n Nh$, the Kakeya maximal function is bounded pointwise by the Hardy-Littlewood maximal function:

$$(2.17) \qquad\qquad \mathcal{K}_N f(x) \le C_n N^{n-1} M f(x).$$

It follows immediately that $\mathcal{K}_N$ is bounded on L^p, $1 < p \le \infty$.

An important problem is to determine the size of the constants as functions of N for the L^p estimates for the Kakeya maximal function. Inequality

(2.17) gives the trivial estimate N^{n-1} for the constant in the weak $(1,1)$ inequality, and it is clear that in L^∞, $\mathcal{K}_N$ has norm 1. Interpolating between these values we get

$$\|\mathcal{K}_N f\|_p \leq C_n N^{(n-1)/p}\|f\|_p, \quad 1 < p < \infty.$$

It is conjectured that the constant can be improved to a power of $\log N$ when $p = n$, which, again by interpolation, would give the following bounds:

(1) if $p \geq n$ then $\|\mathcal{K}_N f\|_p \leq C_n(\log N)^{\alpha_p}\|f\|_p$;

(2) if $1 < p \leq n$ then $\|\mathcal{K}_N f\|_p \leq C_n N^{n/p-1}(\log N)^{\alpha_p}\|f\|_p$.

This conjecture is closely related to two other problems: the Hausdorff dimension of the Kakeya set—a set with Lebesgue measure zero which contains a line segment in each direction (see Stein [**17**, p. 434]); and the boundedness properties of Bochner-Riesz multipliers (see Chapter 8, Sections 5 and 8.3).

This conjecture has been proved completely only when $n = 2$: see the paper by A. Córdoba (*The Kakeya maximal function and the spherical summation multipliers*, Amer. J. Math. **99** (1977), 1–22). In this paper he also discussed the connection with Bochner-Riesz multipliers. Córdoba later proved the result in all dimensions when $1 < p \leq 2$; see *A note on Bochner-Riesz operators* (Duke Math. J. **46** (1979), 505–511). M. Christ, J. Duoandikoetxea and J. L. Rubio de Francia (*Maximal operators related to the Radon transform and the Calderón-Zygmund method of rotations*, Duke Math. J. **53** (1986), 189–209) extended the range to $1 < p \leq (n+1)/2$.

A great deal of activity on this problem has been spurred by the work of J. Bourgain (*Besicovitch type maximal operators and applications to Fourier analysis*, Geom. Funct. Anal. **1** (1991), 147–187). In this paper he proved the conjecture for $1 < p \leq (n+1)/2 + \epsilon_n$, where ϵ_n is given by an inductive formula (for instance, $\epsilon_3 = 1/3$). T. Wolff (*An improved bound for Kakeya type maximal functions*, Rev. Mat. Iberoamericana **11** (1995), 651–674) improved this to $1 < p \leq (n+2)/2$. Recently, J. Bourgain (*On the dimension of Kakeya sets and related maximal inequalities*, Geom. Funct. Anal. **9** (1999), 256–282) has shown that there exists $c > 1/2$ such that the conjecture is true for $p \leq cn$ if n is large enough.

For a discussion of recent results on this problem and its connection with the Kakeya set, see the survey article by T. Wolff (*Recent work connected with the Kakeya problem*, Prospects in Mathematics, H. Rossi, ed., pp. 129–162, Amer. Math. Soc., Providence, 1999).

Chapter 3

The Hilbert Transform

1. The conjugate Poisson kernel

Given a function f in $\mathcal{S}(\mathbb{R})$, its harmonic extension to the upper half-plane is given by $u(x,t) = P_t * f(x)$, where P_t is the Poisson kernel. We can also write (see (1.29))

$$u(z) = \int_0^\infty \hat{f}(\xi)e^{2\pi i z \cdot \xi}\, d\xi + \int_{-\infty}^0 \hat{f}(\xi)e^{2\pi i \bar{z} \cdot \xi}\, d\xi,$$

where $z = x + it$. If we now define

$$iv(z) = \int_0^\infty \hat{f}(\xi)e^{2\pi i z \cdot \xi}\, d\xi - \int_{-\infty}^0 \hat{f}(\xi)e^{2\pi i \bar{z} \cdot \xi}\, d\xi,$$

then v is also harmonic in $\mathbb{R}_+^2$ and both u and v are real if f is. Furthermore, $u + iv$ is analytic, so v is the harmonic conjugate of u.

Clearly, v can also be written as

$$v(z) = \int_{\mathbb{R}} -i\,\mathrm{sgn}(\xi)e^{-2\pi t|\xi|}\hat{f}(\xi)e^{2\pi i x \cdot \xi}\, d\xi,$$

which is equivalent to

(3.1) $$v(x,t) = Q_t * f(x),$$

where

(3.2) $$\hat{Q}_t(\xi) = -i\,\mathrm{sgn}(\xi)e^{-2\pi t|\xi|}.$$

If we invert the Fourier transform we get

(3.3) $$Q_t(x) = \frac{1}{\pi}\frac{x}{t^2 + x^2},$$

the conjugate Poisson kernel. One can immediately verify that $Q(x,t) = Q_t(x)$ is a harmonic function in the upper half-plane and the conjugate of the Poisson kernel $P_t(x)$. More precisely,

$$P_t(x) + iQ_t(x) = \frac{1}{\pi}\frac{t+ix}{t^2+x^2} = \frac{i}{\pi z},$$

which is analytic in $\operatorname{Im} z > 0$.

In Chapter 2 we studied the limit as $t \to 0$ of $u(x,t)$ using the fact that $\{P_t\}$ is an approximation of the identity. We would like to do the same for $v(x,t)$, but we immediately run into an obstacle: $\{Q_t\}$ is not an approximation of the identity and, in fact, Q_t is not integrable for any $t > 0$. Formally,

$$\lim_{t\to 0} Q_t(x) = \frac{1}{\pi x};$$

this is not even locally integrable, so we cannot define its convolution with smooth functions.

2. The principal value of $1/x$

We define a tempered distribution called the principal value of $1/x$, abbreviated p. v. $1/x$, by

$$\text{p. v.}\,\frac{1}{x}(\phi) = \lim_{\epsilon\to 0}\int_{|x|>\epsilon}\frac{\phi(x)}{x}\,dx, \quad \phi \in \mathcal{S}.$$

To see that this expression defines a tempered distribution, we rewrite it as

$$\text{p. v.}\,\frac{1}{x}(\phi) = \int_{|x|<1}\frac{\phi(x)-\phi(0)}{x}\,dx + \int_{|x|>1}\frac{\phi(x)}{x}\,dx;$$

this holds since the integral of $1/x$ on $\epsilon < |x| < 1$ is zero. It is now immediate that

$$\left|\text{p. v.}\,\frac{1}{x}(\phi)\right| \le C(\|\phi'\|_\infty + \|x\phi\|_\infty).$$

Proposition 3.1. *In $\mathcal{S}'$,* $\lim_{t\to 0} Q_t = \frac{1}{\pi}\text{p. v.}\,\frac{1}{x}.$

Proof. For each $\epsilon > 0$, the functions $\psi_\epsilon(x) = x^{-1}\chi_{\{|x|>\epsilon\}}$ are bounded and define tempered distributions. It follows at once from the definition that in $\mathcal{S}'$,

$$\lim_{\epsilon\to 0}\psi_\epsilon = \text{p. v.}\,\frac{1}{x}.$$

Therefore, it will suffice to prove that in $\mathcal{S}'$

$$\lim_{t\to 0}\left(Q_t - \frac{1}{\pi}\psi_t\right) = 0.$$

Fix $\phi \in \mathcal{S}$; then

$$(\pi Q_t - \psi_t)(\phi) = \int_{\mathbb{R}} \frac{x\phi(x)}{t^2 + x^2}\,dx - \int_{|x|>t} \frac{\phi(x)}{x}\,dx$$

$$= \int_{|x|<t} \frac{x\phi(x)}{t^2 + x^2}\,dx + \int_{|x|>t} \left(\frac{x}{t^2 + x^2} - \frac{1}{x}\right)\phi(x)\,dx$$

$$= \int_{|x|<1} \frac{x\phi(tx)}{1 + x^2}\,dx - \int_{|x|>1} \frac{\phi(tx)}{x(1 + x^2)}\,dx.$$

If we take the limit as $t \to 0$ and apply the dominated convergence theorem, we get two integrals of odd functions on symmetric domains. Hence, the limit equals 0. □

As a consequence of this proposition we get that

$$\lim_{t \to 0} Q_t * f(x) = \frac{1}{\pi} \lim_{\epsilon \to 0} \int_{|y|>\epsilon} \frac{f(x - y)}{y}\,dy,$$

and by the continuity of the Fourier transform on $\mathcal{S}'$ and by (3.2) we get

$$\left(\frac{1}{\pi}\,\mathrm{p.\,v.}\,\frac{1}{x}\right)^{\widehat{}}(\xi) = -i\,\mathrm{sgn}(\xi).$$

Given a function $f \in \mathcal{S}$, we define its Hilbert transform by any one of the following equivalent expressions:

$$Hf = \lim_{t \to 0} Q_t * f,$$

$$Hf = \frac{1}{\pi}\,\mathrm{p.\,v.}\,\frac{1}{x} * f,$$

$$(Hf)^{\widehat{}}(\xi) = -i\,\mathrm{sgn}(\xi)\hat{f}(\xi).$$

The third expression also lets us define the Hilbert transform of functions in $L^2(\mathbb{R})$; it satisfies

(3.4) $$\|Hf\|_2 = \|f\|_2,$$

(3.5) $$H(Hf) = -f,$$

(3.6) $$\int Hf \cdot g = -\int f \cdot Hg.$$

3. The theorems of M. Riesz and Kolmogorov

The next theorem shows that the Hilbert transform, now defined for functions in $\mathcal{S}$ or L^2, can be extended to functions in L^p, $1 \le p < \infty$.

Theorem 3.2. *For $f \in \mathcal{S}(\mathbb{R})$, the following assertions are true:*

(1) (Kolmogorov) H *is weak* $(1,1)$:

$$|\{x \in \mathbb{R} : |Hf(x)| > \lambda\}| \leq \frac{C}{\lambda}\|f\|_1.$$

(2) (M. Riesz) H *is strong* (p,p), $1 < p < \infty$:

$$\|Hf\|_p \leq C_p\|f\|_p.$$

Proof. (1) Fix $\lambda > 0$ and f non-negative. Form the Calderón-Zygmund decomposition of f at height λ (see Theorem 2.11); this yields a sequence of disjoint intervals $\{I_j\}$ such that

$$f(x) \leq \lambda \text{ for a.e. } x \notin \Omega = \bigcup_j I_j,$$

$$|\Omega| \leq \frac{1}{\lambda}\|f\|_1,$$

$$\lambda < \frac{1}{|I_j|}\int_{I_j} f \leq 2\lambda.$$

Given this decomposition of $\mathbb{R}$, we now decompose f as the sum of two functions, g and b, defined by

$$g(x) = \begin{cases} f(x) & \text{if } x \notin \Omega, \\ \frac{1}{|I_j|}\int_{I_j} f & \text{if } x \in I_j, \end{cases}$$

and

$$b(x) = \sum_j b_j(x),$$

where

$$b_j(x) = \left(f(x) - \frac{1}{|I_j|}\int_{I_j} f\right)\chi_{I_j}(x).$$

Then $g(x) \leq 2\lambda$ almost everywhere, and b_j is supported on I_j and has zero integral. Since $Hf = Hg + Hb$,

$$|\{x \in \mathbb{R} : |Hf(x)| > \lambda\}|$$
$$\leq |\{x \in \mathbb{R} : |Hg(x)| > \lambda/2\}| + |\{x \in \mathbb{R} : |Hb(x)| > \lambda/2\}|.$$

We estimate the first term using (3.4):

$$|\{x \in \mathbb{R} : |Hg(x)| > \lambda/2\}| \leq \left(\frac{2}{\lambda}\right)^2 \int_{\mathbb{R}} |Hg(x)|^2\,dx$$

$$= \frac{4}{\lambda^2}\int_{\mathbb{R}} g(x)^2\,dx$$

$$\leq \frac{8}{\lambda}\int_{\mathbb{R}} g(x)\,dx$$

$$= \frac{8}{\lambda} \int_{\mathbb{R}} f(x) \, dx.$$

Let $2I_j$ be the interval with the same center as I_j and twice the length, and let $\Omega^* = \bigcup_j 2I_j$. Then $|\Omega^*| \le 2|\Omega|$ and

$$|\{x \in \mathbb{R} : |Hb(x)| > \lambda/2\}| \le |\Omega^*| + |\{x \notin \Omega^* : |Hb(x)| > \lambda/2\}|$$

$$\le \frac{2}{\lambda}\|f\|_1 + \frac{2}{\lambda} \int_{\mathbb{R}\backslash\Omega^*} |Hb(x)| \, dx.$$

Now $|Hb(x)| \le \sum_j |Hb_j(x)|$ almost everywhere: this is immediate if the sum is finite, and otherwise it follows from the fact that $\sum b_j$ and $\sum Hb_j$ converge to b and Hb in L^2. Hence, to complete the proof of the weak $(1,1)$ inequality it will suffice to show that

$$\sum_j \int_{\mathbb{R}\backslash 2I_j} |Hb_j(x)| \, dx \le C\|f\|_1.$$

Even though $b_j \notin \mathcal{S}$, when $x \notin 2I_j$ the formula

$$Hb_j(x) = \int_{I_j} \frac{b_j(y)}{x-y} \, dy$$

is still valid. Denote the center of I_j by c_j; then since b_j has zero integral,

$$\int_{\mathbb{R}\backslash 2I_j} |Hb_j(x)| \, dx = \int_{\mathbb{R}\backslash 2I_j} \left| \int_{I_j} \frac{b_j(y)}{x-y} \, dy \right| dx$$

$$= \int_{\mathbb{R}\backslash 2I_j} \left| \int_{I_j} b_j(y) \left(\frac{1}{x-y} - \frac{1}{x-c_j} \right) dy \right| dx$$

$$\le \int_{I_j} |b_j(y)| \left(\int_{\mathbb{R}\backslash 2I_j} \frac{|y-c_j|}{|x-y||x-c_j|} \, dx \right) dy$$

$$\le \int_{I_j} |b_j(y)| \left(\int_{\mathbb{R}\backslash 2I_j} \frac{|I_j|}{|x-c_j|^2} \, dx \right) dy.$$

The last inequality follows from the fact that $|y - c_j| < |I_j|/2$ and $|x - y| > |x - c_j|/2$. The inner integral equals 2, so

$$\sum_j \int_{\mathbb{R}\backslash 2I_j} |Hb_j(x)| \, dx \le 2 \sum_j \int_{I_j} |b_j(y)| \, dy \le 4\|f\|_1.$$

Our proof of the weak $(1,1)$ inequality is for non-negative f, but this is sufficient since an arbitrary real function can be decomposed into its positive and negative parts, and a complex function into its real and imaginary parts.

(2) Since H is weak $(1,1)$ and strong $(2,2)$, by the Marcinkiewicz interpolation theorem we have the strong (p,p) inequality for $1 < p < 2$. If $p > 2$ we apply (3.6) and the result for $p < 2$:

$$\|Hf\|_p = \sup\left\{\left|\int_{\mathbb{R}} Hf \cdot g\right| : \|g\|_{p'} \leq 1\right\}$$

$$= \sup\left\{\left|\int_{\mathbb{R}} f \cdot Hg\right| : \|g\|_{p'} \leq 1\right\}$$

$$\leq \|f\|_p \sup\{\|Hg\|_{p'} : \|g\|_{p'} \leq 1\}$$

$$\leq C_{p'}\|f\|_p.$$

$\square$

The functions g and b in the proof of the first part of this theorem are traditionally referred to as the good and bad parts of f.

It follows from these proofs that the constants in the strong (p,p) and (p',p') inequalities coincide and tend to infinity as p tends to 1 or infinity. More precisely,

$$C_p = O(p) \quad \text{as} \quad p \to \infty, \quad \text{and} \quad C_p = O((p-1)^{-1}) \quad \text{as} \quad p \to 1.$$

By using the inequalities in Theorem 3.2 we can extend the Hilbert transform to functions in L^p, $1 \leq p < \infty$. If $f \in L^1$ and $\{f_n\}$ is a sequence of functions in $\mathcal{S}$ that converges to f in L^1 (i.e. $\lim \|f_n - f\|_1 = 0$), then by the weak $(1,1)$ inequality the sequence $\{Hf_n\}$ is a Cauchy sequence in measure: for any $\epsilon > 0$,

$$\lim_{m,n\to\infty} |\{x \in \mathbb{R} : |(Hf_n - Hf_m)(x)| > \epsilon\}| = 0.$$

Therefore, it converges in measure to a measurable function which we define to be the Hilbert transform of f.

If $f \in L^p$, $1 < p < \infty$, and $\{f_n\}$ is a sequence of functions in $\mathcal{S}$ that converges to f in L^p, by the strong (p,p) inequality, $\{Hf_n\}$ is a Cauchy sequence in L^p, so it converges to a function in L^p which we call the Hilbert transform of f.

In either case, a subsequence of $\{Hf_n\}$, depending on f, converges pointwise almost everywhere to Hf as defined.

The strong (p,p) inequality is false if $p = 1$ or $p = \infty$; this can easily be seen if we let $f = \chi_{[0,1]}$. Then

$$Hf(x) = \frac{1}{\pi} \log\left|\frac{x}{x-1}\right|,$$

and Hf is neither integrable nor bounded.

In the Schwartz class it is straightforward to characterize the functions whose Hilbert transforms are integrable: for $\phi \in \mathcal{S}$, $H\phi \in L^1$ if and only if $\int \phi = 0$. We leave the proof of this as an exercise for the reader. For more information on the behavior of the Hilbert transform on L^1, see Section 6.5.

In Chapter 6 we will examine the space of integrable functions whose Hilbert transforms are again integrable, and the space (larger than L^∞) in which we can define Hf when f is bounded. (Also see Section 6.6.)

4. Truncated integrals and pointwise convergence

For $\epsilon > 0$, the functions $y^{-1}\chi_{\{|y|>\epsilon\}}$ belong to $L^q(\mathbb{R})$, $1 < q \leq \infty$, so the functions

$$H_\epsilon f(x) = \frac{1}{\pi} \int_{|y|>\epsilon} \frac{f(x-y)}{y} \, dy$$

are well defined if $f \in L^p$, $p \geq 1$. Moreover, H_ϵ satisfies weak $(1,1)$ and strong (p,p) estimates like those in Theorem 3.2 with constants that are uniformly bounded for all ϵ. To see this, we first note that

$$\left(\frac{1}{y} \chi_{\{|y|>\epsilon\}} \right)^{\widehat{}} (\xi) = \lim_{N\to\infty} \int_{\epsilon<|y|<N} \frac{e^{-2\pi i y\xi}}{y} \, dy$$

$$= \lim_{N\to\infty} \int_{\epsilon<|y|<N} -i \frac{\sin(2\pi y\xi)}{y} \, dy$$

$$= -2i \operatorname{sgn}(\xi) \lim_{N\to\infty} \int_{2\pi\epsilon|\xi|}^{2\pi N|\xi|} \frac{\sin(t)}{t} \, dt.$$

This is uniformly bounded, so the strong $(2,2)$ inequality holds with constant independent of ϵ. We can now prove the weak $(1,1)$ inequality exactly as in Theorem 3.2, and the strong (p,p) inequalities follow by interpolation and duality.

If we fix $f \in L^p$, $1 \leq p < \infty$, then the sequence $\{H_\epsilon f\}$ converges to Hf as defined above in L^p norm if $p > 1$ and in measure if $p = 1$. To see this, fix a sequence $\{f_n\}$ converging to f in L^p. Then

$$Hf = \lim_{n\to\infty} Hf_n = \lim_{n\to\infty} \lim_{\epsilon\to 0} H_\epsilon f_n = \lim_{\epsilon\to 0} \lim_{n\to\infty} H_\epsilon f_n = \lim_{\epsilon\to 0} H_\epsilon f;$$

the second and third equalities hold because of the corresponding (uniform) (p,p) inequality.

We now want to show that the same equality holds pointwise almost everywhere.

Theorem 3.3. *Given* $f \in L^p$, $1 \leq p < \infty$, *then*

(3.7) $$Hf(x) = \lim_{\epsilon \to 0} H_\epsilon f(x) \quad a.e. \ x \in \mathbb{R}.$$

Since we know that (3.7) holds for some subsequence $\{H_{\epsilon_k} f\}$, we only need to show that $\lim H_\epsilon f(x)$ exists for almost every x. By Theorem 2.2 (and the remarks following it) it will suffice to show that the maximal operator

$$H^* f(x) = \sup_{\epsilon > 0} |H_\epsilon f(x)|$$

is weak (p, p). This however, follows from the next result.

Theorem 3.4. H^* *is strong* (p, p), $1 < p < \infty$, *and weak* $(1, 1)$.

To prove this we need a lemma which is referred to as Cotlar's inequality.

Lemma 3.5. *If* $f \in \mathcal{S}$ *then* $H^* f(x) \leq M(Hf)(x) + CMf(x)$.

Proof. It will suffice to prove this inequality for each H_ϵ with a constant independent of ϵ.

Fix a function $\phi \in \mathcal{S}(\mathbb{R})$ which is non-negative, even, decreasing on $(0, \infty)$, supported on $\{x \in \mathbb{R} : |x| \leq 1/2\}$ and has integral 1. Let $\phi_\epsilon(x) = \epsilon^{-1}\phi(x/\epsilon)$. Then

$$\frac{1}{y}\chi_{\{|y|>\epsilon\}} = \left(\phi_\epsilon * \text{p. v.} \frac{1}{x}\right)(y) + \left[\frac{1}{y}\chi_{\{|y|>\epsilon\}} - \left(\phi_\epsilon * \text{p. v.} \frac{1}{x}\right)(y)\right],$$

and the convolution of the first term on the right-hand side with f is dominated by $M(Hf)(x)$ (cf. Proposition 2.7). It will suffice to find the pointwise estimate for the second term when $\epsilon = 1$ since it follows for any other ϵ by dilation.

If $|y| > 1$ then

$$\left|\frac{1}{y} - \int_{|x|<1/2} \frac{\phi(x)}{y-x}\,dx\right| = \left|\int_{|x|<1/2} \phi(x)\left(\frac{1}{y} - \frac{1}{y-x}\right)dx\right|$$

$$\leq \int_{|x|<1/2} \frac{\phi(x)|x|}{|y||y-x|}\,dx$$

$$\leq \frac{C}{y^2};$$

if $|y| < 1$ then

$$\left|-\lim_{\delta \to 0}\int_{|x|>\delta} \frac{\phi(y-x)}{x}\,dx\right| \leq \left|\int_{|x|<2} \frac{\phi(y-x)-\phi(y)}{x}\,dx\right| \leq C.$$

Hence,

$$\left| \frac{1}{y} \chi_{\{|y|>\epsilon\}} - \left(\phi_\epsilon * \mathrm{p.\,v.\,} \frac{1}{x} \right)(y) \right| \le \frac{C}{1+y^2},$$

and by Proposition 2.7 the convolution of the right-hand term with f is dominated by $Mf(x)$. $\square$

Proof of Theorem 3.4. Since both the maximal function and the Hilbert transform are strong (p,p), $1 < p < \infty$, it follows at once from Lemma 3.5 that H^* is strong (p,p).

To show that H^* is weak $(1,1)$, we argue initially as in the proof of Theorem 3.2. We may assume that $f \ge 0$. Now fix $\lambda > 0$ and form the Calderón-Zygmund decomposition of f at height λ. Then we can write f as

$$f = g + b = g + \sum_j b_j.$$

The part of the argument involving g proceeds as in Theorem 3.2 using the fact that H^* is strong $(2,2)$. Therefore, the problem reduces to showing that

$$|\{x \notin \Omega^* : H^* b(x) > \lambda\}| \le \frac{C}{\lambda} \|b\|_1.$$

Fix $x \notin \Omega^*$, $\epsilon > 0$ and b_j with support I_j. Then one of the following holds:

(1) $(x - \epsilon, x + \epsilon) \cap I_j = I_j$,

(2) $(x - \epsilon, x + \epsilon) \cap I_j = \emptyset$,

(3) $x - \epsilon \in I_j$ or $x + \epsilon \in I_j$.

In the first case, $H_\epsilon b_j(x) = 0$. In the second, $H_\epsilon b_j(x) = H b_j(x)$; hence, if we let c_j denote the center of I_j, since b_j has zero average,

$$|H_\epsilon b_j(x)| \le \int_{I_j} \left| \frac{1}{x-y} - \frac{1}{x-c_j} \right| |b_j(y)|\, dy \le \frac{|I_j|}{|x-c_j|^2} \|b_j\|_1.$$

In the third case, since $x \notin \Omega^*$, $I_j \subset (x - 3\epsilon, x + 3\epsilon)$, and for all $y \in I_j$, $|x - y| > \epsilon/3$. Therefore,

$$|H_\epsilon b_j(x)| \le \int_{I_j} \frac{|b_j(y)|}{|x-y|}\, dy \le \frac{3}{\epsilon} \int_{x-3\epsilon}^{x+3\epsilon} |b_j(y)|\, dy.$$

If we sum over all j's we get

$$|H_\epsilon b(x)| \le \sum_j \frac{|I_j|}{|x-c_j|^2} \|b_j\|_1 + \frac{3}{\epsilon} \int_{x-3\epsilon}^{x+3\epsilon} |b(y)|\, dy$$

$$\le \sum_j \frac{|I_j|}{|x-c_j|^2} \|b_j\|_1 + C M b(x).$$

It follows from this that

$$|\{x \notin \Omega^* : H^*b(x) > \lambda\}| \leq \left| \left\{ x \notin \Omega^* : \sum_j \frac{|I_j|}{|x - c_j|^2} \|b_j\|_1 > \lambda/2 \right\} \right|$$

$$+ |\{x \in \mathbb{R} : Mb(x) > \lambda/2C\}|$$

$$\leq \frac{2}{\lambda} \|b_j\|_1 \sum_j \int_{\mathbb{R} \setminus 2I_j} \frac{|I_j|}{|x - c_j|^2} \, dx + \frac{C'}{\lambda} \|b\|_1$$

$$\leq \frac{C''}{\lambda} \|b\|_1.$$

$\square$

5. Multipliers

Given a function $m \in L^\infty(\mathbb{R}^n)$, we define a bounded operator T_m on $L^2(\mathbb{R}^n)$ by

$$(3.8) \qquad\qquad (T_m f)\widehat{\ }(\xi) = m(\xi)\hat{f}(\xi).$$

By the Plancherel theorem, $T_m f$ is well defined if $f \in L^2$ and

$$\|T_m f\|_2 \leq \|m\|_\infty \|f\|_2.$$

It is easy to see that the operator norm of T_m is $\|m\|_\infty$: fix $\epsilon > 0$ and let A be a measurable subset of $\{x \in \mathbb{R}^n : |m(x)| > \|m\|_\infty - \epsilon\}$ whose measure is finite and positive, and let f be the L^2 function such that $\hat{f} = \chi_A$. Then

$$\|T_m f\|_2 > (\|m\|_\infty - \epsilon)\|f\|_2.$$

We say that m is the multiplier of the operator T_m, though occasionally we will refer to the operator itself as a multiplier. When T_m can be extended to a bounded operator on L^p we say that m is a multiplier on L^p.

For example, the multiplier of the Hilbert transform, $m(\xi) = -i \operatorname{sgn}(\xi)$, is a multiplier on L^p. More generally, given $a, b \in \mathbb{R}$, $a < b$, define $m_{a,b}(\xi) = \chi_{(a,b)}(\xi)$. Let $S_{a,b}$ be the operator associated with this multiplier:

$$(S_{a,b}f)\widehat{\ }(\xi) = \chi_{(a,b)}(\xi)\hat{f}(\xi).$$

We have the equivalent expression

$$(3.9) \qquad\qquad S_{a,b} = \frac{i}{2} \left(M_a H M_{-a} - M_b H M_{-b} \right),$$

where M_a is the operator given by pointwise multiplication by $e^{2\pi i a x}$,

$$M_a f(x) = e^{2\pi i a x} f(x).$$

To see this, note that by (1.16) the multiplier of $i M_a H M_{-a}$ is $\operatorname{sgn}(\xi - a)$. M_a is clearly bounded on L^p, $1 \leq p \leq \infty$, with norm 1. Therefore, from (3.9) and the strong (p, p) inequality for H, we get that $S_{a,b}$ is bounded on

L^p. By making the obvious changes in the argument we see that this is still true if $a = -\infty$ or $b = \infty$. Hence, we have the following result.

Proposition 3.6. *There exists a constant C_p, $1 < p < \infty$, such that for all a and b, $-\infty \le a < b \le \infty$,*

$$\|S_{a,b}f\|_p \le C_p\|f\|_p.$$

For an application of this result, let $a = -R$, $b = R$. Then $S_{a,b}$ is the partial sum operator S_R introduced in Chapter 1: $S_R f = D_R * f$, where D_R is the Dirichlet kernel. Hence,

$$\|S_R f\|_p \le C_p\|f\|_p$$

with a constant independent of R. This yields the following corollary.

Corollary 3.7. *If $f \in L^p(\mathbb{R})$, $1 < p < \infty$, then*

$$\lim_{R \to \infty} \|S_R f - f\|_p = 0.$$

When $p = 1$ we do not have convergence in norm but only in measure:

$$\lim_{R \to \infty} |\{x \in \mathbb{R} : |S_R f(x) - f(x)| > \epsilon\}| = 0.$$

From this result and from Corollary 3.7 we see that there exists a sequence $\{S_{R_k} f(x)\}$ that converges to $f(x)$ for almost every x, but the sequence depends on f.

Given a family of uniformly bounded operators on L^p, any convex combination of them is also bounded. Hence, starting from Proposition 3.6 we can prove another corollary.

Corollary 3.8. *If m is a function of bounded variation on $\mathbb{R}$, then m is a multiplier on L^p, $1 < p < \infty$.*

Proof. Since m is of bounded variation, the limit of $m(t)$ as $t \to -\infty$ exists, so by adding a constant to m if necessary we may assume that this limit equals 0. Furthermore, we may assume m is normalized so that it is right continuous at each $x \in \mathbb{R}$. Let dm be the Lebesgue-Stieltjes measure associated with m; then

$$m(\xi) = \int_{-\infty}^{\xi} dm(t) = \int_{\mathbb{R}} \chi_{(-\infty,\xi)}(t) \, dm(t) = \int_{\mathbb{R}} \chi_{(t,\infty)}(\xi) \, dm(t).$$

Therefore,

$$(T_m f)\hat{\,}(\xi) = \int_{\mathbb{R}} \chi_{(t,\infty)}(\xi)\hat{f}(\xi) \, dm(t),$$

and so

$$T_m f(x) = \int_{\mathbb{R}} S_{t,\infty} f(x) \, dm(t).$$

By Minkowski's inequality

$$\|T_m f\|_p \leq \int_{\mathbb{R}} \|S_{t,\infty} f\|_p \, |dm|(t) \leq C_p \|f\|_p \int_{\mathbb{R}} |dm|(t);$$

the integral of $|dm|$ is the total variation of m and by assumption this is finite. □

Given a multiplier, we can construct others from it by translation, dilation and rotation.

Proposition 3.9. *If m is a multiplier on $L^p(\mathbb{R}^n)$, then the functions defined by $m(\xi + a)$, $a \in \mathbb{R}^n$, $m(\lambda\xi)$, $\lambda > 0$, and $m(\rho\xi)$, $\rho \in O(n)$ (orthogonal transformations), are multipliers of bounded operators on L^p with the same norm as T_m.*

The proof of this result follows at once from properties (1.16), (1.17) and (1.18) of the Fourier transform.

If m is a multiplier on $L^p(\mathbb{R})$, then the function on $\mathbb{R}^n$ given by $\tilde{m}(\xi) = m(\xi_1)$ is a multiplier on $L^p(\mathbb{R}^n)$. In fact, if T_m is the one-dimensional operator associated with m, then for f defined on $\mathbb{R}^n$,

$$T_{\tilde{m}} f(x) = T_m f(\cdot, x_2, \ldots, x_n)(x_1).$$

Then by Fubini's theorem and the boundedness of T_m on $L^p(\mathbb{R})$,

$$\int_{\mathbb{R}^n} |T_{\tilde{m}} f(x)|^p \, dx = \int_{\mathbb{R}^{n-1}} \left(\int_{\mathbb{R}} |T_m f(\cdot, x_2, \ldots, x_n)(x_1)|^p \, dx_1 \right) dx_2 \cdots dx_n$$

$$\leq C \int_{\mathbb{R}^{n-1}} \int_{\mathbb{R}} |f(x_1, \ldots, x_n)|^p \, dx_1 \cdots dx_n.$$

If we take $m = \chi_{(0,\infty)}$, then by Proposition 3.6 m is a multiplier on $L^p(\mathbb{R})$, $1 < p < \infty$. Hence, by the preceding argument the characteristic function of the half-space $\{\xi \in \mathbb{R}^n : \xi_1 > 0\}$ will be a multiplier on $L^p(\mathbb{R}^n)$. Further, by Proposition 3.9 the same will be true for the characteristic function of any half-space (since it can be gotten from the one above by a rotation and translation). The characteristic function of a convex polyhedron with N faces can be written as the product of N characteristic functions of half-spaces, so it is also a multiplier of $L^p(\mathbb{R}^n)$, $1 < p < \infty$. This fact has the following consequence.

Corollary 3.10. *If $P \subset \mathbb{R}^n$ is a convex polyhedron that contains the origin, then*

$$\lim_{\lambda \to \infty} \|S_{\lambda P} f - f\|_p = 0, \quad 1 < p < \infty,$$

where $S_{\lambda P}$ is the operator whose multiplier is the characteristic function of $\lambda P = \{\lambda x : x \in P\}$.

In light of the above observation, it is perhaps surprising that when $n > 1$, the characteristic function of a ball centered at the origin is not a bounded multiplier on $L^p(\mathbb{R}^n)$, $p \neq 2$. We will examine this and related results for multipliers on $\mathbb{R}^n$ in Chapter 8. (Also see Section 6.8 below.)

6. Notes and further results

6.1. References.

The proof of the theorem of M. Riesz first appeared in *Sur les fonctions conjuguées* (Math. Zeit. **27** (1927), 218–244) but had been announced earlier in *Les fonctions conjuguées et les séries de Fourier* (C. R. Acad. Sci. Paris **178** (1924), 1464–1467). The proof in the text became possible only after the Marcinkiewicz interpolation theorem appeared in 1939. See Section 6.3 below for the original proof by Riesz and another one due to M. Cotlar (*A unified theory of Hilbert transforms and ergodic theorems*, Rev. Mat. Cuyana **1** (1955), 105–167). Additional proofs due to A. P. Calderón (*On the theorems of M. Riesz and Zygmund*, Proc. Amer. Math. Soc. **1** (1950), 533–535) and P. Stein (*On a theorem of M. Riesz*, J. London Math. Soc. **8** (1933), 242–247) are reproduced in Zygmund [**22**]. Kolmogorov's theorem is in *Sur les fonctions harmoniques conjuguées et les séries de Fourier* (Fund. Math. **7** (1925), 23–28). Another proof due to L. H. Loomis (*A note on Hilbert's transform*, Bull. Amer. Math. Soc. **52** (1946), 1082–1086) can be found in Zygmund [**22**] and an elegant proof due to L. Carleson is given by Katznelson [**10**]. Our proof uses the Calderón-Zygmund decomposition in the same way that it appears in Chapter 5 for more general singular integrals. It is derived from the proof of A. P. Calderón and A. Zygmund (*On the existence of certain singular integrals*, Acta Math. **88** (1952), 85–139). Theorem 3.5 is in the paper by M. Cotlar cited above.

6.2. The conjugate function and Fourier series.

The results in this chapter can also be developed for functions defined on the unit circle. Historically, they evolved in close connection with the theory of Fourier series discussed in Chapter 1.

Given a function $f \in L^1(\mathbb{T})$ (equivalently, a function in $L^1([0,1])$), its harmonic extension to the unit disk is gotten by convolution with the Poisson kernel

$$P_r(t) = \frac{1 - r^2}{1 - 2r\cos(2\pi t) + r^2}, \quad 0 \leq r < 1,$$

and the harmonic conjugate of $P_r * f(t)$ is gotten by convolution with the conjugate Poisson kernel

$$Q_r(t) = \frac{2r\sin(2\pi t)}{1 - 2r\cos(2\pi t) + r^2}, \quad 0 \le r < 1.$$

The analogue of the Hilbert transform is the conjugation operator which is defined by

$$(3.10) \qquad \tilde{f}(x) = \lim_{r \to 1^-} Q_r * f(x) = \lim_{\epsilon \to 0} \int_{\epsilon < t < 1/2} \frac{f(x-t) - f(x+t)}{\tan(\pi t)} \, dt.$$

Both limits can be shown to exist for almost every x.

The theorems of M. Riesz and Kolmogorov hold for the conjugation operator. Hence, by an argument similar to the one in Section 5 it can be shown that the partial sum operators $S_N f$ of the Fourier series of f are uniformly bounded on L^p, and so $S_N f$ converges to f in L^p. (Cf. Chapter 1, Section 4.)

Given a function $f \in L^1(\mathbb{T})$, its conjugate Fourier series is the trigonometric series

$$\tilde{S}[f](x) = \sum_{-\infty}^{\infty} -i\,\mathrm{sgn}(k)\hat{f}(k)e^{2\pi i k x};$$

when the Fourier series of f is written as in (1.1), then the conjugate series is gotten by switching the coefficients of the sine and cosine terms and taking their difference instead of their sum:

$$\tilde{S}[f](x) = \sum_{k=0}^{\infty} a_k \sin(2\pi k x) - b_k \cos(2\pi k x).$$

When $\tilde{f} \in L^1$ then $\tilde{S}[f]$ coincides with the Fourier series of $\tilde{f}$.

Even for continuous functions the second limit in (3.10) exists because of subtle cancellation and not because the numerator gets small for t close to zero. It can be shown using the Baire category theory that there exists a continuous function f such that for every $x \in [0,1]$,

$$\int_0^{1/2} \frac{|f(x-t) - f(x+t)|}{\tan(\pi t)} \, dt = \infty.$$

The same phenomenon occurs with the Hilbert transform.

For these and further results, see the books by Bary [1], Katznelson [10], Koosis [11] and Zygmund [21].

6.3. Other proofs of the M. Riesz theorem.

The original proof of M. Riesz of the L^p boundedness of the conjugate function is based on the analyticity of powers of an analytic function. The easiest case is when $p = 2k$, k an integer. Given a function f on the unit circle, let $u = P_r * f$ and $v = Q_r * f$; then $F(z) = u + iv$ is analytic in the unit disc and hence so is $F(z)^{2k}$. By Cauchy's theorem

$$\frac{1}{2\pi i} \int_{|z|=r} \frac{F(z)^{2k}}{z}\, dz = \frac{1}{2\pi} \int_0^{2\pi} F(re^{it})^{2k}\, dt = F(0)^{2k}.$$

If $F(0) = 0$ then by taking the real part of $F(re^{it})$ we get that

$$\int_0^{2\pi} |v(re^{it})|^{2k}\, dt \le \sum_{j=1}^k \binom{2k}{2j} \int_0^{2\pi} |u(re^{it})|^{2j}\, |v(re^{it})|^{2k-2j}\, dt.$$

By applying Hölder's inequality (with the appropriate exponent) to each term on the right-hand side, we get

$$\int_0^{2\pi} |v(re^{it})|^{2k}\, dt \le C_k \int_0^{2\pi} |u(re^{it})|^{2k}\, dt,$$

where C_k is independent of the radius of the circle. Taking the limit as the radius tends to 1, u tends to f and v to $\tilde{f}$. (When $F(0) = \hat{f}(0) \ne 0$ replace f by $f - \hat{f}(0)$.)

From the inequality for $p = 2k$, the whole theorem can be obtained using interpolation and duality, but since interpolation was not available in 1923, Riesz next considered the case when $p > 1$ is not an integer. In order to get that $(u+iv)^p$ is analytic, he assumed $u > 0$ (which is true if f is non-negative and not identically zero) and then used a clever estimate. For technical reasons, this argument does not work for p an odd integer, and the inequality for these values of p is gotten by duality. In a letter dated November 1923, Riesz explained to Hardy how he arrived at the proof and showed him the essential details (reproduced in M. L. Cartwright, *Manuscripts of Hardy, Littlewood, M. Riesz and Titchmarsh*, Bull. London Math. Soc. **14** (1982), 472–532).

From the fact that $(u + iv)^2 = u^2 - v^2 + 2iuv$ is analytic we deduce $H(f^2 - (Hf)^2) = 2f \cdot Hf$, which gives the following formula due to Cotlar:

(3.11) $$(Hf)^2 = f^2 + 2H(f \cdot Hf).$$

An alternative way to prove this (proposed by Cotlar in his paper) is to show directly that

$$\widehat{Hf} * \widehat{Hf} = \hat{f} * \hat{f} - 2i\,\mathrm{sgn}(\xi)(\hat{f} * \widehat{Hf}).$$

It follows from (3.11) that if $\|Hf\|_p \le C_p\|f\|_p$, then $\|Hf\|_{2p} \le (C_p + \sqrt{C_p^2 + 1})\|f\|_{2p}$. In fact,

$$\begin{aligned}
\|Hf\|_{2p}^2 &= \|(Hf)^2\|_p \\
&\le \|f^2\|_p + 2\|H(f \cdot Hf)\|_p \\
&\le \|f\|_{2p}^2 + 2C_p\|f \cdot Hf\|_p
\end{aligned}$$

$$\leq \|f\|_{2p}^2 + 2C_p\|f\|_{2p}\|Hf\|_{2p}$$

and the desired inequality follows by solving a quadratic equation.

If we begin with (3.4) and repeatedly apply this inequality we get, for instance, that $\|Hf\|_{2^k} \leq (2^k - 1)\|f\|_{2^k}$ for integers $k \geq 1$. By the Riesz-Thorin interpolation theorem (Theorem 1.19), we get

$$\|Hf\|_p \leq C_p\|f\|_p, \quad p \geq 2.$$

We get the Riesz theorem for $p < 2$ by using duality as in the proof of Theorem 3.2.

An elementary real-variable proof when $p = 2$ (without using the Fourier transform) is the following:

$$\|H_\epsilon f\|^2 = \langle f, -H_\epsilon H_\epsilon f \rangle \leq \|f\|_2 \|H_\epsilon H_\epsilon f\|_2,$$

and the kernel of $H_\epsilon H_\epsilon$, which is the convolution of $y^{-1}\chi_{\{|y|>\epsilon\}}$ with itself, can be computed explicitly and shown to be in L^1. (By a dilation argument, it suffices to consider the case $\epsilon = 1$.) This proof is attributed to N. Lusin (1951) by E. M. Dyn'kin (*Methods of the theory of singular integrals: Hilbert transform and Calderón-Zygmund theory*, Commutative Harmonic Analysis, I, V. Havin and N. Nikolskii, eds., pp. 167–259, Springer-Verlag, Berlin, 1991). A similar argument had been used earlier by Schur for a discrete version of the operator.

Another real-variable proof when $p = 2$ using Cotlar's lemma is in Chapter 9, Section 1.

6.4. The size of constants.

The best constants in the theorems of Kolmogorov and M. Riesz are known. For the strong (p,p) inequality, $1 < p < \infty$, the best constants are $C_p = \tan(\pi/2p)$, $1 < p \leq 2$, and $C_p = \cot(\pi/2p)$, $2 \leq p < \infty$. This was first proved by S. K. Pichorides (*On the best values of the constants in the theorems of M. Riesz, Zygmund and Kolmogorov*, Studia Math. **44** (1972), 165–179); a much simpler proof was later given by L. Grafakos (*Best bounds for the Hilbert transform on $L^p(\mathbb{R}^1)$*, Math. Res. Let. **4** (1997), 469–471).

In the proof of the M. Riesz theorem due to Cotlar given above, we get the estimate $C_{2p} \leq C_p + \sqrt{C_p^2 + 1}$. If we begin with $C_2 = 1$, the resulting bounds for C_{2^k} are sharp. This fact was first observed by I. Gohberg and N. Krupnik (*Norm of the Hilbert transformation in the space L^p*, Funct. Anal. Appl. **2** (1968), 180–181).

The best constant in the weak $(1,1)$ inequality has a more complex expression:

$$C_1 = \frac{1 + \frac{1}{3^2} + \frac{1}{5^2} + \cdots}{1 - \frac{1}{3^2} + \frac{1}{5^2} - \cdots}.$$

This was first proved by B. Davis (*On the weak type $(1,1)$ inequality for conjugate functions*, Proc. Amer. Math. Soc. **44** (1974), 307–311) using Brownian motion. A non-probabilistic proof was later given by A. Baernstein (*Some sharp inequalities for conjugate functions*, Indiana Univ. Math. J. **27** (1978), 833–852).

6.5. The Hilbert transform on L^1.

As we noted in Section 3, if $f \in L^1$ then Hf need not be. However, unlike the case of the maximal function, there exist $f \in L^1$ such that $Hf \in L^1$. For example, if $f = \chi_{(0,1)} - \chi_{(-1,0)}$ then $Hf(x) = \log(|x^2 - 1|/x^2)$ is integrable.

A simple necessary condition for Hf to be integrable if $f \in L^1$ is that $\hat{f}(0) = \int f = 0$. If f is such that the identity $(Hf)\widehat{\ }(\xi) = -i\,\mathrm{sgn}(\xi)\hat{f}(\xi)$ holds, then it suffices to note that the Fourier transform of an integrable function is continuous, and $\hat{f}(\xi)$ and $-i\,\mathrm{sgn}(\xi)\hat{f}(\xi)$ are both continuous only if $\hat{f}(0) = 0$. This argument clearly works if $f \in L^1 \cap L^2$ since in this case the Fourier transform identity is valid. But one can show that this identity holds if $f, Hf \in L^1$. This would follow if $\phi * (Hf) = H(\phi * f)$ for every $\phi \in \mathcal{S}$: take the Fourier transform of both sides and simplify. This equality can be proved as is done for more general singular integrals in the paper by A. P. Calderón and O. Capri (*On the convergence in L^1 of singular integrals*, Studia Math. **78** (1984), 321–327).

Similarly, when $f, Hf \in L^1$ we have the identity $H(Hf) = -f$. We originally gave this in (3.5) for L^2 functions, and it can be extended to $L^p, 1 < p < \infty$, using the results in this chapter. For f and Hf integrable, a proof using complex analysis is due to E. Hille and J. D. Tamarkin (*On the absolute integrability of the Fourier transform*, Fund. Math. **25** (1935), 329–352). The interesting paper by J. F. Toland (*A few remarks about the Hilbert transform*, J. Funct. Anal. **145** (1997), 151–174) examines this question and provides additional historical information.

In general, $Hf \notin L^1$, so we cannot even define the Hilbert transform of Hf. Nevertheless, if we replace the Lebesgue integral with a more general one, then it is possible to define $H(Hf)$ and to get the identity. (See Zygmund [**21**, Chapter 7].) The above-cited paper by Toland uses this extended notion of the integral.

6.6. $L \log L$ estimates.

The following result characterizes the local integrability of the Hilbert transform; it is analogous to Theorem 2.18 for the maximal function.

Theorem 3.11. *Let B and C be two open balls such that $\bar{B} \subset C$.*

(1) *If $f \log^+ |f| \in L^1(C)$, then $Hf \in L^1(B)$.*

(2) *Conversely, if $f \geq 0$ and $Hf \in L^1(C)$, then $f \log^+ |f| \in L^1(B)$.*

The first part of the theorem is due to A. P. Calderón and A. Zygmund (see the paper cited above). It can be sharpened using Orlicz spaces (cf. Chapter 2, Section 8.4, and Zygmund [**21**, Chapter 4]). The second part is due to E. M. Stein (*Note on the class $L \log L$*, Studia Math. **32** (1969), 305–310). The hypothesis $f \geq 0$ can be replaced by a weaker condition which measures (in some sense) the degree to which $P_t * f$ differs from a positive harmonic function. See the article by J. Brossard and L. Chevalier (*Classe $L \log L$ et densité de l'intégrale d'aire dans $\mathbb{R}_+^{n+1}$*, Ann. of Math. **128** (1988), 603–618).

6.7. Translation invariant operators and multipliers.

Let τ_h be the translation operator: $\tau_h f(x) = f(x - h)$. An operator T is said to be translation invariant if it commutes with τ_h: $\tau_h \circ T = T \circ \tau_h$, $h \in \mathbb{R}^n$. The Hilbert transform, for example, is translation invariant. Such operators are completely characterized by the following result.

Theorem 3.12. *Given a linear operator T which is translation invariant and bounded from $L^p(\mathbb{R}^n)$ to $L^q(\mathbb{R}^n)$ for any pair (p, q), $1 \leq p, q \leq \infty$, then there exists a unique tempered distribution K such that $Tf = K * f$, $f \in \mathcal{S}$.*

If such a T is bounded from L^p to L^q and not zero, then p cannot be greater than q. An elegant and very simple proof of this fact is due to L. Hörmander (*Estimates for translation invariant operators in L^p-spaces*, Acta Math. **104** (1960), 93–139). First note that $\lim_{h \to \infty} \|f + \tau_h f\|_p = 2^{1/p} \|f\|_p$. Let $\|T\|_{p,q}$ be the norm of T as a bounded operator from L^p to L^q. Since T commutes with translations,

$$\|Tf + \tau_h Tf\|_q \leq \|T\|_{p,q} \|f + \tau_h f\|_p;$$

if we let h tend to infinity we get

$$\|Tf\|_q \leq 2^{1/p - 1/q} \|T\|_{p,q} \|f\|_p,$$

and this is possible only when $p \leq q$.

Clearly, if $Tf = K * f$ then T is linear and translation invariant. By the properties of the Fourier transform, $(Tf)\hat{} = \hat{K}\hat{f}$, which implies that $\hat{K}$ is a multiplier of T, at least if $\hat{K} \in L^\infty$, following the definition in Section 5. But if T is bounded on L^p, then by duality (since its adjoint is the convolution with kernel $\tilde{K}(x) = K(-x)$) it is bounded on $L^{p'}$. Thus by interpolation it is bounded on L^2, so the condition that $\hat{K} \in L^\infty$ is necessary, and our assumption that a multiplier m is in L^∞ is justified.

It would be interesting to characterize the distributions K that define bounded operators (equivalently, to characterize the multipliers on L^p), but a complete answer is known only in two cases.

Proposition 3.13.

(1) T *is bounded on* $L^2(\mathbb{R}^n)$ *if and only if* $\hat{K} \in L^\infty$ *and the norm of* T *as an operator on* L^2 *is the norm of* $\hat{K}$ *in* L^∞.

(2) T *is bounded on* $L^1(\mathbb{R}^n)$ *if and only if* K *is a finite Borel measure, and the operator norm of* T *equals the total variation of the measure.*

Note that since p. v. $1/x$ is not a measure, Proposition 3.13 gives another proof that the Hilbert transform is not bounded on L^1.

For all of these results, see Stein and Weiss [**18**, Chapter 1].

6.8. Multipliers of Fourier series.

The multipliers of trigonometric series are precisely bounded sequences, $\{\lambda(k)\}_{k \in \mathbb{Z}}$. The associated operator is defined for $f \in L^2(\mathbb{T})$ by

$$T_\lambda f(x) = \sum_{k \in \mathbb{Z}} \lambda(k) \hat{f}(k) e^{2\pi i k x}.$$

(For multiple Fourier series the definition is the same except that we take $k \in \mathbb{Z}^n$.) T_λ can be written as the convolution of f with a distribution whose Fourier coefficients are $\{\lambda(k)\}$, and there are results analogous to those in Proposition 3.13.

If we know the boundedness properties of a multiplier on $L^p(\mathbb{R})$, then we can deduce results for multipliers of series by restricting the multiplier to the integers.

Theorem 3.14. *Given* $1 \leq p \leq \infty$, *suppose the operator* T *defined by* $Tf = K * f$ *is bounded on* $L^p(\mathbb{R})$. *If* $\hat{K}$ *is continuous at each point of* $\mathbb{Z}$ *and* $\lambda(k) = \hat{K}(k)$, *then the operator* T_λ *associated with this sequence is bounded on* $L^p(\mathbb{T})$ *and* $\|T_\lambda\| \leq \|T\|$.

There is also an analogous n-dimensional result. For a proof see Stein and Weiss [**18**, Chapter 6].

Starting from Theorem 3.14, one can deduce results for the partial sum operators S_N of a Fourier series from the corresponding results for S_R in

Section 5, and in particular one gets the convergence in L^p norm of the partial sums of a Fourier series. (Cf. Chapter 1, Section 4.)

6.9. The Hilbert transform of characteristic functions.

If A is a subset of $\mathbb{R}$ with finite measure, one can show that

$$|\{x \in \mathbb{R} : |H(\chi_A)(x)| > \lambda\}| = \frac{2|A|}{\sinh(\pi\lambda)}.$$

This result was first proved by E. M. Stein and G. Weiss (*An extension of a theorem of Marcinkiewicz and some of its applications*, J. Math. Mech. **8** (1959), 263–284). A simple proof is given by Zygmund [**22**, p. 15].

Chapter 4

Singular Integrals (I)

1. Definition and examples

The singular integrals we are interested in are operators of the form

$$(4.1) \qquad Tf(x) = \lim_{\epsilon \to 0} \int_{|y|>\epsilon} \frac{\Omega(y')}{|y|^n} f(x-y) \, dy,$$

where Ω is defined on the unit sphere in $\mathbb{R}^n$, S^{n-1}, is integrable with zero average and where $y' = y/|y|$.

With these hypotheses, (4.1) is defined for Schwartz functions since it is the convolution of f with the tempered distribution p. v. $\Omega(x')/|x|^n$, defined by

$$(4.2) \quad \text{p. v.} \, \frac{\Omega(x')}{|x|^n}(\phi) = \lim_{\epsilon \to 0} \int_{|x|>\epsilon} \frac{\Omega(x')}{|x|^n} \phi(x) \, dx$$

$$= \int_{|x|<1} \frac{\Omega(x')}{|x|^n} [\phi(x) - \phi(0)] \, dx + \int_{|x|>1} \frac{\Omega(x')}{|x|^n} \phi(x) \, dx.$$

(The second equality follows since Ω has zero average.) Since $\phi \in \mathcal{S}$, both integrals converge. Note that we could also assume, for instance, that ϕ in (4.2) or f in (4.1) is a Lipschitz function of order a with compact support.

Proposition 4.1. *A necessary condition for the limit in* (4.1) *or* (4.2) *to exist is that* Ω *have zero average on* S^{n-1}.

Proof. Let $f \in \mathcal{S}(\mathbb{R}^n)$ be such that $f(x) = 1$ for any $|x| \le 2$. Then for $|x| < 1$,

$$Tf(x) = \int_{|y|>1} \frac{\Omega(y')}{|y|^n} f(x-y) \, dy + \lim_{\epsilon \to 0} \int_{\epsilon<|y|<1} \frac{\Omega(y')}{|y|^n} \, dy.$$

The first integral always converges but the second equals

$$\lim_{\epsilon \to 0} \int_{S^{n-1}} \Omega(y') \, d\sigma(y') \cdot \log(1/\epsilon),$$

and this is finite only if the integral of Ω on S^{n-1} is zero.   □

When $n = 1$ the unit sphere reduces to two points, 1 and -1, and Ω must take opposite values on them. Thus on the real line, any operator of the type in (4.1) is a multiple of the Hilbert transform.

In higher dimensions we consider two examples given by A. P. Calderón and A. Zygmund. First, let $f(x_1, x_2)$ be the density of a mass distribution in the plane. Then its Newtonian potential in the half-space $\mathbb{R}^3_+$ is

$$u(x_1, x_2, x_3) = \int_{\mathbb{R}^2} \frac{f(y_1, y_2)}{(x_1 - y_1)^2 + (x_2 - y_2)^2 + x_3^2} \, dy_1 dy_2.$$

The strength of the gravitational field is gotten by taking partial derivatives of the potential. The component in the x_3 direction is equivalent to a multiple of the Poisson integral which we have already considered. The other two are similar to one another; for example, for the first we formally have that

$$\lim_{x_3 \to 0} \frac{\partial u}{\partial x_1}(x_1, x_2, x_3) = - \int_{\mathbb{R}^2} \frac{f(y_1, y_2)(x_1 - y_1)}{[(x_1 - y_1)^2 + (x_2 - y_2)^2]^{3/2}} \, dy_1 dy_2.$$

This integral does not converge in general, but it exists as a principal value if f is smooth and is in fact the value of the limit of $\partial u/\partial x_1$. It corresponds to a singular integral of the form (4.1) in $\mathbb{R}^2$ with $\Omega(x') = -x_1/|x|$. (In polar coordinates this becomes $\cos(\theta)$.)

The second example is gotten from the logarithmic potential associated with a mass distribution $f(x_1, x_2)$ in the plane (i.e. the solution of the equation $\Delta u = f$):

$$u(x_1, x_2) = \int_{\mathbb{R}^2} f(y_1, y_2) \log \left(\frac{1}{[(x_1 - y_1)^2 + (x_2 - y_2)^2]^{1/2}} \right) dy_1 dy_2.$$

This integral converges absolutely if, for example, f has compact support, and partial derivatives can be taken under the integral sign. However, this is not possible for second derivatives: one can show that $\partial^2 u/\partial x_1 \partial x_2$ is given by an operator of the form (4.1) with $\Omega(x') = 2x_1 x_2/|x|^2$. For more information on this operator, see Section 5.

2. The Fourier transform of the kernel

A function f is homogeneous of degree a if for any $x \in \mathbb{R}^n$ and any $\lambda > 0$,

$$f(\lambda x) = \lambda^a f(x).$$

Given any function ϕ, define $\phi_\lambda(x) = \lambda^{-n}\phi(\lambda^{-1}x)$; then

$$\int_{\mathbb{R}^n} f(x)\phi_\lambda(x)\,dx = \lambda^a \int_{\mathbb{R}^n} f(x)\phi(x)\,dx,$$

so we can define the homogeneity of a distribution as follows.

Definition 4.2. A distribution T is homogeneous of degree a if for every test function ϕ it satisfies

$$T(\phi_\lambda) = \lambda^a T(\phi).$$

A simple computation shows that the distribution given by (4.2) is homogeneous of degree $-n$; details are left to the reader.

Proposition 4.3. *If T is a tempered distribution which is homogeneous of degree a, then its Fourier transform is homogeneous of degree $-n - a$.*

Proof. By Definition 1.16 and property (1.18), if $\phi \in \mathcal{S}$ then

$$\hat{T}(\phi_\lambda) = T(\hat{\phi}(\lambda\cdot)) = \lambda^{-n}T(\hat{\phi}_{\lambda^{-1}}) = \lambda^{-n-a}T(\hat{\phi}) = \lambda^{-n-a}\hat{T}(\phi).$$

$\square$

As a corollary to this proposition we can easily calculate the Fourier transform of $f(x) = |x|^{-a}$ if $n/2 < a < n$. For in this case f is the sum of an L^1 function (its restriction to $\{|x| < 1\}$) and an L^2 function, so by Proposition 4.3, $\hat{f}$ is a homogeneous function of degree $a - n$. Hence, since $\hat{f}$ is rotationally invariant, $\hat{f}(\xi) = c_{a,n}|\xi|^{a-n}$. We calculate $c_{a,n}$ using Lemma 1.14 and (1.21):

$$\int_{\mathbb{R}^n} e^{-\pi|x|^2}|x|^{-a}\,dx = c_{a,n}\int_{\mathbb{R}^n} e^{-\pi|x|^2}|x|^{a-n}\,dx;$$

since

$$\int_0^\infty e^{-\pi r^2} r^b\,dr = \frac{1}{2}\pi^{-\frac{1+b}{2}}\Gamma\left(\frac{1+b}{2}\right),$$

we see that

(4.3) $$\left(|x|^{-a}\right)^{\widehat{\;}}(\xi) = \frac{\pi^{a-\frac{n}{2}}\Gamma\left(\frac{n-a}{2}\right)}{\Gamma\left(\frac{a}{2}\right)}|\xi|^{a-n}.$$

In fact, this formula holds for all a, $0 < a < n$. For $0 < a < n/2$ it follows from the inversion formula (1.22). Further, since $|x|^{-a}$ tends to $|x|^{n/2}$ as $a \to n/2$, and since the Fourier transform is continuous, (4.3) holds with $a = n/2$.

Theorem 4.4. *If Ω is an integrable function on S^{n-1} with zero average, then the Fourier transform of* p. v. $\Omega(x')/|x|^n$ *is a homogeneous function of degree 0 given by*

$$(4.4) \qquad m(\xi) = \int_{S^{n-1}} \Omega(u) \left[\log\left(\frac{1}{|u \cdot \xi'|}\right) - i\frac{\pi}{2} \operatorname{sgn}(u \cdot \xi') \right] d\sigma(u).$$

Proof. By Proposition 4.3 the Fourier transform is homogeneous of degree 0; therefore, we may now assume that $|\xi| = 1$. Since Ω has zero average,

$$m(\xi) = \lim_{\epsilon \to 0} \int_{\epsilon < |y| < 1/\epsilon} \frac{\Omega(y')}{|y|^n} e^{-2\pi i y \cdot \xi} \, dy$$

$$= \lim_{\epsilon \to 0} \int_{S^{n-1}} \Omega(u) \left[\int_{\epsilon}^{1} (e^{-2\pi i r u \cdot \xi} - 1) \frac{dr}{r} + \int_{1}^{1/\epsilon} e^{-2\pi i r u \cdot \xi} \frac{dr}{r} \right] d\sigma(u).$$

Thus $m(\xi) = I_1 - iI_2$, where

$$I_1 = \lim_{\epsilon \to 0} \int_{S^{n-1}} \Omega(u) \left[\int_{\epsilon}^{1} (\cos(2\pi r u \cdot \xi) - 1) \frac{dr}{r} \right.$$

$$\left. + \int_{1}^{1/\epsilon} \cos(2\pi r u \cdot \xi) \frac{dr}{r} \right] d\sigma(u),$$

$$I_2 = \lim_{\epsilon \to 0} \int_{S^{n-1}} \Omega(u) \left[\int_{\epsilon}^{1/\epsilon} \sin(2\pi r u \cdot \xi) \frac{dr}{r} \right] d\sigma(u).$$

By the dominated convergence theorem we can exchange the limit and outer integral. In each inner integral make the change of variables $s = 2\pi r |u \cdot \xi|$. We may assume that $u \cdot \xi \neq 0$, so in I_2 we get

$$\int_{2\pi|u\cdot\xi|\epsilon}^{2\pi|u\cdot\xi|/\epsilon} \sin(s) \operatorname{sgn}(u \cdot \xi) \frac{ds}{s}.$$

As $\epsilon \to 0$ this becomes

$$\operatorname{sgn}(u \cdot \xi) \int_{0}^{\infty} \frac{\sin(s)}{s} \, ds = \frac{\pi}{2} \operatorname{sgn}(u \cdot \xi).$$

After the change of variables in I_1 we get

$$\int_{2\pi|u\cdot\xi|\epsilon}^{1} (\cos(s) - 1) \frac{ds}{s} + \int_{1}^{2\pi|u\cdot\xi|/\epsilon} \cos(s) \frac{ds}{s} - \int_{1}^{2\pi|u\cdot\xi|} \frac{ds}{s};$$

as $\epsilon \to 0$ this becomes

$$\int_{0}^{1} (\cos(s) - 1) \frac{ds}{s} + \int_{1}^{\infty} \frac{\cos(s)}{s} \, ds - \log|2\pi| - \log|u \cdot \xi|.$$

If we integrate against Ω, which has zero average on S^{n-1}, the constant terms disappear and we get the desired formula for m. $\qquad\square$

In formula (4.4) the factor multiplied against Ω has two terms: the first is even and its contribution is zero if Ω is odd; it is not bounded but any power of it is integrable. The second is odd and its contribution is zero if Ω is even; further, it is bounded. Since any function Ω on S^{n-1} can be decomposed into its even and odd parts,

$$\Omega_e(u) = \frac{1}{2}(\Omega(u) + \Omega(-u)), \quad \Omega_o(u) = \frac{1}{2}(\Omega(u) - \Omega(-u)),$$

we immediately get the following corollary.

Corollary 4.5. *Given a function Ω with zero average on S^{n-1}, suppose that $\Omega_o \in L^1(S^{n-1})$ and $\Omega_e \in L^q(S^{n-1})$ for some $q > 1$. Then the Fourier transform of* p. v. $\Omega(x')/|x|^n$ *is bounded.*

From (4.4) one can easily find an integrable function Ω such that m is not bounded. Nevertheless, in Corollary 4.5 we can substitute the weaker hypothesis $\Omega_e \in L \log L(S^{n-1})$, that is,

$$\int_{S^{n-1}} |\Omega_e(u)| \log^+ |\Omega_e(u)| \, d\sigma(u) < \infty.$$

(Recall that $\log^+ t = \max(0, \log t)$.) The sufficiency of this condition follows from the inequality

$$AB \leq A \log A + e^B, \qquad A \geq 1, \, B \geq 0.$$

For in the region $D = \{u \in S^{n-1} : |\Omega(u)| \geq 1\}$,

$$\left| \int_D \Omega(u) \log\left(\frac{1}{|u \cdot \xi'|} \right) d\sigma(u) \right|$$
$$\leq \int_D 2|\Omega(u)| \log(2|\Omega(u)|) \, d\sigma(u) + \int_D |u \cdot \xi'|^{-1/2} \, d\sigma(u).$$

Ω is bounded in the complement of D, and so the integral is finite.

3. The method of rotations

Corollary 4.5 together with the Plancherel theorem gives sufficient conditions for operators T as in (4.1) to be bounded on L^2. In this and the following section we develop techniques due to Calderón and Zygmund which will let us prove they are bounded on L^p, $1 < p < \infty$.

Let T be a one-dimensional operator which is bounded on $L^p(\mathbb{R})$ and let $u \in S^{n-1}$. Starting from T we can define a bounded operator T_u on $\mathbb{R}^n$ as follows: let $L_u = \{\lambda u : \lambda \in \mathbb{R}\}$ and let $L_u^\perp$ be its orthogonal complement in $\mathbb{R}^n$. Then given any $x \in \mathbb{R}^n$, there exists a unique $x_1 \in \mathbb{R}$ and $\bar{x} \in L_u^\perp$ such that $x = x_1 u + \bar{x}$. Now define $T_u f(x)$ to be the value at x_1 of the image under T of the one-dimensional function $f(\cdot u + \bar{x})$. If C_p is the norm of T in $L^p(\mathbb{R})$, then by Fubini's theorem,

$$
\int_{\mathbb{R}^n} |T_u f(x)|^p \, dx = \int_{L_u^\perp} \int_{\mathbb{R}} |T(f(\cdot u + \bar{x})(x_1)|^p \, dx_1 dx
$$

$$
\leq C_p^p \int_{L_u^\perp} \int_{\mathbb{R}} |f(\cdot u + \bar{x})(x_1)|^p \, dx_1 dx
$$

$$
= C_p^p \int_{\mathbb{R}^n} |f(x)|^p \, dx.
$$

Operators gotten in this way include the directional Hardy-Littlewood maximal function,

$$
M_u f(x) = \sup_{h>0} \frac{1}{2h} \int_{-h}^{h} |f(x - tu)| \, dt,
$$

and the directional Hilbert transform,

$$
H_u f(x) = \frac{1}{\pi} \lim_{\epsilon \to 0} \int_{|t|>\epsilon} f(x - tu) \frac{dt}{t}.
$$

Since the operators T_u obtained from the operator T are uniformly bounded on $L^p(\mathbb{R}^n)$, any convex combination of them is also a bounded operator. Hence, the next result is an immediate consequence of Minkowski's integral inequality.

Proposition 4.6. *Given a one-dimensional operator T which is bounded on $L^p(\mathbb{R})$ with norm C_p, let T_u be the directional operators defined from T. Then for any $\Omega \in L^1(S^{n-1})$, the operator T_Ω defined by*

$$
T_\Omega f(x) = \int_{S^{n-1}} \Omega(u) T_u f(x) \, d\sigma(u)
$$

is bounded on $L^p(\mathbb{R}^n)$ with norm at most $C_p \|\Omega\|_1$.

By using this result we can pass from a one-dimensional result to one in higher dimensions. Its most common application is in the *method of rotations*, which uses integration in polar coordinates to get directional operators in its radial part. For example, given $\Omega \in L^1(S^{n-1})$, define the "rough" maximal function

$$
(4.5) \qquad M_\Omega f(x) = \sup_{R>0} \frac{1}{|B(0,R)|} \int_{B(0,R)} |\Omega(y')||f(x-y)| \, dy.
$$

If we rewrite this integral in polar coordinates we get

$$
M_\Omega f(x) = \sup_{R>0} \frac{1}{|B(0,1)|R^n} \int_{S^{n-1}} |\Omega(u)| \int_0^R |f(x-ru)| r^{n-1} \, dr d\sigma(u)
$$

$$\leq \frac{1}{|B(0,1)|} \int_{S^{n-1}} |\Omega(u)| M_u f(x) \, d\sigma(u).$$

Corollary 4.7. *If $\Omega \in L^1(S^{n-1})$ then M_Ω is bounded on $L^p(\mathbb{R}^n)$, $1 < p \leq \infty$.*

If we let $\Omega(u) = 1$ for all u, then M_Ω becomes the Hardy-Littlewood maximal function in $\mathbb{R}^n$; thus the method of rotations shows it is bounded on $L^p(\mathbb{R}^n)$, $p > 1$, starting from the one-dimensional case. Further, it is interesting to note that the L^p constant we get is $O(n)$ since $|S^{n-1}|/|B(0,1)| = n$. (See Chapter 2, Section 8.5.) On the other hand, the method of rotations does not give us the weak $(1,1)$ result. (See Section 7.6.)

We can also apply Proposition 4.6 to operators of the form (4.1) when Ω is odd. In fact, if we fix a Schwartz function f, then

$$Tf(x) = \lim_{\epsilon \to 0} \int_{S^{n-1}} \Omega(u) \int_\epsilon^\infty f(x - ru) \frac{dr}{r} d\sigma(u)$$

$$= \lim_{\epsilon \to 0} \frac{1}{2} \int_{S^{n-1}} \Omega(u) \int_{|r|>\epsilon} f(x - ru) \frac{dr}{r} d\sigma(u);$$

since Ω has zero average, we can argue as we did in (4.2) to get

$$= \frac{1}{2} \lim_{\epsilon \to 0} \int_{S^{n-1}} \Omega(u) \int_{\epsilon<|r|<1} (f(x - ru) - f(x)) \frac{dr}{r} d\sigma(u)$$

$$+ \frac{1}{2} \int_{S^{n-1}} \Omega(u) \int_{|r|>1} f(x - ru) \frac{dr}{r} d\sigma(u).$$

Because $f \in \mathcal{S}$, the inner integral is uniformly bounded, so we can apply the dominated convergence theorem to get

$$= \frac{\pi}{2} \int_{S^{n-1}} \Omega(u) H_u f(x) \, d\sigma(u).$$

Since the Hilbert transform is strong (p,p), $1 < p < \infty$, we have proved the following.

Corollary 4.8. *If Ω is an odd integrable function on S^{n-1}, then the operator T defined by (4.1) is bounded on $L^p(\mathbb{R}^n)$, $1 < p < \infty$.*

In Corollary 4.8 we implicitly defined Tf for $f \in L^p$ as a limit in L^p norm. However, as with the Hilbert transform, we can show that (4.1) holds for almost every x. By an argument similar to the one above we can show that the maximal operator associated with the singular integral,

$$(4.6) \qquad T^*f(x) = \sup_{\epsilon>0} \left| \int_{|y|>\epsilon} \frac{\Omega(y')}{|y|^n} f(x - y) \, dy \right|,$$

satisfies

$$T^* f(x) \le \frac{\pi}{2} \int_{S^{n-1}} |\Omega(u)| H_u^* f(x) \, d\sigma(u),$$

where H_u^* is the directional operator defined from the maximal Hilbert transform. (See Chapter 3, Section 4.) Therefore, we can apply Proposition 4.6 and Theorem 2.2 to get the following.

Corollary 4.9. *With the same hypotheses as before, the operator T^* defined by (4.6) is strong (p,p), $1 < p < \infty$. In particular, given $f \in L^p$, the limit (4.1) holds for almost every $x \in \mathbb{R}^n$.*

An important family of operators with odd kernels consists of the Riesz transforms,

$$(4.7) \qquad R_j f(x) = c_n \, \mathrm{p.\,v.} \int_{\mathbb{R}^n} \frac{y_j}{|y|^{n+1}} f(x-y) \, dy, \quad 1 \le j \le n,$$

where

$$c_n = \Gamma\left(\frac{n+1}{2}\right) \pi^{-\frac{n+1}{2}}.$$

The constant is fixed so that for $f \in L^2$,

$$(4.8) \qquad (R_j f)\widehat{\;}(\xi) = -i \frac{\xi_j}{|\xi|} \hat{f}(\xi);$$

this in turn implies that

$$(4.9) \qquad \sum_{j=1}^{n} R_j^2 = -I,$$

where I is the identity operator in L^2. Since the Schwartz functions are dense in L^p, $p > 1$, this identity in fact holds in every L^p space.

To prove (4.8) one could use Theorem 4.4 directly; instead we will argue as follows. With equality in the sense of distributions,

$$\frac{\partial}{\partial x_j} |x|^{-n+1} = (1-n) \, \mathrm{p.\,v.} \, \frac{x_j}{|x|^{n+1}},$$

so if we apply (4.3) we get

$$\left(\mathrm{p.\,v.} \, \frac{x_j}{|x|^{n+1}}\right)\widehat{\;}(\xi) = \frac{1}{1-n} \left(\frac{\partial}{\partial x_j} |x|^{-n+1}\right)\widehat{\;}(\xi)$$

$$= \frac{2\pi i \xi_j}{1-n} (|x|^{-n+1})\widehat{\;}(\xi)$$

$$= \frac{2\pi i \xi_j}{1-n} \frac{\pi^{\frac{n}{2}-1} \Gamma\left(\frac{1}{2}\right)}{\Gamma\left(\frac{n-1}{2}\right)} |\xi|^{-1}$$

$$= -i \frac{\pi^{\frac{n+1}{2}}}{\Gamma\left(\frac{n+1}{2}\right)} \cdot \frac{\xi_j}{|\xi|}.$$

4. Singular integrals with even kernel

If the function Ω in the singular integral (4.1) is even, then the method of rotations does not apply since we cannot represent the singular integral in terms of the Hilbert transform. However, we ought to be able to argue as follows: by (4.9),

$$Tf = -\sum_{j=1}^{n} R_j^2(Tf) = -\sum_{j=1}^{n} R_j(R_jT)f,$$

and the operator R_jT is odd since it is the composition of an odd and even operator. If we can show that R_jT has a representation of the form (4.1), then by Corollary 4.8, T is bounded on L^p.

In the rest of this section we will make this argument precise by showing that R_jT has the requisite representation.

Let Ω be an even function with zero average in $L^q(S^{n-1})$, for some $q > 1$, and for $\epsilon > 0$ let

(4.10) $$K_\epsilon(x) = \frac{\Omega(x')}{|x|^n} \chi_{\{|x|>\epsilon\}}.$$

Note that $K_\epsilon \in L^r$, $1 < r \leq q$. Thus if $f \in C_c^\infty(\mathbb{R}^n)$ then by taking the Fourier transform we see that

(4.11) $$R_j(K_\epsilon * f) = (R_j K_\epsilon) * f.$$

Lemma 4.10. *With the preceding hypotheses, there exists a function $\widetilde{K}_j$ which is odd, homogeneous of degree $-n$ and such that*

$$\lim_{\epsilon \to 0} R_j K_\epsilon(x) = \widetilde{K}_j(x)$$

in the L^∞ norm on every compact set that does not contain the origin.

Proof. Fix $x \neq 0$ and let $0 < \epsilon < \nu < |x|/2$. Then for almost every such x, by Corollary 4.9

$$R_j K_\epsilon(x) - R_j K_\nu(x) = c_n \lim_{\delta \to 0} \int_{\mathbb{R}^n} \frac{x_j - y_j}{|x-y|^{n+1}} \chi_{\{|x-y|>\delta\}} [K_\epsilon(y) - K_\nu(y)] \, dy$$

$$= c_n \int_{\epsilon < |y| < \nu} \frac{x_j - y_j}{|x-y|^{n+1}} \frac{\Omega(y')}{|y|^n} \, dy;$$

since Ω has zero average,

$$= c_n \int_{\epsilon < |y| < \nu} \left(\frac{x_j - y_j}{|x-y|^{n+1}} - \frac{x_j}{|x|^{n+1}} \right) \frac{\Omega(y')}{|y|^n} \, dy.$$

Therefore, if we apply the mean value theorem to the integrand we get

$$(4.12) \qquad |R_j K_\epsilon(x) - R_j K_\nu(x)| \leq \frac{C}{|x|^{n+1}} \int_{\epsilon < |y| < \nu} \frac{|\Omega(y')|}{|y|^{n-1}} \, dy \leq \frac{C\|\Omega\|_1}{|x|^{n+1}} \nu.$$

Hence, for any $\alpha > 0$, $\{R_j K_\epsilon\}$ is a Cauchy sequence in the L^∞ norm on $\{|x| > \alpha\}$. So for almost every x we can define K_j^* by

$$K_j^*(x) = \lim_{\epsilon \to 0} R_j K_\epsilon(x).$$

The function $R_j K_\epsilon$ is odd, so (by modifying K_j^* on a set of measure zero if necessary) K_j^* is also an odd function.

To find the desired function $\widetilde{K}_j$, fix $\lambda > 0$; then again for almost every x,

$$R_j K_\epsilon(\lambda x) = \lim_{\delta \to 0} c_n \int_{|\lambda x - y| > \delta} \frac{\lambda x_j - y_j}{|\lambda x - y|^{n+1}} K_\epsilon(y) \, dy$$

$$= \lim_{\delta \to 0} c_n \int_{|x-y| > \delta/\lambda} \frac{x_j - y_j}{|x - y|^{n+1}} \lambda^{-n} K_{\epsilon/\lambda}(y) \, dy$$

$$= \lambda^{-n} R_j K_{\epsilon/\lambda}(x).$$

Hence, for almost every x, $K_j^*(\lambda x) = \lambda^{-n} K_j^*(x)$. The set of measure zero where equality does not hold depends on λ, but since K_j^* is measurable, the set

$$D = \{(x, \lambda) \subset \mathbb{R}^n \times (0, \infty) : K_j^*(\lambda x) \neq \lambda^{-n} K_j^*(x)\}$$

has measure zero. Therefore, by Fubini's theorem there exists a sphere centered at the origin of radius ρ, S_ρ, such that $D \cap S_\rho$ has measure zero. We now define

$$\widetilde{K}_j(x) = \begin{cases} \left(\dfrac{\rho}{|x|}\right)^n K_j^*\left(\dfrac{\rho x}{|x|}\right) & \text{if } x \neq 0 \text{ and } \rho x/|x| \notin D \cap S_\rho; \\ 0 & \text{otherwise.} \end{cases}$$

This function is measurable, homogeneous of degree $-n$ (by definition) and odd. Further, $K_j^*(x) = \widetilde{K}_j(x)$ almost everywhere. To see this, let $x \neq 0$ be such that $x_0 = \rho x/|x| \notin D \cap S_\rho$. (The set of x such that $x_0 \in D \cap S_\rho$ has measure zero since $D \cap S_\rho$ has measure zero.) Then for almost every λ,

$$\widetilde{K}_j(\lambda x_0) = \lambda^{-n} \widetilde{K}_j(x_0) = \lambda^{-n} K_j^*(x_0) = K_j^*(\lambda x_0).$$

$\square$

Lemma 4.11. *The kernel $\widetilde{K}_j$ defined in Lemma 4.10 satisfies*

$$\int_{S^{n-1}} |\widetilde{K}_j(u)| \, d\sigma(u) \leq C_q \|\Omega\|_q.$$

Furthermore, if $\widetilde{K}_{j,\epsilon}(x) = \widetilde{K}_j(x)\chi_{\{|x|>\epsilon\}}$, *then* $\Delta_\epsilon = R_j K_\epsilon - \widetilde{K}_{j,\epsilon} \in L^1(\mathbb{R}^n)$ *and* $\|\Delta_\epsilon\|_1 \le C'_q \|\Omega\|_q$.

Proof. By the homogeneity of $\widetilde{K}_j$,

$$
\int_{S^{n-1}} |\widetilde{K}_j(u)|\, d\sigma(u) = \frac{1}{\log 2} \int_{1<|x|<2} |\widetilde{K}_j(x)|\, dx
$$

$$
\le \frac{1}{\log 2} \int_{1<|x|<2} |\widetilde{K}_j(x) - R_j K_{1/2}(x)|\, dx
$$

$$
+ \frac{1}{\log 2} \int_{1<|x|<2} |R_j K_{1/2}(x)|\, dx.
$$

In (4.12) let $\nu = 1/2$ and $|x| > 1$; then if we take the limit as $\epsilon \to 0$ we get

$$(4.13) \qquad\qquad |\widetilde{K}_j(x) - R_j K_{1/2}(x)| \le \frac{C\|\Omega\|_1}{|x|^{n+1}}.$$

Therefore, the first integral on the right-hand side above is bounded by $C\|\Omega\|_1 \le C\|\Omega\|_q$. To bound the second integral, note that

$$
\int_{1<|x|<2} |R_j K_{1/2}(x)|\, dx \le C\|R_j K_{1/2}\|_q \le C\|K_{1/2}\|_q \le C\|\Omega\|_q.
$$

To prove the second assertion it will suffice to show that $\|\Delta_1\|_1 < \infty$ since $\Delta_\epsilon = \epsilon^{-n}\Delta_1(\epsilon^{-1}x)$. But then

$$
\|\Delta_1\|_1 = \int_{\mathbb{R}^n} |R_j K_1(x) - \widetilde{K}_{j,1}(x)|\, dx
$$

$$
\le \int_{|x|<2} |R_j K_1(x)|\, dx + \int_{1<|x|<2} |\widetilde{K}_j(x)|\, dx + \int_{|x|>2} |\Delta_1(x)|\, dx.
$$

The first integral is bounded by $C\|R_j K_1\|_q \le C\|K_1\|_q \le C\|\Omega\|_q$; above we showed that the second integral has the same bound. To see that the third integral is bounded, we argue as we did for (4.13) to get $|\Delta_1(x)| \le C\|\Omega\|_1 |x|^{-n-1}$. $\qquad\square$

Theorem 4.12. *Let* Ω *be a function on* S^{n-1} *with zero average such that its odd part is in* $L^1(S^{n-1})$ *and its even part is in* $L^q(S^{n-1})$ *for some* $q > 1$. *Then the singular integral* T *in (4.1) is bounded on* $L^p(\mathbb{R}^n)$, $1 < p < \infty$.

Proof. By Corollary 4.8 we may assume Ω is even. Further, by arguing as we did for the Hilbert transform, it will suffice to establish the L^p inequality for functions $f \in C_c^\infty(\mathbb{R}^n)$. For such f, $Tf = \lim_{\epsilon \to 0} K_\epsilon * f$. From (4.9) and (4.11) we see that

$$
K_\epsilon * f = -\sum_{j=1}^n R_j \left((R_j K_\epsilon) * f\right),
$$

and in the notation of Lemma 4.11,

$$(R_j K_\epsilon) * f = \widetilde{K}_{j,\epsilon} * f + \Delta_\epsilon * f.$$

By Lemma 4.10, $\widetilde{K}_j$ is an odd, homogeneous kernel of degree $-n$, so by Corollary 4.9,

$$\|\widetilde{K}_{j,\epsilon} * f\|_p \leq C \int_{S^{n-1}} |\widetilde{K}_j(u)| \, d\sigma(u) \|f\|_p \leq C \|\Omega\|_q \|f\|_p.$$

By Lemma 4.11,

$$\|\Delta_\epsilon * f\|_p \leq \|\Delta_\epsilon\|_1 \|f\|_p \leq C \|\Omega\|_q \|f\|_p.$$

If we combine these estimates and use the fact that R_j is bounded in L^p we see that

$$\|K_\epsilon * f\|_p \leq C \|\Omega\|_q \|f\|_p.$$

Since the right-hand side is independent of ϵ, by Fatou's lemma we get

$$\|Tf\|_p \leq C \|\Omega\|_q \|f\|_p$$

and this completes our proof.   □

Another proof of Theorem 4.12 is given below in Chapter 8. (See Corollary 8.21.)

5. An operator algebra

Let $P(\xi) = \sum_a b_a \xi^a$ be a polynomial in n variables with constant coefficients and let $P(D)$ be the associated differential polynomial, that is, the operator given by

$$P(D)f = \sum_a b_a D^a f.$$

It follows from (1.19) that

$$(P(D)f)\widehat{\ }(\xi) = P(2\pi i \xi) \hat{f}(\xi).$$

Define the operator Λ to be the square root of the positive operator $-\Delta$:

(4.14) $$(\Lambda f)\widehat{\ }(\xi) = 2\pi |\xi| \hat{f}(\xi).$$

If P is a homogeneous polynomial of degree m, then

(4.15) $$P(D)f = T(\Lambda^m f),$$

where the operator T is defined by

$$(Tf)\widehat{\ }(\xi) = i^m \frac{P(\xi)}{|\xi|^m} \hat{f}(\xi).$$

The multiplier $P(\xi)/|\xi|^m$ is homogeneous of degree zero and its restriction to S^{n-1} coincides with $P(\xi')$, so it is a C^∞ function. (In fact, it can be shown that T is a linear combination of compositions of Riesz transforms.)

The operator T is not a singular integral of the type given in (4.1) since $P(\xi)$ may not have zero average on S^{n-1}. However, we can get such a singular integral by subtracting a constant, that is, a multiple of the identity operator.

This particular operator T is a special case of the operators in the following result.

Theorem 4.13. *If $m \in C^\infty(\mathbb{R}^n \setminus \{0\})$ is a homogeneous function of degree 0, and T_m is the operator defined by $(T_m f)\widehat{\ } = m\hat{f}$, then there exist $a \in \mathbb{C}$ and $\Omega \in C^\infty(S^{n-1})$ with zero average such that for any $f \in \mathcal{S}$,*

$$T_m f = af + \mathrm{p.\,v.}\,\frac{\Omega(x')}{|x|^n} * f.$$

Since any homogeneous function of degree 0 is the sum of a constant and a homogeneous function of degree 0 with zero average on S^{n-1}, Theorem 4.13 is an immediate consequence of the following lemma.

Lemma 4.14. *Let $m \in C^\infty(\mathbb{R}^n \setminus \{0\})$ be a homogeneous function of degree 0 with zero average on S^{n-1}. Then there exists $\Omega \in C^\infty(S^{n-1})$ with zero average such that $\hat{m}(\xi) = \mathrm{p.\,v.}\,\Omega(x')/|x|^n$.*

Proof. Since m is a tempered distribution, $\hat{m}$ exists. Hence,

$$\left(\frac{\partial^n m}{\partial x_i^n}\right)\widehat{\ }\,(\xi) = C\xi_i^n \hat{m}(\xi),$$

where C is a constant. The function $\partial^n m/\partial x_i^n$ is homogeneous of degree $-n$, in $C^\infty(\mathbb{R}^n \setminus \{0\})$ and has zero average on S^{n-1}. Furthermore,

$$\frac{\partial^n m}{\partial x_i^n} = \mathrm{p.\,v.}\,\frac{\partial^n m}{\partial x_i^n} + \sum_{|a|\leq k} C_a D^a \delta,$$

where δ is the Dirac measure at the origin, since the difference between $\partial^n m/\partial \xi_i^n$ and p. v. $\partial^n m/\partial \xi_i^n$ is a distribution supported at the origin. If we take the Fourier transform of both sides of this equation we get

$$C\xi_i^n \hat{m}(\xi) = \left(\mathrm{p.\,v.}\,\frac{\partial^n m}{\partial x_i^n}\right)\widehat{\ }\,(\xi) + \sum_{|a|\leq k} C_a (2\pi i \xi)^a.$$

The left-hand side and the first term on the right-hand side are homogeneous distributions of degree 0, so the polynomial on the right-hand side reduces to a constant. Thus the right-hand side is a homogeneous function of degree 0 which is in $C^\infty(\mathbb{R}^n \setminus \{0\})$. Since this is valid for $1 \le i \le n$, $\hat{m}$ coincides on $\mathbb{R}^n \setminus \{0\}$ with a homogeneous function of degree $-n$. We will denote its restriction to S^{n-1} by Ω.

To see that Ω has zero average on S^{n-1}, fix a radial function $\phi \in \mathcal{S}$ which is supported on the annulus $1 \le |x| \le 2$ and which is positive on the interior. Then

$$\hat{m}(\phi) = \int_{\mathbb{R}^n} \frac{\Omega(x')}{|x|^n} \phi(x)\, dx = c \int_{S^{n-1}} \Omega(u)\, d\sigma(u),$$

where $c > 0$; furthermore, since $\hat{\phi}$ is radial and m is homogeneous,

$$\hat{m}(\phi) = m(\hat{\phi}) = c' \int_{S^{n-1}} m(u)\, d\sigma(u) = 0.$$

Finally, to see that $\hat{m}$ is identical to p. v. $\Omega(x')/|x|^n$, consider their difference,

$$\hat{m} - \text{p. v.}\, \frac{\Omega(x')}{|x|^n},$$

which is supported at the origin. If we take the inverse Fourier transform of this difference we get a polynomial which must be constant since both m and $(\text{p. v.}\, \Omega(x')/|x|^n)\hat{\ }$ are bounded. Further, this constant must be zero since both m and Ω have zero average on S^{n-1}. $\qquad\square$

Theorem 4.15. *The set $\mathcal{A}$ of operators defined by Theorem 4.13 is a commutative algebra. An element of $\mathcal{A}$ is invertible if and only if m is never zero on S^{n-1}.*

Proof. To see that $\mathcal{A}$ is an algebra, it is enough to note that given m_1 and m_2 with associated operators T_{m_1} and T_{m_2}, $T_{m_1} \circ T_{m_2} = T_{m_1 m_2}$.

Since the identity has the function 1 as its multiplier, T_m is invertible if and only if $T_{1/m} \in \mathcal{A}$, and $1/m \in C^\infty(\mathbb{R}^n \setminus \{0\})$ precisely when $m(\xi) \ne 0$ for any $\xi \in S^{n-1}$. $\qquad\square$

The operator T in (4.15) associated with the polynomial P is thus invertible if and only if $P(\xi)$ is never zero on S^{n-1}, that is, if $P(D)$ is an elliptic operator. If the coefficients of P are real, then m must be even and $\Lambda^m = (-\Delta)^{m/2}$. Thus the problem of solving $P(D)u = f$ reduces to solving $(-\Delta)^{m/2}u = T^{-1}f$. (For more on this operator, see Section 7.7.)

6. Singular integrals with variable kernel

Let $P(x, D)$ be a homogeneous differential polynomial with variable coefficients:

$$P(x, D) = \sum_{|a|=m} b_a(x) D^a.$$

Since for $f \in \mathcal{S}$,

$$D^a f(x) = \int_{\mathbb{R}^n} (2\pi i \xi)^a \hat{f}(\xi) e^{2\pi i x \cdot \xi} \, d\xi,$$

we have that

$$P(x, D) f(x) = \int_{\mathbb{R}^n} P(x, 2\pi i \xi) \hat{f}(\xi) e^{2\pi i x \cdot \xi} \, d\xi.$$

Further, with Λ as defined by (4.14), this has a representation analogous to (4.15):

(4.16) $$P(x, D) f = T(\Lambda^m f),$$

where T is defined by

(4.17) $$Tf(x) = \int_{\mathbb{R}^n} \sigma(x, \xi) \hat{f}(\xi) e^{2\pi i x \cdot \xi} \, d\xi,$$

$$\sigma(x, \xi) = \frac{P(x, i\xi)}{|\xi|^m}.$$

The function σ is homogeneous of degree 0 in the variable ξ. If we substitute the definition of $\hat{f}(\xi)$ into (4.17) we get

$$Tf(x) = \int_{\mathbb{R}^n} \sigma(x, \xi) \int_{\mathbb{R}^n} f(y) e^{-2\pi i y \cdot \xi} \, dy \, e^{2\pi i x \cdot \xi} \, d\xi.$$

Thus formally,

(4.18) $$Tf(x) = \int_{\mathbb{R}^n} K(x, x - y) f(y) \, dy,$$

where

(4.19) $$K(x, z) = \int_{\mathbb{R}^n} \sigma(x, \xi) e^{2\pi i z \cdot \xi} \, d\xi.$$

In other words, for fixed x, $K(x, \cdot)$ is the inverse Fourier transform of $\sigma(x, \cdot)$. By Theorem 4.13, for each x there exists a constant $a(x)$ and a function $\Omega(x, \cdot) \in C^\infty(S^{n-1})$ with zero average on S^{n-1} such that

$$K(x, z) = a(x) \delta(z) + \text{p. v.} \, \frac{\Omega(x, z')}{|z|^n}.$$

This example is the motivation for studying singular integrals with variable kernel:

$$(4.20) \qquad Tf(x) = \lim_{\epsilon \to 0} \int_{|y|>\epsilon} \frac{\Omega(x,y')}{|y|^n} f(x-y) \, dy.$$

We can again apply the method of rotations.

Theorem 4.16. *Let $\Omega(x,y)$ be a function which is homogeneous of degree 0 in y and such that:*

(1) $\Omega(x,-y) = -\Omega(x,y)$;

(2) $\Omega^*(u) = \sup_x |\Omega(x,u)| \in L^1(S^{n-1})$.

Then the operator T given by (4.20) is bounded on $L^p(\mathbb{R}^n)$, $1 < p < \infty$.

Proof. Because Ω is odd, we can argue as in the proof of Corollary 4.8 (where the kernel does not depend on x) to get

$$(4.21) \qquad Tf(x) = \frac{\pi}{2} \int_{S^{n-1}} \Omega(x,u) H_u f(x) \, d\sigma(u), \quad f \in \mathcal{S}.$$

Therefore,

$$|Tf(x)| \le \frac{\pi}{2} \int_{S^{n-1}} \Omega^*(u) |H_u f(x)| \, d\sigma(u)$$

and the desired result follows at once from Proposition 4.6. □

Theorem 4.17. *If in the statement of Theorem 4.16 we replace (2) by*

$$(4.22) \qquad \sup_x \left(\int_{S^{n-1}} |\Omega(x,u)|^q \, d\sigma(u) \right)^q = B_q < \infty$$

for some q, $1 < q < \infty$, then T is bounded on $L^p(\mathbb{R}^n)$, $q' \le p < \infty$.

Proof. Apply Hölder's inequality with exponents q and q' to get

$$(4.23) \qquad |Tf(x)| \le \frac{\pi}{2} B_q \left(\int_{S^{n-1}} |H_u f(x)|^{q'} \, d\sigma(u) \right)^{1/q'}.$$

If we raise this to the q'-th power and integrate with respect to x we get that

$$\|Tf\|_{q'} \le C\|f\|_{q'}.$$

If condition (4.22) holds for some value of q, then it holds for any smaller value, so we obtain the desired inequality for all p, $q' \le p < \infty$. □

When Ω is even there is a result analogous to Theorem 4.17 whose proof resembles that of Theorem 4.12. It can be found in the first article by A. P. Calderón and A. Zygmund cited in Section 7.1.

Operators of the form (4.17) are a special class of pseudo-differential operators. For more information, see Chapter 5, Section 6.9.

7. Notes and further results

7.1. References.

The method of rotations was introduced in an article by A. P. Calderón and A. Zygmund (*On singular integrals*, Amer. J. Math. **78** (1956), 289–309). The examples in Section 1 come from an earlier article by them (*On the existence of certain singular integrals*, Acta Math. **88** (1952), 85–139) which will be discussed in Chapter 5. The proof of Theorem 4.12 for even kernels is taken from course notes by A. P. Calderón (*Singular integrals and their applications to hyperbolic differential equations*, University of Buenos Aires, 1960). It can also be found in the books by Zygmund [**22**] and Neri [**13**]. For a general overview of singular integrals and their applications, see the survey article by A. P. Calderón (*Singular integrals*, Bull. Amer. Math. Soc. **72** (1966), 427–465).

7.2. Spherical harmonics.

A solid harmonic is a homogeneous harmonic polynomial, and its restriction to S^{n-1} is called a spherical harmonic. The spherical harmonics of different degrees are orthogonal with respect to the inner product on $L^2(S^{n-1})$, and among those of a fixed degree there exists an orthogonal subcollection. Thus $L^2(S^{n-1})$ has an orthogonal basis composed of spherical harmonics. Note that if $n = 2$, the basis of spherical harmonics for $L^2(S^1)$ is just $\{e^{ik\theta}, k \in \mathbb{Z}\}$.

The functions $Y_k(x)e^{-\pi|x|^2}$, where Y_k is a solid harmonic of degree k, are eigenfunctions of the Fourier transform:

$$\left(Y_k(x)e^{-\pi|x|^2}\right)^{\widehat{}} (\xi) = i^{-k}Y_k(\xi)e^{-\pi|\xi|^2}.$$

(This is referred to as the Bochner-Hecke formula.)

The utility of spherical harmonics for studying singular integrals is suggested by the following formula: for $k \geq 1$,

$$\left(\mathrm{p.\,v.}\, \frac{Y_k(x')}{|x|^n}\right)^{\widehat{}} (\xi) = i^{-k}\pi^{\frac{n}{2}}\frac{\Gamma\left(\frac{k}{2}\right)}{\Gamma\left(\frac{n+k}{2}\right)}Y_k(\xi').$$

For a singular integral with $\Omega \in L^2(S^{n-1})$ and even, one can give a different proof of Theorem 4.12 using the decomposition of Ω into spherical harmonics. (See Stein and Weiss [18, Chapter 6].)

The properties and uses of spherical harmonics can be found in the books by Stein [15], Stein and Weiss [18] and Neri [13]. Another discussion of spherical harmonics, as part of the general theory of harmonic functions, can be found in the book by S. Axler, P. Bourdon and W. Ramey (*Harmonic Function Theory*, Springer-Verlag, New York, 1992).

7.3. Operator algebras.

Besides the operator algebra studied in Section 5, Calderón and Zygmund considered others of the same type. (See *Algebras of certain singular integral operators*, Amer. J. Math. **78** (1956), 310–320.) In particular, let A_q be the set of operators

$$Tf(x) = af(x) + \lim_{\epsilon \to 0} \int_{|y| > \epsilon} \frac{\Omega(y')}{|y|^n} f(x - y) \, dy,$$

where $a \in \mathbb{C}$ and $\Omega \in L^q(S^{n-1})$. If we define

$$\|T\|_q = |a| + \|\Omega\|_{L^q(S^{n-1})},$$

then there exists a constant B_q which depends only on q such that

$$\|T_1 \circ T_2\|_q \le B_q \|T_1\|_q \|T_2\|_q.$$

The set A_q is a semi-simple commutative Banach algebra.

For more information on algebras of singular integrals, see the article by A. P. Calderón (*Algebras of singular integral operators*, Singular Integrals, Proc. Sympos. Pure Math. **X**, pp. 18–55, Amer. Math. Soc., Providence, 1967).

7.4. More on the method of rotations.

In the proof of Theorem 4.17, we could deduce that $\|Tf\|_p \le C\|f\|_p$ from inequality (4.23) provided that

$$(4.24) \qquad \left(\int_{\mathbb{R}^n} \left(\int_{S^{n-1}} |H_u f(x)|^{q'} \, d\sigma(u) \right)^{p/q'} dx \right)^{1/p} \le C\|f\|_p.$$

In the proof of Theorem 4.17 we used that inequality (4.24) is immediate if $p \ge q'$. However, there are also values $p < q'$ for which (4.24) is true, and this allows us to improve the theorem.

If f is the characteristic function of the ball, then one can show that (4.24) cannot hold unless

$$\frac{n}{p} < \frac{n-1}{q'} + 1.$$

It is conjectured that if $1 < p < \infty$ and p and q' satisfy this condition, then inequality (4.24) holds. It is also conjectured that (4.24) holds for this range of p and q' if H_u is replaced by the associated maximal operator, H_u^*, or by the directional maximal function, M_u.

The following results are known: when $n = 2$ the conjecture for H_u was proved by A. P. Calderón and A. Zygmund (*On singular integrals with variable kernel*, Appl. Anal. **7** (1978), 221–238); when $n \geq 3$ they proved it for $1 < p \leq 2$. M. Cowling and G. Mauceri (*Inequalities for some maximal functions, I*, Trans. Amer. Math. Soc. **287** (1985), 431–455) showed that the same range holds for M_u. M. Christ, J. Duoandikoetxea and J. L. Rubio de Francia (*Maximal operators related to the Radon transform and the Calderón-Zygmund method of rotations*, Duke Math. J. **53** (1986), 189–209) showed that the conjecture is true for all these operators and for p in the range

$$1 < p \leq \max\left(2, \frac{n+1}{2}\right).$$

7.5. $L \log L$ results.

As we noted at the end of Section 2, if $\Omega \in L \log L(S^{n-1})$ is even then the Fourier transform of p. v. $\Omega(x')/|x|^n$ is bounded. Further, Theorem 4.12 can be extended to the case when the even part of Ω is in $L \log L(S^{n-1})$. (See the first article by Calderón and Zygmund cited in Section 7.1.)

These are the best possible results. In the same paper, Calderón and Zygmund noted that if ϕ is any function such that $\phi(t)/t \log t \to 0$ as $t \to \infty$, then there exists an even function Ω such that $\phi(\Omega) \in L^1(S^{n-1})$ but the Fourier transform of p. v. $\Omega(x')/|x|^n$ is unbounded.

Later, M. Weiss and A. Zygmund (*An example in the theory of singular integrals*, Studia Math. **26** (1965), 101–111) showed that given any such ϕ there exists an even Ω, $\phi(\Omega) \in L^1(S^{n-1})$, and a continuous function $f \in L^p(\mathbb{R}^n)$ for every $p \geq 1$, such that for almost every x,

$$\limsup_{\epsilon \to 0} \left| \int_{|y| > \epsilon} \frac{\Omega(y')}{|y|^n} f(x - y)\, dy \right| = \infty.$$

7.6. Weak $(1, 1)$ inequalities.

Proposition 4.6 does not extend to weak $(1, 1)$ inequalities because the Lorentz space $L^{1,\infty}$ is not a normed space. (See Chapter 2, Section 8.3.) Hence, we cannot use the method of rotations to prove weak $(1, 1)$ inequalities for singular integrals of the type (4.1) or even for the rough maximal function M_Ω defined in (4.5). However, the following results are known:

If $\Omega \in L\log L(S^{n-1})$ then M_Ω is weak $(1,1)$. For $n = 2$ this was proved by M. Christ (*Weak type* $(1,1)$ *bounds for rough operators*, Ann. of Math. **128** (1988), 19–42); for $n \geq 2$ this is due to M. Christ and J. L. Rubio de Francia (*Weak type* $(1,1)$ *bounds for rough operators, II*, Invent. Math. **93** (1988), 225–237). It is unknown whether M_Ω is weak $(1,1)$ if $\Omega \in L^1(S^{n-1})$.

If $\Omega \in L\log L(S^{n-1})$ then the operator T in (4.1) is weak $(1,1)$. This was proved by A. Seeger (*Singular integral operators with rough convolution kernels*, J. Amer. Math. Soc. **9** (1996), 95–105). Partial results were obtained earlier by M. Christ and J. L. Rubio de Francia (in the above papers) and by S. Hoffman (*Weak* $(1,1)$ *boundedness of singular integrals with nonsmooth kernels*, Proc. Amer. Math. Soc. **103** (1988), 260–264). By the counter-examples given above this is the best possible result for T for arbitrary Ω. However, it is unknown whether T is weak $(1,1)$ when $\Omega \in L^1(S^{n-1})$ and is odd. P. Sjögren and F. Soria (*Rough maximal operators and rough singular integral operators applied to integrable radial functions*, Rev. Mat. Iberoamericana **13** (1997), 1–18) have shown that for arbitrary $\Omega \in L^1(S^{n-1})$, T is weak $(1,1)$ when restricted to radial functions.

7.7. Fractional integrals and Sobolev spaces.

If $\phi \in \mathcal{S}$ then

$$(-\Delta\phi)^\wedge(\xi) = 4\pi^2|\xi|^2\hat{\phi}(\xi);$$

in Section 5 we defined the square root of the operator $-\Delta$ by

$$(\Lambda\phi)^\wedge(\xi) = 2\pi|\xi|\hat{\phi}(\xi).$$

More generally we can define any fractional power of the Laplacian by

$$\left((-\Delta)^{a/2}\phi\right)^\wedge(\xi) = (2\pi|\xi|)^a\hat{\phi}(\xi).$$

Comparing this to the Fourier transform of $|x|^{-a}$, $0 < a < n$ (see (4.3)), we are led to define the so-called fractional integral operator I_a (also referred to as the Riesz potential) by

$$I_a\phi(x) = \frac{1}{\gamma_a}\int_{\mathbb{R}^n}\frac{\phi(y)}{|x-y|^{n-a}}\,dy,$$

where

$$\gamma_a = \pi^{\frac{n}{2}-a}\frac{\Gamma\left(\frac{a}{2}\right)}{\Gamma\left(\frac{n-a}{2}\right)}.$$

Then with equality in the sense of distributions,

$$(I_a\phi)^\wedge(\xi) = |\xi|^{-a}\hat{\phi}(\xi).$$

If we consider the behavior of I_a on L^p, then homogeneity considerations show that the norm inequality

(4.25) $$\|I_a f\|_q \le C\|f\|_p$$

can hold only if

(4.26) $$\frac{1}{q} = \frac{1}{p} - \frac{a}{n}.$$

In fact, this condition is also sufficient for $1 < p < n/a$.

Theorem 4.18. *Let $0 < a < n$, $1 \le p < n/a$, and define q by (4.26). Then (4.25) holds. If $p = 1$ then I_a satisfies the weak $(1, n/(n-a))$ inequality*

$$|\{x \in \mathbb{R}^n : |I_a f(x)| > \lambda\}| \le C \left(\frac{\|f\|_1}{\lambda}\right)^{n/(n-a)}.$$

For a proof, see Stein [**15**, Chapter 5]. Another proof uses the following inequality due to L. Hedberg (*On certain convolution inequalities*, Proc. Amer. Math. Soc. **36** (1972), 505–510):

(4.27) $$I_a f(x) \le C_a \|f\|_p^{ap/n} M f(x)^{1-ap/n}, \qquad 1 \le p < n/a,$$

where M is the Hardy-Littlewood maximal function. To prove it decompose the integral defining I_a into two parts, one over $\{x : |x - y| \le A\}$ and the other over $\{x : |x - y| > A\}$; apply Proposition 2.7 to the first part and Hölder's inequality to the second. Now choose A so that both terms are the same size. Theorem 4.18 then follows from (4.27) and from the boundedness of M.

Closely related to the fractional integral operator is the fractional maximal function,

$$M_a f(x) = \sup_{r>0} \frac{1}{|B_r|^{1-a/n}} \int_{B_r} |f(x-y)|\, dy, \quad 0 < a < n.$$

M_a satisfies the same norm inequalities as I_a. The weak $(1, n/(n-a))$ inequality can be proved using covering lemma arguments (see Chapter 2, Section 8.6), and M_a is strong $(n/a, \infty)$: by Hölder's inequality

$$\frac{1}{|B_r|^{1-a/n}} \int_{B_r} |f(x-y)|\, dy \le \left(\int_{B_r} |f(x-y)|^{n/a}\, dy\right)^{a/n} \le \|f\|_{n/a}.$$

The strong (p, q) inequalities then follow by interpolation.

For any positive f it is easy to see that $M_a f(x) \le C I_a f(x)$. The reverse inequality does not hold in general, but the two quantities are comparable in norm.

Theorem 4.19. *For* $1 < p < \infty$ *and* $0 < a < n$, *there exists a constant* $C_{a,p}$ *such that*

$$\|I_a f\|_p \leq C_{a,p}\|M_a f\|_p.$$

This result is due to B. Muckenhoupt and R. Wheeden (*Weighted norm inequalities for fractional integrals*, Trans. Amer. Math. Soc. **192** (1974), 261–274). Also see D. R. Adams, *A note on Riesz potentials* (Duke Math. J. **42** (1975), 765–778) and D. R. Adams and L. Hedberg (*Function Spaces and Potential Theory*, Springer-Verlag, Berlin, 1996).

An important application of Theorem 4.18 is in proving the Sobolev embedding theorem. For $1 \leq p < \infty$ and $k \geq 1$ an integer, define the Sobolev space $L_k^p(\mathbb{R}^n)$ to be the space of all functions f such that f and all its derivatives (defined as distributions) up to order k are in L^p. More precisely, let L_k^p be the closure of C_c^∞ under the norm

$$\|f\|_{L_k^p} = \sum_{|a| \leq k} \|D^a f\|_p.$$

Theorem 4.20. *Fix* $1 \leq p < \infty$ *and* $k \geq 1$ *an integer. Then*

(1) *if* $p < n/k$, *then* $L_k^p(\mathbb{R}^n) \subset L^r(\mathbb{R}^n)$ *for all* r, $p \leq r \leq q$, *where* $1/q = 1/p - k/n$;

(2) *if* $p = n/k$, *then* $L_k^p(\mathbb{R}^n) \subset L^r(\mathbb{R}^n)$ *for all* r, $p \leq r < \infty$;

(3) *if* $p > n/k$ *and* $f \in L_k^p(\mathbb{R}^n)$, *then* f *differs from a continuous function on a set of measure* 0.

This result is due to S. L. Sobolev (*On a theorem in functional analysis*, Mat. Sb. **46** (1938), 471–497; English translation in Amer. Math. Soc. Transl. ser. 2, **34** (1963), 39–68).

For all the results in this section, see Stein [**15**, Chapter 5], the book by Adams and Hedberg cited above, and the books by R. Adams (*Sobolev Spaces*, Academic Press, New York, 1975) and W. Ziemer (*Weakly Differentiable Functions*, Springer-Verlag, New York, 1989).

Singular Integrals (II)

1. The Calderón-Zygmund theorem

In the previous chapter we used the Hilbert transform to study singular integrals. In this chapter we are going to consider singular integrals whose kernels have the same essential properties as the kernel of the Hilbert transform. This will let us generalize Theorem 3.2 to get the following result.

Theorem 5.1 (Calderón-Zygmund). *Let K be a tempered distribution in $\mathbb{R}^n$ which coincides with a locally integrable function on $\mathbb{R}^n \setminus \{0\}$ and is such that*

$$(5.1) \qquad\qquad |\hat{K}(\xi)| \leq A,$$

$$(5.2) \qquad \int_{|x|>2|y|} |K(x-y) - K(x)|\, dx \leq B, \quad y \in \mathbb{R}^n.$$

Then for $1 < p < \infty$,

$$\|K * f\|_p \leq C_p \|f\|_p,$$

and

$$|\{x \in \mathbb{R}^n : |K * f(x)| > \lambda\}| \leq \frac{C}{\lambda} \|f\|_1.$$

We will show that these inequalities are true for $f \in \mathcal{S}$, but they can be extended to arbitrary $f \in L^p$ as we did for the Hilbert transform. Condition (5.2) is usually referred to as the Hörmander condition; in practice it is often deduced from another, stronger, condition called the gradient condition.

Proposition 5.2. *The Hörmander condition* (5.2) *holds if for every* $x \neq 0$

(5.3) $$|\nabla K(x)| \leq \frac{C}{|x|^{n+1}}.$$

This follows from the mean value theorem; details are left to the reader.

Proof of Theorem 5.1. Since this proof is (essentially) a repetition of the proof of Theorem 3.2, we will omit the details.

Let $f \in \mathcal{S}$ and let $Tf = K*f$. From (5.1) it follows that $\|Tf\|_2 \leq A\|f\|_2$. It will suffice to prove that T is weak $(1,1)$ since the strong (p,p) inequality, $1 < p < 2$, follows by interpolation, and for $p > 2$ it follows by duality since the adjoint operator T^* has kernel $K^*(x) = K(-x)$ which also satisfies (5.1) and (5.2).

To show that f is weak $(1,1)$, fix $\lambda > 0$ and form the Calderón-Zygmund decomposition of f at height λ. Then, as in Theorem 3.2, we can write $f = g + b$, where $g \in L^2$ and is bounded by $2^n \lambda$ and b is the sum of functions which are supported on disjoint cubes Q_j and have zero average. The argument now proceeds as before, and the proof reduces to showing that

(5.4) $$\int_{\mathbb{R}^n \backslash Q_j^*} |Tb_j(x)| \, dx \leq C \int_{Q_j} |b_j(x)| \, dx,$$

where Q_j^* is the cube with the same same center as Q_j and whose sides are $2\sqrt{n}$ times longer. Denote their common center by c_j. Inequality (5.4) follows from the Hörmander condition (5.2): since each b_j has zero integral, if $x \notin Q_j^*$

$$Tb_j(x) = \int_{Q_j} K(x-y)b_j(y) \, dy = \int_{Q_j} [K(x-y) - K(x-c_j)]b_j(y) \, dy;$$

hence,

$$\int_{\mathbb{R}^n \backslash Q_j^*} |Tb_j(x)| \, dx \leq \int_{Q_j} |b_j(y)| \left(\int_{\mathbb{R}^n \backslash Q_j^*} |K(x-y) - K(x-c_j)| \, dx \right) dy.$$

Since

$$\mathbb{R}^n \backslash Q_j^* \subset \{x \in \mathbb{R}^n : |x - c_j| > 2|y - c_j|\},$$

the term in parentheses is bounded by B, the constant in (5.2). $\qquad \square$

We now consider singular integrals with a homogeneous kernel of degree $-n$, such as we studied in the previous chapter: $K(x) = \Omega(x')/|x|^n$. What must we assume about Ω for the Hörmander condition (5.2) to hold? Clearly,

$\Omega \in C^1(S^{n-1})$ is sufficient by Proposition 5.2. But much weaker conditions are sufficient. For example, define

$$\omega_\infty(t) = \sup\{|\Omega(u_1) - \Omega(u_2)| : |u_1 - u_2| \leq t, \ u_1, u_2 \in S^{n-1}\}.$$

Then we have the following result.

Proposition 5.3. *If Ω satisfies*

$$(5.5) \qquad\qquad \int_0^1 \frac{\omega_\infty(t)}{t}\, dt < \infty,$$

then the kernel $\Omega(x')/|x|^n$ satisfies (5.2).

Condition (5.5) is referred to as a Dini-type condition.

Proof.

$$|K(x-y) - K(x)| = \left| \frac{\Omega((x-y)')}{|x-y|^n} - \frac{\Omega(x')}{|x|^n} \right|$$

$$\leq \frac{|\Omega((x-y)') - \Omega(x')|}{|x-y|^n} + |\Omega(x')| \left| \frac{1}{|x-y|^n} - \frac{1}{|x|^n} \right|.$$

Condition (5.5) implies that Ω is bounded, so on the set $\{|x| > 2|y|\}$ the second term is bounded by $C|y|/|x|^{n+1}$. Thus its integral on this set is finite.

On this set we also have that

$$|(x-y)' - x'| \leq 4\frac{|y|}{|x|},$$

so

$$\int_{|x|>2|y|} \frac{|\Omega((x-y)') - \Omega(x')|}{|x-y|^n}\, dx \leq \int_{|x|>2|y|} \frac{\omega_\infty(4|y|/|x|)}{(|x|/2)^n}\, dx$$

$$= 2^n |S^{n-1}| \int_0^2 \frac{\omega_\infty(t)}{t}\, dt$$

$$\leq C.$$

$\square$

For similar results, see Section 6.2.

From Proposition 5.3 and Corollary 4.5 we immediately get the following corollary to Theorem 5.1.

Corollary 5.4. *If Ω is a function defined on S^{n-1} with zero integral and satisfying (5.5), then the operator*

$$Tf(x) = \mathrm{p.\,v.} \int_{\mathbb{R}^n} \frac{\Omega(y')}{|y|^n} f(x-y)\, dy$$

is strong (p,p), $1 < p < \infty$, and weak $(1,1)$.

Since (5.5) implies that Ω is bounded, we already had the strong (p,p) inequality via the method of rotations. Nevertheless, we now also have the weak $(1,1)$ inequality.

2. Truncated integrals and the principal value

In Theorem 5.1 we assumed that the operator was bounded on L^2 (via the hypothesis that $\hat{K} \in L^\infty$). In this section we give conditions on K which imply this property and which make the associated operator bounded on L^p, $1 < p < \infty$. Given $K \in L^1_{\text{loc}}(\mathbb{R}^n \setminus \{0\})$, define $K_{\epsilon,R}(x) = K(x)\chi_{\{\epsilon < |x| < R\}}$.

Proposition 5.5. *Let $K \in L^1_{\text{loc}}(\mathbb{R}^n \setminus \{0\})$ be such that*

$$(5.6) \qquad \left| \int_{a<|x|<b} K(x)\,dx \right| \leq A, \quad 0 < a < b < \infty;$$

$$(5.7) \qquad \int_{a<|x|<2a} |K(x)|\,dx \leq B, \quad a > 0;$$

$$(5.8) \qquad \int_{|x|>2|y|} |K(x-y) - K(x)|\,dx \leq C, \quad y \in \mathbb{R}^n.$$

Then for all $\xi \in \mathbb{R}^n$, $|\widehat{K_{\epsilon,R}}(\xi)| \leq C$, where C is independent of ϵ and R.

Condition (5.7) is equivalent to

$$(5.9) \qquad \int_{|x|<a} |x||K(x)|\,dx \leq B'a, \quad a > 0.$$

To see this, note that

$$\int_{|x|<a} |x||K(x)|\,dx \leq \sum_{k=0}^{\infty} \int_{2^{-k-1}a<|x|<2^{-k}a} |x||K(x)|\,dx \leq \sum_{k=0}^{\infty} 2^{-k}aB,$$

and

$$\int_{a<|x|<2a} |K(x)|\,dx \leq \int_{|x|<2a} \frac{|x|}{a}|K(x)|\,dx \leq 2B'.$$

Proof. If we fix ξ then whenever $\epsilon < |\xi|^{-1} < R$,

$$\widehat{K_{\epsilon,R}}(\xi) = \int_{\epsilon<|x|<R} K(x)e^{-2\pi i x \cdot \xi}\,dx$$

$$= \int_{\epsilon<|x|<|\xi|^{-1}} K(x)e^{-2\pi i x \cdot \xi}\,dx + \int_{|\xi|^{-1}<|x|<R} K(x)e^{-2\pi i x \cdot \xi}\,dx$$

$$= I_1 + I_2.$$

(If $|\xi|^{-1} < \epsilon$ or if $|\xi|^{-1} > R$, then it suffices to consider just one of the two integrals.) We treat I_1 first:

$$I_1 = \int_{\epsilon < |x| < |\xi|^{-1}} K(x)\, dx + \int_{\epsilon < |x| < |\xi|^{-1}} K(x)(e^{-2\pi i x \cdot \xi} - 1)\, dx,$$

so

$$|I_1| \leq \left| \int_{\epsilon < |x| < |\xi|^{-1}} K(x)\, dx \right| + 2\pi |\xi| \int_{\epsilon < |x| < |\xi|^{-1}} |x| |K(x)|\, dx \leq C(A + B).$$

To evaluate I_2, let $z = \frac{1}{2}\xi |\xi|^{-2}$, so that $\exp(2\pi i z \cdot \xi) = -1$; then if we make the change of variables $x \mapsto x - z$ in I_2 we get

$$I_2 = -\int_{|\xi|^{-1} < |x-z| < R} K(x - z) e^{-2\pi i x \cdot \xi}\, dx.$$

Hence,

$$2I_2 = \int_{|\xi|^{-1} < |x| < R} K(x) e^{-2\pi i x \cdot \xi}\, dx - \int_{|\xi|^{-1} < |x-z| < R} K(x - z) e^{-2\pi i x \cdot \xi}\, dx;$$

this in turn implies that

$$2|I_2| \leq \int_{|\xi|^{-1} < |x|} |K(x) - K(x - z)|\, dx$$

$$+ \int_{\frac{1}{2}|\xi|^{-1} < |x| < \frac{3}{2}|\xi|^{-1}} |K(x)|\, dx$$

$$+ \int_{R - \frac{1}{2}|\xi|^{-1} < |x| < R + \frac{1}{2}|\xi|^{-1}} |K(x)|\, dx.$$

The first integral is bounded by C since $|\xi|^{-1} = 2|z|$. The other two integrals are bounded by $2B$: since $|\xi|^{-1} < R$, $R + \frac{1}{2}|\xi|^{-1} < 3(R - \frac{1}{2}|\xi|^{-1})$. □

Corollary 5.6. *If K satisfies the hypotheses of Proposition 5.5, then*

$$\|K_{\epsilon,R} * f\|_p \leq C_p \|f\|_p, \quad 1 < p < \infty,$$

and

$$|\{x \in \mathbb{R}^n : |K_{\epsilon,R} * f(x)| > \lambda\}| \leq \frac{C_1}{\lambda} \|f\|_1,$$

with constants independent of ϵ and R.

When $p = 2$ this result follows immediately from Proposition 5.5; for the rest note that (5.8) implies the Hörmander condition,

$$\int_{|x| > 2|y|} |K_{\epsilon,R}(x - y) - K_{\epsilon,R}(x)|\, dx \leq C,$$

with C independent of ϵ and R. The details are left as an exercise for the reader.

When the kernel is homogeneous, $K(x) = \Omega(x')/|x|^n$, conditions (5.6) and (5.7) are equivalent to $\Omega \in L^1(S^{n-1})$ and

$$\int_{S^{n-1}} \Omega(u) \, d\sigma(u) = 0.$$

Since $K_{\epsilon,R} \in L^1$, $K_{\epsilon,R} * f$ is well defined for $f \in L^p$. Ideally we could define the singular integral T by the pointwise limit

$$Tf(x) = \lim_{\substack{\epsilon \to 0 \\ R \to \infty}} K_{\epsilon,R} * f(x),$$

but this limit need not exist even if $f \in \mathcal{S}$. In this case we have convergence as $R \to \infty$, so the problem reduces to determining when the principal value distribution of K,

$$\mathrm{p.\,v.}\, K(\phi) = \lim_{\epsilon \to 0} \int_{|x|>\epsilon} K(x)\phi(x) \, dx, \quad \phi \in \mathcal{S},$$

exists.

Proposition 5.7. *Given a function K which satisfies condition (5.7), the tempered distribution* $\mathrm{p.\,v.}\, K$ *exists if and only if*

$$\lim_{\epsilon \to 0} \int_{\epsilon < |x| < 1} K(x) \, dx$$

exists.

Proof. Suppose that the tempered distribution exists. If we fix $\phi \in \mathcal{S}$ which is identically 1 on $B(0,1)$, then

$$\mathrm{p.\,v.}\, K(\phi) = \lim_{\epsilon \to 0} \int_{\epsilon < |x| < 1} K(x) \, dx + \int_{|x|>1} K(x)\phi(x) \, dx.$$

The second integral exists since

$$\int_{|x|>1} |K(x)\phi(x)| \, dx \leq \||x|\phi\|_\infty \sum_{k=0}^{\infty} 2^{-k} \int_{2^k < |x| \leq 2^{k+1}} |K(x)| \, dx \leq 2B \||x|\phi\|_\infty.$$

Therefore, the limit of the first integral must also exist.

Conversely, suppose the limit exists; denote it by L. Then

$$\mathrm{p.\,v.}\, K(\phi) = \phi(0)L + \int_{|x|<1} K(x)(\phi(x) - \phi(0)) \, dx + \int_{|x|>1} K(x)\phi(x) \, dx.$$

Again, the second integral always exists. The first integral exists since $|\phi(x) - \phi(0)| \leq |x|\|\nabla\phi\|_\infty$, and so by (5.9)

$$\int_{|x|<1} |K(x)||\phi(x) - \phi(0)| \, dx \leq \|\nabla\phi\|_\infty \int_{|x|<1} |x||K(x)| \, dx \leq 2B\|\nabla\phi\|_\infty.$$

$\square$

Corollary 5.8. *If we add to the hypotheses of Proposition* 5.5 *the assumption that*

$$\lim_{\epsilon \to 0} \int_{\epsilon < |x| < 1} K(x) \, dx$$

exists, then

$$Tf(x) = \lim_{\epsilon \to 0} \int_{|y| > \epsilon} K(y) f(x - y) \, dy$$

can be extended to an operator which is bounded on L^p, $1 < p < \infty$, and is weak $(1,1)$.

Example 5.9 (An application to $K(x) = |x|^{-n-it}$). The function $|x|^{-n-it}$ is locally integrable on $\mathbb{R}^n \setminus \{0\}$ and satisfies the hypotheses of Proposition 5.5. In fact,

$$\left| \int_{a < |x| < b} \frac{dx}{|x|^{n+it}} \right| = \left| |S^{n-1}| \frac{b^{it} - a^{-it}}{-it} \right| \le \frac{2}{t} |S^{n-1}|,$$

$$\int_{a < |x| < 2a} \frac{dx}{|x|^n} = |S^{n-1}| \log 2,$$

$$|\nabla K(x)| \le \frac{|n + it|}{|x|^{n+1}}.$$

Hence, $\|K_{\epsilon,R} * f\|_p \le C_p \|f\|_p$ with C_p independent of ϵ and R.

However, the limit of the truncated integrals does not exist almost everywhere since

$$\int_{\epsilon < |x| < 1} \frac{dx}{|x|^{n+it}} = |S^{n-1}| \frac{1 - \epsilon^{-it}}{-it},$$

and the limit of ϵ^{-it} as $\epsilon \to 0$ does not exist. The limit does exist if we choose an appropriate subsequence $\{\epsilon_k\}$, for example, $\epsilon_k = e^{-2\pi k/t}$. If we take this sequence then

$$\lim_{k,R \to \infty} K_{\epsilon_k,R} * f(x) = \int_{|y| < 1} \frac{f(x - y) - f(x)}{|y|^{n+it}} \, dy + \int_{|y| > 1} \frac{f(x - y)}{|y|^{n+it}} \, dy,$$

and this defines an operator which is strong (p,p), $1 < p < \infty$, and weak $(1,1)$. This operator is the convolution of f with the tempered distribution which we will refer to as p. v. $|x|^{-n-it}$, even though it depends on our choice of the sequence $\{\epsilon_k\}$:

$$\text{p. v. } \frac{1}{|x|^{n+it}}(\phi) = \int_{|x| < 1} \frac{\phi(x) - \phi(0)}{|x|^{n+it}} \, dx + \int_{|x| > 1} \frac{\phi(x)}{|x|^{n+it}} \, dx.$$

Despite its appearance this distribution is not homogeneous of degree $-n - it$ (see Definition 4.2); that is, it does not satisfy

$$\text{p. v.} \frac{1}{|x|^{n+it}}(\phi_\lambda) = \lambda^{-n-it} \text{ p. v.} \frac{1}{|x|^{n+it}}(\phi),$$

where $\phi_\lambda(x) = \lambda^{-n}\phi(\lambda^{-1}x)$. This can be shown by a straightforward computation, but here we are going to give an indirect argument which also yields its Fourier transform.

Given z such that $\text{Re } z < n$, the function $|x|^{-z}$ is locally integrable and homogeneous of degree $-z$. It defines a tempered distribution which is also homogeneous of degree $-z$:

$$\frac{1}{|x|^z}(\phi) = \int \frac{\phi(x)}{|x|^z}\, dx.$$

We can rewrite this as

$$\frac{1}{|x|^z}(\phi) = \int_{|x|<1} \frac{\phi(x) - \phi(0)}{|x|^z}\, dx + \phi(0) \int_{|x|<1} \frac{dx}{|x|^z} + \int_{|x|>1} \frac{\phi(x)}{|x|^z}\, dx$$

$$= \int_{|x|<1} \frac{\phi(x) - \phi(0)}{|x|^z}\, dx + \int_{|x|>1} \frac{\phi(x)}{|x|^z}\, dx + \frac{|S^{n-1}|}{n - z}\phi(0);$$

this expression makes sense for $\text{Re } z < n+1$ except if $z = n$. This distribution is homogeneous of degree $-z$, and if we let $z = n + it$, we see that it differs from the one we call p. v. $|x|^{-n-it}$ by a multiple of the Dirac delta. (This is homogeneous of degree $-n$, which implies that p. v. $|x|^{-n-it}$ cannot be homogeneous.) This new distribution is thus the unique distribution that is homogeneous of degree $-n - it$ and which coincides away from the origin with the locally integrable function $|x|^{-n-it}$.

Given the Fourier transform of $|x|^{-z}$ (see (4.3)),

$$\left(\frac{1}{|x|^z}\right)^{\widehat{\;}}(\xi) = \pi^{z-\frac{n}{2}} \frac{\Gamma\left(\frac{n-z}{2}\right)}{\Gamma\left(\frac{z}{2}\right)} \frac{1}{|\xi|^{-z+n}},$$

if we let $z = n + it$ we get the Fourier transform of the homogeneous distribution, which in turn gives us the Fourier transform of p. v. $|x|^{-n-it}$:

$$\left(\text{p. v.} \frac{1}{|x|^{n+it}}\right)^{\widehat{\;}}(\xi) = \pi^{\frac{n}{2}+it} \frac{\Gamma\left(\frac{-it}{2}\right)}{\Gamma\left(\frac{n+it}{2}\right)} |\xi|^{it} + \frac{1}{it}|S^{n-1}|.$$

3. Generalized Calderón-Zygmund operators

Up to this point the operators we have been studying could be written as convolutions with tempered distributions. One practical advantage of this hypothesis is that we could use the Fourier transform to deduce the L^2 boundedness of the operator. If we assume this then the boundedness on the remaining L^p spaces only depends on the Hörmander condition, which can be adapted to operators which are not convolution operators.

Let Δ be the diagonal of $\mathbb{R}^n \times \mathbb{R}^n$: $\Delta = \{(x,x) : x \in \mathbb{R}^n\}$. By a proof nearly identical to that of Theorem 5.1 we can show the following.

Theorem 5.10. *Let T be a bounded operator on $L^2(\mathbb{R}^n)$, and let K be a function on $\mathbb{R}^n \times \mathbb{R}^n \setminus \Delta$ such that if $f \in L^2(\mathbb{R}^n)$ has compact support then*

$$Tf(x) = \int_{\mathbb{R}^n} K(x,y)f(y)\,dy, \qquad x \notin \mathrm{supp}(f).$$

Further, suppose that K also satisfies

(5.10)
$$\int_{|x-y|>2|y-z|} |K(x,y) - K(x,z)|\,dx \leq C,$$

(5.11)
$$\int_{|x-y|>2|x-w|} |K(x,y) - K(w,y)|\,dy \leq C.$$

Then T is weak $(1,1)$ and strong (p,p), $1 < p < \infty$.

The given representation holds only for functions in L^2 of compact support, but this suffices for the proof since it is only applied to the functions b_j gotten from the Calderón-Zygmund decomposition. condition (5.10) is used to prove the weak $(1,1)$ inequality for T, and condition (5.11) is used to prove the same inequality for its adjoint.

Following the terminology of Coifman and Meyer [2], we say that $K : \mathbb{R}^n \times \mathbb{R}^n \setminus \Delta \to \mathbb{C}$ is a standard kernel if there exists $\delta > 0$ such that

(5.12)
$$|K(x,y)| \leq \frac{C}{|x-y|^n},$$

(5.13)
$$|K(x,y) - K(x,z)| \leq C\frac{|y-z|^\delta}{|x-y|^{n+\delta}} \quad \text{if} \quad |x-y| > 2|y-z|,$$

(5.14)
$$|K(x,y) - K(w,y)| \leq C\frac{|x-w|^\delta}{|x-y|^{n+\delta}} \quad \text{if} \quad |x-y| > 2|x-w|.$$

Standard kernels clearly satisfy the Hörmander conditions (5.10) and (5.11).

The following are examples of operators which have this type of kernel.

(1) *The Cauchy integral along a Lipschitz curve.* Let A be a Lipschitz function on $\mathbb{R}$ (i.e. $A' = a \in L^\infty$) and let $\Gamma = (t, A(t))$ be a plane curve. With this parameterization we can regard any function f defined on Γ as a function of t and conversely. Given $f \in \mathcal{S}(\mathbb{R})$, the Cauchy integral

$$C_\Gamma f(z) = \frac{1}{2\pi i}\int_{-\infty}^{\infty} \frac{f(t)(1+ia(t))}{t+iA(t)-z}\,dt$$

defines an analytic function in the open set

$$\Omega_+ = \{z = x + iy \in \mathbb{C} : y > A(x)\}.$$

Its boundary values on Γ,

$$\lim_{\epsilon \to 0} C_\Gamma f(x + i(A(x) + \epsilon)),$$

are given by

$$\frac{1}{2} \left[f(x) + \frac{i}{\pi} \lim_{\epsilon \to 0} \int_{|x-t|>\epsilon} \frac{f(t)(1 + ia(t))}{x - t + i(A(x) - A(t))} \, dt \right].$$

This leads us to consider the operator

$$Tf(x) = \lim_{\epsilon \to 0} \int_{|x-y|>\epsilon} \frac{f(y)}{x - y + i(A(x) - A(y))} \, dy,$$

whose kernel,

(5.15) $$K(x, y) = \frac{1}{x - y + i(A(x) - A(y))},$$

satisfies (5.13) and (5.14) with $\delta = 1$.

(2) *Calderón commutators.* If $\|A'\|_\infty$ then we expand the kernel (5.15) as a geometric series:

$$K(x, y) = \frac{1}{x - y} \sum_{k=0}^\infty \left(i \frac{A(x) - A(y)}{x - y} \right)^k.$$

It is, therefore, natural to consider the following operators: given a Lipschitz function A on $\mathbb{R}$ and an integer $k \geq 0$, define

$$T_k f(x) = \lim_{\epsilon \to 0} \int_{|x-y|>\epsilon} \left(\frac{A(x) - A(y)}{x - y} \right)^k \frac{f(y)}{x - y} \, dy.$$

The associated kernels,

$$K_k(x, y) = \left(\frac{A(x) - A(y)}{x - y} \right)^k \frac{1}{x - y},$$

are also standard kernels with $\delta = 1$.

Definition 5.11. An operator T is a (generalized) Calderón-Zygmund operator if

(1) T is bounded on $L^2(\mathbb{R}^n)$;

(2) there exists a standard kernel K such that for $f \in L^2$ with compact support,

$$Tf(x) = \int_{\mathbb{R}^n} K(x, y) f(y) \, dy, \quad x \notin \text{supp}(f).$$

Theorem 5.10 implies that a Calderón-Zygmund operator is bounded on L^p, $1 < p < \infty$, and is weak $(1, 1)$. Hence, given an operator with a standard kernel, the problem reduces to showing that it is bounded on L^2. We will return to this question in Chapter 9.

4. Calderón-Zygmund singular integrals

The examples in the previous section suggest that for any Calderón-Zygmund operator,

$$Tf(x) = \lim_{\epsilon \to 0} \int_{|x-y|>\epsilon} K(x,y)f(y)\,dy,$$

at least for $f \in \mathcal{S}$. However, this is not necessarily the case. From (5.12) we can deduce that

$$T_\epsilon f(x) = \int_{|x-y|>\epsilon} K(x,y)f(y)\,dy$$

makes sense for $f \in \mathcal{S}(\mathbb{R}^n)$. Nevertheless, the limit as $\epsilon \to 0$ need not exist or may exist and be different from $Tf(x)$. An example of the first is the operator we defined in Section 2 as convolution with p. v. $|x|^{-n-it}$, whose kernel, $K(x,y) = |x-y|^{-n-it}$, is standard. (Recall that this operator is strong $(2,2)$ and so a Calderón-Zygmund operator.)

By an argument identical to that in Proposition 5.7 we can prove the following result.

Proposition 5.12. *The limit*

(5.16)
$$\lim_{\epsilon \to 0} T_\epsilon f(x)$$

exists almost everywhere for $f \in C_c^\infty$ if and only if

$$\lim_{\epsilon \to 0} \int_{\epsilon < |x-y| < 1} K(x,y)\,dy$$

exists almost everywhere.

The existence of the limit (5.16) does not imply that it is equal to $Tf(x)$: for example, consider the identity operator I. This is a Calderón-Zygmund operator associated with the kernel $K(x,y) = 0$—clearly, $If(x) = 0$ if $x \notin \text{supp}(f)$—but (5.16) equals 0.

Furthermore, this example shows us that an operator is not characterized by its kernel since the zero operator also has the zero kernel. In general, so does any pointwise multiplication operator $Tf(x) = a(x)f(x)$, $a \in L^\infty$. However, these are the only ones; this is shown by the following result whose proof is left to the reader.

Proposition 5.13. *If two Calderón-Zygmund operators are associated with the same kernel, then their difference is a pointwise multiplication operator.*

It is important to assume that a Calderón-Zygmund operator is bounded on L^2 since without this or a similar hypothesis, Proposition 5.13 would be false. For example, the derivative is an operator with kernel 0 ($f'(x) = 0$ if $x \notin \operatorname{supp}(f)$) but it is not a pointwise multiplication operator.

A Calderón-Zygmund singular integral is a Calderón-Zygmund operator that satisfies

$$(5.17) \qquad Tf(x) = \lim_{\epsilon \to 0} T_\epsilon f(x).$$

To determine when this equality holds for $f \in L^p(\mathbb{R}^n)$, we will proceed as we did for the Hilbert transform and examine the maximal operator

$$T^* f(x) = \sup_{\epsilon > 0} |T_\epsilon f(x)|.$$

By Theorem 2.2, if T^* is weak (p, p) then the set

$$\{f \in L^p : \lim_{\epsilon \to 0} T_\epsilon f(x) \text{ exists a.e.}\}$$

is closed in L^p. Hence, if (5.17) holds for a dense subset, say $f \in C_c^\infty$, then it holds for any $f \in L^p$.

Theorem 5.14. *If T is a Calderón-Zygmund operator then T^* is strong (p, p), $1 < p < \infty$, and weak $(1, 1)$.*

The proof of Theorem 5.14 depends on the following result which is analogous to Cotlar's inequality (Lemma 3.5).

Lemma 5.15. *If T is a Calderón-Zygmund operator then for any ν, $0 < \nu \le 1$, and for any $f \in C_c^\infty$,*

$$(5.18) \qquad T^* f(x) \le C_\nu \left(M(|Tf|^\nu)(x)^{1/\nu} + Mf(x) \right).$$

To prove this we need the following result due to Kolmogorov.

Lemma 5.16. *Given an operator S which is weak $(1, 1)$, ν, $0 < \nu < 1$, and a set E of finite measure, there exists a constant C depending only on ν such that*

$$\int_E |Sf(x)|^\nu \, dx \le C |E|^{1-\nu} \|f\|_1^\nu.$$

Proof. By (2.1) and the weak $(1, 1)$ inequality,

$$\int_E |Sf(x)|^\nu \, dx = \nu \int_0^\infty \lambda^{\nu-1} |\{x \in E : |Sf(x)| > \lambda\}| \, d\lambda$$
$$\le \nu \int_0^\infty \lambda^{\nu-1} \min\left(|E|, \frac{C}{\lambda}\|f\|_1\right) d\lambda$$
$$= \nu \int_0^{C\|f\|_1/|E|} \lambda^{\nu-1} |E| \, d\lambda + \nu \int_{C\|f\|_1/|E|}^\infty C\lambda^{\nu-2}\|f\|_1 \, d\lambda.$$

The desired inequality follows from this immediately. $\qquad\square$

Proof of Lemma 5.15. We will prove that

$$T_\epsilon f(0) \le C\left(M(|Tf|^\nu)(0)^{1/\nu} + Mf(0)\right)$$

with C independent of ϵ. Our argument will be translation invariant and so actually yields (5.18).

Fix $\epsilon > 0$; let $Q = B(0,\epsilon/2)$ and $2Q = B(0,\epsilon)$, and define $f_1 = f\chi_{2Q}$ and $f_2 = f - f_1$. Then

$$Tf_2(0) = \int_{|y|>\epsilon} K(0,y)f(y)\,dy = T_\epsilon f(0).$$

If $z \in Q$ then, since K is a standard kernel,

$$\begin{aligned}
|Tf_2(z) - Tf_2(0)| &= \left|\int_{|y|>\epsilon}(K(z,y)-K(0,y))f(y)\,dy\right| \\
&\le C|z|^\delta \int_{|y|>\epsilon}\frac{|f(y)|}{|y|^{n+\delta}}\,dy \\
&\le C\epsilon^\delta \sum_{k=0}^\infty \int_{2^k\epsilon<|y|<2^{k+1}\epsilon}\frac{|f(y)|}{|y|^{n+\delta}}\,dy \\
&\le C\sum_{k=0}^\infty 2^{-k\delta}\frac{1}{(2^k\epsilon)^n}\int_{|y|<2^{k+1}\epsilon}|f(y)|\,dy \\
&\le C_\delta Mf(0).
\end{aligned}$$

It follows from this inequality that

$$(5.19)\qquad |T_\epsilon f(0)| \le CMf(0) + |Tf(z)| + |Tf_1(z)|.$$

If $T_\epsilon f(0) = 0$ then there is nothing to prove. If not, fix λ such that $0 < \lambda < |T_\epsilon f(0)|$ and let

$$\begin{aligned}
Q_1 &= \{z \in Q : |Tf(z)| > \lambda/3\}, \\
Q_2 &= \{z \in Q : |Tf_1(z)| > \lambda/3\},
\end{aligned}$$

and

$$Q_3 = \begin{cases} \emptyset & \text{if } CMf(0) \le \lambda/3, \\ Q & \text{if } CMf(0) > \lambda/3. \end{cases}$$

Then $Q = Q_1 \cup Q_2 \cup Q_3$, so $|Q| \le |Q_1| + |Q_2| + |Q_3|$. However,

$$|Q_1| \le \frac{3}{\lambda}\int_Q |Tf(z)|\,dz \le \frac{3}{\lambda}|Q|M(Tf)(0),$$

and by the weak $(1,1)$ inequality for T,

$$|Q_2| = |\{z \in Q : |Tf_1(z)| > \lambda/3\}| \le \frac{3C}{\lambda} \int_Q |f(z)|\, dz \le \frac{3C}{\lambda}|Q|Mf(0).$$

If $Q_3 = Q$ then $\lambda \le 3CMf(0)$; if $Q_3 = \emptyset$ then

$$|Q| \le |Q_1| + |Q_2| \le \frac{3C}{\lambda}|Q|(M(Tf)(0) + Mf(0)).$$

Hence, in every case we have that

$$\lambda \le C\left(M(Tf)(0) + Mf(0)\right).$$

This is true for any $\lambda < |T_\epsilon f(0)|$ and so (5.18) holds when $\nu = 1$.

If $0 < \nu < 1$, then it follows from (5.19) that

$$|T_\epsilon f(0)|^\nu \le CMf(0)^\nu + |Tf(z)|^\nu + |Tf_1(z)|^\nu.$$

If we integrate in z over Q, divide by $|Q|$ and raise to the power $1/\nu$, we get

$$|T_\epsilon f(0)|^\nu \le C\left(Mf(0) + M(|Tf|^\nu)(0)^{1/\nu} + \left(\frac{1}{|Q|}\int_Q |Tf_1(z)|^\nu\, dz\right)^{1/\nu}\right).$$

By Lemma 5.16,

$$\left(\frac{1}{|Q|}\int_Q |Tf_1(z)|^\nu\, dz\right)^{1/\nu} \le C|Q|^{-1}\|f_1\|_1 \le CMf(0),$$

and this completes the proof. $\square$

Proof of Theorem 5.14. Inequality (5.18) with $\nu = 1$ immediately implies that T^* is strong (p,p) since both T and M are.

To show that T^* is weak $(1,1)$ we could argue as we did in the proof of Theorem 3.4; instead we will give a different proof which uses (5.18) with $\nu < 1$. From this inequality we have that

$$|\{x \in \mathbb{R}^n : T^*f(x) > \lambda\}| \le |\{x \in \mathbb{R}^n : Mf(x) > \lambda/2C\}|$$
$$+ |\{x \in \mathbb{R}^n : M(|Tf|^\nu)(x)^{1/\nu} > \lambda/2C\}|,$$

and the first term on the right-hand side satisfies the desired estimate. As for the second term, by Lemma 2.12

$$|\{x \in \mathbb{R}^n : M(|Tf|^\nu)(x)^{1/\nu} > \lambda\}| \le 2^n|\{x \in \mathbb{R}^n : M_d(|Tf|^\nu)(x) > 4^{-n}\lambda^\nu\}|,$$

where M_d is the dyadic maximal operator (2.9). Let $E = \{x \in \mathbb{R}^n : M_d(|Tf|^\nu)(x) > \lambda^\nu\}$; then E has finite measure if $f \in C_c^\infty$. But then

$$|E| \le \frac{1}{\lambda^\nu}\int_E |Tf(y)|^\nu\, dy;$$

by the proof of Theorem 2.10 it suffices to take the integral over E instead of all of $\mathbb{R}^n$. Therefore, by Lemma 5.16

$$|E| \leq C\lambda^\nu |E|^{1-\nu} \|f\|_1^\nu.$$

The desired inequality now follows if we replace λ^ν by $4^{-n}\lambda^\nu$. $\qquad\square$

5. A vector-valued extension

Let B be a separable Banach space. A function F from $\mathbb{R}^n$ to B is (strongly) measurable if for each $b' \in B^*$ (the dual of B) the map $x \mapsto \langle F(x), b' \rangle$ is measurable. If F is measurable then it follows that the scalar function $x \mapsto \|F(x)\|_B$ is also measurable. Therefore, we can define $L^p(B)$ as the space of (equivalence classes of) measurable functions from $\mathbb{R}^n$ to B such that

$$\|F\|_{L^p(B)} = \left(\int_{\mathbb{R}^n} \|F(x)\|_B^p \, dx \right)^{1/p} < \infty, \quad 1 \leq p < \infty,$$

and $\|f\|_\infty = \sup\{\|F(x)\|_B : x \in \mathbb{R}^n\}$. The space $L^p(B)$, $1 \leq p \leq \infty$, is a Banach space.

If f is a scalar function in L^p and $b \in B$, define the function $f \cdot b$ from $\mathbb{R}^n$ to B by $(f \cdot b)(x) = f(x)b$. This function is in $L^p(B)$ and its norm is $\|f\|_p \|b\|_B$. The subspace of $L^p(B)$ consisting of finite linear combinations of functions of this type, denoted by $L^p \otimes B$, is dense if $1 \leq p < \infty$.

Given $F = \sum_j f_j \cdot b_j \in L^1 \otimes B$, define its integral to be the element of B given by

$$\int_{\mathbb{R}^n} F(x) \, dx = \sum_j \left(\int_{\mathbb{R}^n} f_j(x) \, dx \right) b_j.$$

The map $F \mapsto \int F(x) \, dx$ extends to $L^1(B)$ by continuity. For a function $F \in L^1(B)$, this integral is the unique element of B that satisfies

$$\left\langle \int_{\mathbb{R}^n} F(x) \, dx, b' \right\rangle = \int_{\mathbb{R}^n} \langle F(x), b' \rangle \, dx$$

for all $b' \in B^*$.

If $F \in L^p(B)$ and $G \in L^{p'}(B^*)$, then $\langle F, G \rangle(x) = \langle F(x), G(x) \rangle$ is integrable; furthermore,

$$\|G\|_{L^{p'}(B^*)} = \sup \left\{ \left| \int_{\mathbb{R}^n} \langle F(x), G(x) \rangle \, dx \right| : \|F\|_{L^p(B)} \leq 1 \right\}.$$

From this we see that $L^{p'}(B^*) \subset (L^p(B))^*$. Equality is not true in general, but is, for example, if $1 \leq p < \infty$ and B is reflexive.

Let A and B be Banach spaces and let $\mathcal{L}(A, B)$ be the space of bounded linear operators from A to B. Suppose that K is a function defined on

$\mathbb{R}^n \times \mathbb{R}^n \setminus \Delta$ which takes values in $\mathcal{L}(A, B)$ and T is an operator which has K as its associated kernel: if $f \in L^\infty(A)$ and has compact support, then

$$T f(x) = \int_{\mathbb{R}^n} K(x, y) \cdot f(y) \, dy, \quad x \notin \mathrm{supp}(f).$$

For such operators there is a vectorial analogue of Theorem 5.10.

Theorem 5.17. *Let T be a bounded operator from $L^r(A)$ to $L^r(B)$ for some r, $1 < r < \infty$, with associated kernel K. If K satisfies*

$$(5.20) \qquad \int_{|x-y|>2|y-z|} \|K(x, y) - K(x, z)\|_{\mathcal{L}(A,B)} \, dx \leq C,$$

$$(5.21) \qquad \int_{|x-y|>2|x-w|} \|K(x, y) - K(w, y)\|_{\mathcal{L}(A,B)} \, dy \leq C,$$

then T is bounded from $L^p(A)$ to $L^p(B)$, $1 < p < \infty$, and is weak $(1, 1)$, that is,

$$|\{x \in \mathbb{R}^n : \|T f(x)\|_B > \lambda\}| \leq \frac{C}{\lambda} \|f\|_{L^1(A)}.$$

The proof of Theorem 5.17 initially follows the outline of the scalar result: inequality (5.20) together with the boundedness from $L^r(A)$ to $L^r(B)$ yields the weak $(1, 1)$ inequality; then the Marcinkiewicz interpolation theorem (which can easily be shown to be true in these spaces) shows that T is bounded for $1 < p \leq r$.

To prove that T is bounded for $r < p < \infty$ we must pass to the adjoint operator. However, this presents a problem since, as we noted above, $L^{p'}(A^*)$ need not be equal to $L^p(A)^*$. When A is reflexive (and it will always be so in our applications in Chapter 8) they are equal, and in that case it is enough to note that the kernel associated with the adjoint operator T^* is $\tilde{K}(x, y) = K^*(y, x) \in \mathcal{L}(B^*, A^*)$. Inequality (5.21) for K is equivalent to (5.20) for $\tilde{K}$, so by repeating the above argument we get that T^* is bounded for $1 < p \leq r'$.

When $L^{p'}(A^*) \neq L^p(A)^*$ we must first consider the finite dimensional subspaces of A. Given such a subspace A_0, let $T_0 : L^r(A_0) \to L^r(B)$ be the restriction of T to functions with values in A_0. The kernel associated with T_0 is $K_0 \in \mathcal{L}(A_0, B)$, the restriction of K to A_0. Since $\|K_0\| \leq \|K\|$, inequalities (5.20) and (5.21) hold for K_0 with constants independent of the subspace A_0. Therefore, arguing as before,

$$T_0^* : L^q(B^*) \to L^q(A_0^*), \quad 1 < q \leq r',$$

with a constant independent of A_0. So by duality, T_0 is bounded from $L^p(A_0)$ to $L^p(B)$, $r < p < \infty$, with a constant independent of A_0. That it is bounded on all of $L^p(A)$ now follows since $L^p \otimes A$ is dense in $L^p(A)$.

We leave it to the reader to fill in the details of the outlined proof of Theorem 5.17 by following the scalar model.

6. Notes and further results

6.1. References.

The Calderón-Zygmund decomposition and its application to proving the weak $(1,1)$ inequalities for singular integrals appeared in the classic article by both authors (*On the existence of certain singular integrals*, Acta Math. **88** (1952), 85–139). In this article they used the gradient condition (5.3); L. Hörmander first observed that (5.2) is sufficient (*Estimates for translation invariant operators in L^p-spaces*, Acta Math. **104** (1960), 93–139). Also see Stein [**15**]. Proposition 5.5 is due to A. Benedek, A. P. Calderón and R. Panzone (*Convolution operators with Banach-space valued functions*, Proc. Nat. Acad. Sci. U.S.A. **48** (1962), 356–365). The tempered distribution p. v. $|x|^{-n-it}$ and its generalizations were first considered by B. Muckenhoupt (*On certain singular integrals*, Pacific J. Math. **10** (1960), 239–261). For more on generalized Calderón-Zygmund operators, consult Coifman and Meyer [**2**], Journé [**8**] and Stein [**17**]. The Cauchy integral has a long history: see, for example, the book by N. T. Mushkelishvili (*Singular Integral Equations*, P. Noordhoff, Groningen, 1953). The associated commutators were first studied by A. P. Calderón (*Commutators of singular integral operators*, Proc. Nat. Acad. Sci. U.S.A. **53** (1965), 1092–1099). Commutators are discussed again in Chapter 9. For more on vector-valued singular integrals see García-Cuerva and Rubio de Francia [**6**, Chapter 5], the article by J. L. Rubio de Francia, F. J. Ruiz and J. L. Torrea (*Calderón-Zygmund theory for operator-valued kernels*, Adv. in Math. **62** (1986), 7–48) or the monograph by J. L. Torrea (*Integrales Singulares Vectoriales*, Notas de Algebra y Análisis 12, Univ. Nacional del Sur, Bahía Blanca, 1984).

The survey article by C. Fefferman (*Recent progress in classical Fourier analysis*, Proceedings of the I.C.M. (Vancouver, B.C., 1974), Vol. 1, pp. 95–118, Canad. Math. Congress, Montreal, 1975) contains a succinct discussion of singular integrals and their connection to many other problems in analysis.

6.2. A more general Dini-type condition.

The Hörmander condition (5.2) holds for kernels of the form $K(x) = \Omega(x')/|x|^n$ under weaker hypotheses than those in Proposition 5.3. Given $\rho \in O(n)$, let

$$\|\rho\| = \sup\{|u - \rho u| : u \in S^{n-1}\}.$$

If we define

$$\omega_1(t) = \sup_{\|\rho\| \le t} \int_{S^{n-1}} |\Omega(\rho u) - \Omega(u)| \, d\sigma(u),$$

then the Dini-type condition

$$\int_0^1 \frac{\omega_1(t)}{t} \, dt < \infty$$

implies that (5.2) holds for K. This condition also implies that $\Omega \in L \log^+ L$. This result is due to A. P. Calderón, M. Weiss and A. Zygmund (*On the existence of singular integrals*, Singular Integrals, Proc. Sympos. Pure Math. **X**, pp. 56–73, Amer. Math. Soc., Providence, 1967). Later, Calderón and Zygmund proved that this condition is also necessary for the Hörmander condition to hold (*A note on singular integrals*, Studia Math. **65** (1979), 77–87).

6.3. Nonisotropic dilations.

The Euclidean norm $|\cdot|$ on $\mathbb{R}^n$ is associated with a family of dilations

$$\delta_t(x) = (tx_1, \dots, tx_n)$$

in the sense that $|\delta_t(x)| = t|x|$, $t > 0$, $x \in \mathbb{R}^n$.

Given $a_1, \dots, a_n > 0$, we can define a family of dilations that act on each variable differently:

$$\delta_t(x) = (t^{a_1} x_1, \dots, t^{a_n} x_n).$$

Then for each δ_t there exists a quasi-norm $\|\cdot\|$ such that

$$\|\delta_t(x)\| = t\|x\|$$

and if $z \in S^{n-1}$ then $\|z\| = 1$. Define $\|\cdot\|$ as follows: given $x \in \mathbb{R}^n$, there exists a unique $x' \in S^{n-1}$ such that $\delta_t(x') = x$ for some $t > 0$. Let $\|x\| = t$. This is not an actual norm since the triangle inequality is only satisfied up to a constant $L \ge 1$:

$$\|x + y\| \le L(\|x\| + \|y\|).$$

Given $\mathbb{R}^n$ with this quasi-norm we can get results analogous to Theorem 5.10 by considering conditions like

$$\int_{\|x-y\| \ge 2\|y-z\|} |K(x,y) - K(x,z)| \, dx \le C$$

and the symmetric condition gotten by changing the order of the variables.

This kind of singular integral appears primarily in connection with the parabolic operators introduced by E. Fabes and N. Rivière (*Singular integrals with mixed homogeneity*, Studia Math. **27** (1966), 19–38). Also see C. Sadosky (*On some properties of a class of singular integrals*, Studia Math.

27 (1966), 73–86) and M. de Guzmán (*Singular integral operators with generalized homogeneity*, Rev. Acad. Ciencias Madrid **64** (1970), 77–137). In Chapter 8, Section 7, we will use the method of rotations to study the kernels associated with this structure.

6.4. Spaces of homogeneous type.

Singular integrals can be studied in very general spaces. R. Coifman and G. Weiss considered this question in their book *Analyse harmonique non-conmutative sur certains espaces homogènes* (Lecture Notes in Math. **242**, Springer-Verlag, Berlin, 1971). For a discussion in a slightly less general setting, see Stein [**17**, Chapter 1].

Let X be a space with pseudo-metric ρ, that is, a function $\rho : X \times X \to [0, \infty)$ such that

(1) $\rho(x, y) = 0$ if and only if $x = y$;

(2) $\rho(x, y) = \rho(y, x)$;

(3) there exists $L > 0$ such that $\rho(x, z) \leq L(\rho(x, y) + \rho(y, z))$.

A space of homogeneous type is a topological space X with a pseudo-metric ρ such that the balls $B(x, r)$ form a basis of open neighborhoods of X, and there exists a positive integer N such that for any $x \in X$ and $r > 0$, the ball $B(x, r)$ contains at most N points x_i such that $\rho(x_i, x_j) > r/2$. The second property holds if there exists a Borel measure μ on X such that

$$0 < \mu(B(x, r)) \leq A\mu(B(x, r/2)) < \infty.$$

(Such a measure μ is called a doubling measure. We first discussed doubling measures in Chapter 2, Section 8.6.)

If X is a space of homogeneous type, then given a kernel $K(x, y) \in L^2(X \times X, d\mu \otimes d\mu)$ we can define the operator

$$Tf(x) = \int_X K(x, y) f(y) \, d\mu(y).$$

If $\|Tf\|_q \leq C_q \|f\|_q$ for some $q > 1$, and if for any $y, z \in X$,

(5.22) $$\int_{\rho(x,y) \geq 2L\rho(y,z)} |K(x, y) - K(x, z)| \, d\mu(x) \leq C,$$

then T is strong (p, p), $1 < p \leq q$, and weak $(1, 1)$.

Very recently, in connection with the study of the Cauchy integral, the question has arisen of extending the theory of singular integrals to nonhomogeneous spaces: topological spaces X with a pseudo-metric ρ and a measure μ which is not doubling. F. Nazarov, S. Treil and A. Volberg (*Weak type estimates and Cotlar inequalities for Calderón-Zygmund operators on nonhomogeneous spaces*, Int. Math. Res. Let. **9** (1998), 463–487) have shown that the above result remains true if: ρ is a metric; there exists a constant $\nu > 0$ such that for all $x \in X$ and $r > 0$, $\mu(B(x,r)) \leq r^{\nu}$; and we replace (5.22) with the assumption that there exists $\delta > 0$ such that

$$|K(x,y) - K(x,z)| \leq C\frac{\rho(y,z)^{\delta}}{\rho(x,y)^{\nu+\delta}}, \quad \text{if } \rho(x,y) \geq 2\rho(y,z).$$

6.5. The size of constants.

In the proof of Theorem 5.1, if we form the Calderón-Zygmund decomposition at height $A^{-1}\lambda$, then the weak $(1,1)$ constant becomes $C_n(A+B)$, and by interpolation the strong (p,p) constant is dominated by

$$\frac{C'_n(A+B)p^2}{p-1}, \quad 1 < p < \infty.$$

In general, this is the best possible constant asymptotically as $p \to 1$ or $p \to \infty$. To see this, suppose the kernel K satisfies the gradient condition with constant C (5.3) and also satisfies

$$|K(x)| \geq \frac{c}{|x|^n}, \quad |x| > 0.$$

Let $B = B(0,1)$ and let $B^* = B(0,R)$, where R is such that $C/R < c/2$. Fix $f = |B|^{-1/p}\chi_B$; then $\|f\|_p = 1$. Further, for $x \notin B^*$,

$$|Tf(x)| \geq |B|^{1-1/p} - |B|^{-1/p}\int_B |K(x-y) - K(x)|\,dy$$

$$\geq \frac{c|B|^{1-1/p}}{|x|^n} - \frac{C|B|^{1+1/n-1/p}}{|x|^{n+1}}$$

$$\geq \frac{c|B|^{1-1/p}}{2|x|^n}.$$

It follows from this that for p small, $\|Tf\|_p = O((p-1)^{-1})$. If we apply the same argument to the adjoint operator, then by duality we get that for p large, $\|Tf\|_p = O(p)$.

This proof can easily be adapted to the case when K is the kernel of one of the Riesz transforms, and a similar argument holds for Calderón-Zygmund operators. (See Stein [**17**, p. 42].)

6.6. More on truncated integrals.

Given a Calderón-Zygmund singular integral T, that is, a Calderón-Zygmund operator that satisfies (5.17), it is natural to ask when $T_\epsilon f$ converges to Tf in L^p. If $1 < p < \infty$, this is immediate: if $f \in L^p$ then by Theorem 5.14, $T^*f \in L^p$, so convergence follows from the dominated convergence theorem. This argument fails when $p = 1$, but nevertheless it can be shown that if $f, Tf \in L^1$, then $T_\epsilon f \to Tf$ in L^1. This result is due to

A. Calderón and O. Capri (*On the convergence in L^1 of singular integrals*, Studia Math. **78** (1984), 321–327).

6.7. Vector-valued singular integrals and maximal functions.

The vector-valued extension of the theory of singular integral operators in Section 5 has wide application, since many of the operators in harmonic analysis can be viewed as vector-valued singular integrals. This approach is due to Rubio de Francia, Ruiz and Torrea (see the reference given in Section 6.1).

Here we will show that the Hardy-Littlewood maximal function can be treated as a vector-valued singular integral. We first extend Theorem 5.17 to include the case when T is a bounded operator from $L^\infty(A)$ to $L^\infty(B)$. The proof is essentially the same. Fix f, form the Calderón-Zygmund decomposition of $\|f\|_A$ at height λ, and decompose f as $g + b$, where $\|g(x)\|_A \leq 2^n\lambda$ a.e. Then, since T is bounded from $L^\infty(A)$ to $L^\infty(B)$, for some constant $\beta > 0$,

$$\{x \in \mathbb{R}^n : \|Tf(x)\|_B > \beta\lambda\} \subset \{x \in \mathbb{R}^n : \|Tb(x)\|_B > \lambda\}.$$

The proof then continues as before.

Now fix a non-negative function $\phi \in \mathcal{S}$ such that $\phi \geq 1$ on $B(0,1)$. Define the maximal operator

$$M_\phi f(x) = \sup_{t>0} |\phi_t * f(x)|,$$

where $\phi_t(x) = t^{-n}\phi(x/t)$. Since $\phi \in \mathcal{S}$, it suffices to take the supremum over rational t. By our choice of ϕ, $Mf(x) \leq M_\phi(|f|)(x)$. (The reverse inequality was proved in Proposition 2.7.) Thus, to prove norm inequalities for M it will suffice to prove them for M_ϕ.

Let $A = \mathbb{R}$ and $B = \ell^\infty(\mathbb{Q}_+)$, and define the vector-valued function $K(x) = \{\phi_t(x)\}_{t \in \mathbb{Q}_+}$. Then K takes values in $\mathcal{L}(A, B)$ and we can define an operator T to be convolution with K. Since

$$\|Tf(x)\|_B = M_\phi f(x),$$

it follows that $T : L^\infty(A) \to L^\infty(B)$ is bounded. Further, since $\phi \in \mathcal{S}$,

$$\sup_{t>0} |\phi_t(x - y) - \phi_t(x)| \leq \frac{C|y|}{|x|^{n+1}}, \quad |x| > 2|y| > 0,$$

which implies the Hörmander condition (5.20) for K. Hence, by Theorem 5.17 (as extended above), $T : L^p(A) \to L^p(B)$; equivalently, M_ϕ is bounded on L^p.

The boundedness of M_ϕ was originally proved by F. Zo (*A note on approximation of the identity*, Studia Math. **55** (1976), 111–122).

6.8. Strongly singular integrals.

In Theorem 5.1, given an arbitrary tempered distribution with bounded Fourier transform, the Hörmander condition (5.2) seems to be the weakest hypothesis possible to get L^p boundedness. It is of interest, however, to see how this hypothesis can be weakened if stronger conditions are assumed on the Fourier transform. The prototypical operator motivating this is the convolution operator $T_{a,b} = K_{a,b} * f$, $0 < a < 1$ and $b > 0$, where

$$\hat{K}_{a,b}(\xi) = \phi(\xi)\frac{e^{i|\xi|^a}}{|\xi|^b},$$

and ϕ is a C^∞ function which vanishes near the origin and is identically equal to one outside of some compact set. This integral arises in the study of the L^p convergence of multiple Fourier series (cf. Chapter 1, Section 10.2).

Clearly,

$$|\hat{K}_{a,b}(\xi)| \leq \frac{A}{(1 + |\xi|)^b},$$

and it can be shown that for x close to the origin,

$$|K_{a,b}(x)| \approx \frac{B}{|x|^{n+\delta}},$$

where $\delta = (na/2 - b)/(1-a)$. Hence, this kernel does not satisfy the gradient condition (5.3). (It also fails to satisfy the Hörmander condition; this fact follows from the next result.)

However, these two growth conditions are sufficient to determine the behavior of $T_{a,b}$ on L^p.

Theorem 5.18. *The operator $T_{a,b}$ is bounded on L^p if*

$$(5.23) \qquad \left|\frac{1}{2} - \frac{1}{p}\right| < \frac{(b/n)(n/2 + \delta)}{b + \delta}, \qquad \delta = \frac{na/2 - b}{1 - a},$$

and is unbounded if the reverse inequality holds. If equality holds in (5.23), then $T_{a,b}$ maps L^p into the Lorentz space $L^{p,p'}$.

The L^p boundedness of $T_{a,b}$ was first shown by I. Hirschmann (*On multiplier transformations*, Duke Math. J. **25** (1959), 221–242) when $n = 1$ and by S. Wainger (*Special trigonometric series in k dimensions*, Mem. Amer. Math. Soc. **59** (1965)) in higher dimensions. Also see the survey article by E. M. Stein (*Singular integrals, harmonic functions and differentiability properties of functions of several variables*, Singular Integrals, Proc. Sympos. Pure Math. **X**, pp. 316–335, Amer. Math. Soc., Providence, 1967).

The endpoint inequalities were proved by C. Fefferman (*Inequalities for strongly singular convolution operators*, Acta Math. **124** (1970), 9–36). He showed that they are consequences of the following general result, which further illustrates the delicate relationship between the conditions on K and $\hat{K}$.

Theorem 5.19. *Let K be a tempered distribution on $\mathbb{R}^n$ with compact support which coincides with a locally integrable function away from the origin. Suppose there exists θ, $0 < \theta < 1$, such that*

$$|\hat{K}(\xi)| \leq \frac{A}{(1 + |\xi|)^{-n\theta/2}}, \quad \xi \in \mathbb{R}^n,$$

$$\int_{|x| > 2|y|^{1-\theta}} |K(x - y) - K(x)| \, dx \leq B, \quad |y| \leq 1.$$

Then the operator $Tf = K * f$ is bounded on L^p, $1 < p < \infty$, and satisfies a weak $(1, 1)$ inequality.

This result was later generalized by P. Sjölin (*L^p estimates for strongly singular convolution operators in $\mathbb{R}^n$*, Ark. Mat. **14** (1976), 59–64).

6.9. Pseudo-differential operators.

Pseudo-differential operators are generalizations of differential operators and singular integrals. They are formally defined as in equation (4.17), that is,

$$Tf(x) = \int_{\mathbb{R}^n} \sigma(x, \xi) \hat{f}(\xi) e^{2\pi i x \cdot \xi} \, d\xi,$$

where σ, the symbol of T, is a complex-valued function defined on $\mathbb{R}^n \times \mathbb{R}^n$. Conditions must be imposed on σ to ensure that Tf is well defined for $f \in C_c^\infty(\mathbb{R}^n)$.

If $\sigma(x, \xi) = m(\xi)$ is independent of x, then T is the multiplier associated with m; if $\sigma(x, \xi) = b(x)$ is independent of ξ, T corresponds to pointwise multiplication by b. Although in these cases T is bounded on L^2 if and only if m or b are bounded functions, this is not true in general. For example, $\sigma(x, \xi) = b(x)m(\xi)$ with $m, b \in L^2$ can be unbounded, but by applying Hölder's inequality it is immediate that T is always bounded on L^2.

Symbols are classified according to their size and the size of their derivatives. The simplest classification is motivated by the study of elliptic differential operators: given $m \in \mathbb{Z}$, we say that $\sigma \in S^m$ if

$$|D_x^\beta D_\xi^\alpha \sigma(x, \xi)| \leq C_{\alpha, \beta} (1 + |\xi|)^{m - |\alpha|}.$$

Pseudo-differential operators can be rewritten as

$$(5.24) \qquad Tf(x) = \int_{\mathbb{R}^n} K(x, x - y) f(y) \, dy,$$

where K is given by (4.19). When $\sigma \in S^0$ then one can show that K satisfies a Hörmander condition (cf. (5.10) and (5.11)) and that T is bounded on L^2.

Hence the theory developed in this chapter applies and T is bounded on L^p, $1 < p < \infty$.

The composition of pseudo-differential operators yields a corresponding symbolic calculus. In the simplest cases (pointwise multiplication and multipliers) the symbol of the composition of two operators is the product of the symbols. (Cf. Theorem 4.15.) In general, given pseudo-differential operators T_1 and T_2 with symbols in S^{m_1} and S^{m_2}, their composition is a pseudo-differential operator with symbol in $S^{m_1+m_2}$. Further, the symbol of $T_1 \circ T_2$ has an asymptotic expansion whose dominant term is the product of the symbols of T_1 and T_2 and the remaining terms are symbols of pseudo-differential operators in $S^{m_1+m_2-j}$, $j > 0$.

If $\sigma \in S^m$ is an elliptic operator (that is, it has a lower bound $|\sigma(x,\xi)| \geq C(1 + |\xi|)^m$), then there exists a symbol in S^{-m} such that the composition of the corresponding operators is the identity (which is in S^0) plus an error term with symbol in S^{-1}. Thus, the theory of pseudo-differential operators with symbols in S^m is readily applicable to the problem of the inversion of elliptic operators.

When considering the corresponding problem for other differential operators, a more general class of symbols arises. We say that $\sigma \in S_{\rho,\delta}^m$ if

$$|D_x^\beta D_\xi^\alpha \sigma(x,\xi)| \leq A_{\alpha,\beta}(1 + |\xi|)^{m-\rho|\alpha|+\delta|\beta|} .$$

This class includes the previous one: with this notation S^m becomes $S_{1,0}^m$.

If T is a pseudo-differential operator with symbol in $S_{\rho,\delta}^m$, then it can again be written in the form (5.24). One can show that the kernel K satisfies the standard estimates (5.12), (5.13) and (5.14) if and only if $m = 0$ and $\rho = \delta \leq 1$. A remarkable result due to A. P. Calderón and R. Vaillancourt (*A class of bounded pseudo-differential operators*, Proc. Nat. Acad. Sci. U.S.A. **69** (1972), 1185–1187) gives us that a pseudo-differential operator with symbol in $S_{\rho,\rho}^0$ for some $0 \leq \rho < 1$ is bounded on L^2, and so we can again apply the techniques of this chapter to show that it is bounded on L^p. The proof of Calderón and Vaillancourt uses Cotlar's lemma (see Chapter 9, Section 1). Their result is false when $\rho = 1$: there exist symbols in $S_{1,1}^0$ (and so in L^∞) whose associated pseudo-differential operators are unbounded on L^2.

When $m \neq 0$, the properties of pseudo-differential operators whose symbols are in $S_{\rho,\delta}^m$ are studied using a scale of spaces which measure the regularity of functions; for example, the Sobolev spaces (see Chapter 4, Section 7.7) or the Lipschitz spaces (see Stein [**15**, Chapter 5]).

For further results on pseudo-differential operators and additional references see Stein [**17**], Journé [**8**] and Coifman and Meyer [**2**].

Chapter 6

H^1 and BMO

1. The space atomic H^1

In Chapter 3, Section 3, we saw that the Hilbert transform of an integrable function is not, in general, in L^1, and that a necessary condition for this is that the function have zero integral. Here we are going to define a subspace of L^1 whose image under any singular integral is in L^1. We begin by defining its basic elements—atoms.

Definition 6.1. An atom is a complex-valued function a defined on $\mathbb{R}^n$ which is supported on a cube Q and is such that

$$\int_Q a(x)\,dx = 0 \quad \text{and} \quad \|a\|_\infty \leq \frac{1}{|Q|}.$$

Proposition 6.2. *Let T be an operator as in the hypotheses of Theorem 5.10 whose kernel satisfies condition (5.10). Then there exists a constant C such that, given any atom a,*

$$\|Ta\|_1 \leq C.$$

Proof. Since $a \in L^2$, Ta is well defined. Let Q^* be the cube with the same center as Q, c_Q, and side length $2\sqrt{n}$ times larger. Then, since T is bounded on L^2,

$$\int_{Q^*} |Ta(x)|\,dx \leq |Q^*|^{1/2} \left(\int_{Q^*} |Ta(x)|^2\,dx \right)^{1/2}$$

$$\leq C|Q|^{1/2} \left(\int_Q |a(x)|^2 \, dx \right)^{1/2}$$

$$\leq C.$$

Further, since a has zero average, by condition (5.10)

$$\int_{\mathbb{R}^n \setminus Q^*} |Ta(x)| \, dx = \int_{\mathbb{R}^n \setminus Q^*} \left| \int_Q K(x,y)a(y) \, dy \right| dx$$

$$= \int_{\mathbb{R}^n \setminus Q^*} \left| \int_Q [K(x,y) - K(x,c_Q)]a(y) \, dy \right| dx$$

$$\leq \int_Q \int_{\mathbb{R}^n \setminus Q^*} |K(x,y) - K(x,c_Q)| \, dx \, |a(y)| \, dy$$

$$\leq C.$$

$\square$

We now define the space atomic H^1, denoted by H^1_{at}, by

$$H^1_{\mathrm{at}}(\mathbb{R}^n) = \left\{ \sum_j \lambda_j a_j : a_j \text{ atoms}, \ \lambda_j \in \mathbb{C}, \ \sum_j |\lambda_j| < \infty \right\}.$$

Clearly, H^1_{at} is contained in L^1. Define a norm on H^1_{at} by

$$\|f\|_{H^1_{\mathrm{at}}} = \inf \left\{ \sum_j |\lambda_j| : f = \sum \lambda_j a_j \right\}.$$

With this norm H^1_{at} is a Banach space. (Details are left to the reader.) Further, it follows immediately from Proposition 6.2 that singular integrals are bounded from H^1_{at} to L^1.

Corollary 6.3. *Let T be an operator as in Proposition 6.2, and let $f \in H^1_{\mathrm{at}}$. Then*

$$\|Tf\|_1 \leq C\|f\|_{H^1_{\mathrm{at}}}.$$

The space H^1_{at} is the largest subspace of $L^1(\mathbb{R}^n)$ for which Corollary 6.3 holds in the following sense: let $R_1, \ldots, R_n$ be the Riesz transforms in $\mathbb{R}^n$ (the Hilbert transform if $n = 1$), and define the space

$$H^1(\mathbb{R}^n) = \{ f \in L^1(\mathbb{R}^n) : R_j f \in L^1(\mathbb{R}^n), 1 \leq j \leq n \}$$

with the norm

$$\|f\|_{H^1} = \|f\|_1 + \sum_{j=1}^n \|R_j f\|_1.$$

Then the following is true.

Theorem 6.4. $H^1(\mathbb{R}^n) = H^1_{\text{at}}(\mathbb{R}^n)$ *and their norms are equivalent.*

We will not prove Theorem 6.4; a proof can be found in either García-Cuerva and Rubio de Francia [**6**, Chapter 3] or Stein [**17**, Chapter 3].

2. The space BMO

Given a function $f \in L^1_{\text{loc}}(\mathbb{R}^n)$ and a cube Q, let f_Q denote the average of f on Q:

$$f_Q = \frac{1}{|Q|} \int_Q f.$$

Define the sharp maximal function by

(6.1) $$M^\# f(x) = \sup_{Q \ni x} \frac{1}{|Q|} \int_Q |f - f_Q|,$$

where the supremum is taken over all cubes Q containing x. Each of these integrals measures the mean oscillation of f on the cube Q; we say that f has bounded mean oscillation if the function $M^\# f$ is bounded. The space of functions with this property is denoted by BMO:

$$BMO = \{f \in L^1_{\text{loc}} : M^\# f \in L^\infty\}.$$

We define a norm on BMO by

$$\|f\|_* = \|M^\# f\|_\infty.$$

This is not properly a norm since any function which is constant almost everywhere has zero oscillation. However, these are the only functions with this property, and it is customary to think of BMO as the quotient of the above space by the space of constant functions. In other words, two functions which differ by a constant coincide as functions in BMO. On this space $\|\cdot\|_*$ is a norm and the space is a Banach space.

It is easy to see that we have the pointwise inequality

$$M^\# f(x) \leq C_n M f(x)$$

with the Hardy-Littlewood maximal function. The constant depends on the dimension n, but if we replace M by M'', the variant of the maximal operator where the supremum is taken over all cubes containing x (see (2.6)), the constant is 2.

Proposition 6.5.

(6.2) $$\frac{1}{2}\|f\|_* \leq \sup_Q \inf_{a \in \mathbb{C}} \frac{1}{|Q|} \int_Q |f(x) - a| \, dx \leq \|f\|_*;$$

(6.3) $$M^\#(|f|)(x) \leq 2M^\# f(x).$$

Proof. The second inequality in (6.2) is immediate. To prove the first, note that for all a,

$$\int_Q |f(x) - f_Q| \, dx \le \int_Q |f(x) - a| \, dx + \int_Q |a - f_Q| \, dx \le 2 \int_Q |f(x) - a| \, dx.$$

Now divide both sides by $|Q|$, take the infimum over all a and then the supremum over Q.

Inequality (6.3) follows from (6.2) (with $a = |f_Q|$) since

$$\frac{1}{|Q|} \int_Q ||f(x)| - |f_Q|| \, dx \le \frac{1}{|Q|} \int_Q |f(x) - f_Q| \, dx.$$

$\square$

Inequality (6.2) defines a norm equivalent to $\| \cdot \|_*$, one which provides a way to show that $f \in BMO$ without using its average on Q: it suffices to find a constant a (that can depend on Q) such that

$$\frac{1}{|Q|} \int_Q |f(x) - a| \, dx \le C$$

with C independent of Q.

It follows from (6.3) that if $f \in BMO$ then $|f|$ is also in BMO. However, the converse is not true. This confirms what the definition suggests: being in BMO is not just a question of size. Clearly $L^\infty \subset BMO$, but there are also unbounded BMO functions. The typical example on $\mathbb{R}$ is

$$f(x) = \begin{cases} \log\left(\dfrac{1}{|x|}\right) & |x| < 1, \\ 0 & |x| \ge 1. \end{cases}$$

But it is easy to see that the function $\text{sgn}(x)f(x) \notin BMO$ even though f is its absolute value.

The next result shows the connection between BMO and singular integrals.

Theorem 6.6. *Let T be an operator as in the hypotheses of Theorem 5.10 whose kernel satisfies condition (5.11). Then if f is a bounded function of compact support, $Tf \in BMO$ and*

$$\|Tf\|_* \le C\|f\|_\infty.$$

Proof. Fix a cube Q in $\mathbb{R}^n$ with center c_Q, and let Q^* be the cube centered at c_Q whose side length is $2\sqrt{n}$ times that of Q. Decompose f as $f = f_1 + f_2$, where $f_1 = f\chi_{Q^*}$.

Let $a = Tf_2(c_Q)$. Then, since (5.11) holds and since T is bounded on L^2,

$$\frac{1}{|Q|} \int_Q |Tf(x) - a|\, dx$$

$$\leq \frac{1}{|Q|} \int_Q |Tf_1(x)|\, dx$$

$$+ \frac{1}{|Q|} \int_Q |Tf_2(x) - Tf_2(c_Q)|\, dx$$

$$\leq \left(\frac{1}{|Q|} \int_Q |Tf_1(x)|^2\, dx \right)^{1/2}$$

$$+ \frac{1}{|Q|} \int_Q \left| \int_{\mathbb{R}^n \setminus Q^*} [K(x,y) - K(c_Q, y)] f(y)\, dy \right| dx$$

$$\leq C \left(\frac{1}{|Q|} \int_{Q^*} |f(x)|^2\, dx \right)^{1/2}$$

$$+ \frac{1}{|Q|} \int_Q \int_{\mathbb{R}^n \setminus Q^*} |K(x,y) - K(c_Q, y)|\, dy\, dx \cdot \|f\|_\infty$$

$$\leq C\|f\|_\infty.$$

$\square$

Theorem 6.6 is a first step towards our goal of finding a space which contains the images of bounded functions under singular integrals. However, the set of bounded functions with compact support is not dense in L^∞, so we cannot extend T to the whole space by continuity. Instead, we will extend the definition of T to one which holds on all of L^∞.

Let f be a bounded function and let Q be a cube in $\mathbb{R}^n$ centered at the origin. Define Q^* as above and again decompose f as $f_1 + f_2$, $f_1 = f\chi_{Q^*}$. Since f_1 is bounded and has compact support, Tf_1 is well defined as an L^2 function; hence $Tf_1(x)$ exists for almost every x. For $x \in Q$ define

(6.4) $$Tf(x) = Tf_1(x) + \int_{\mathbb{R}^n} [K(x,y) - K(0,y)] f_2(y)\, dy.$$

This integral converges since it is bounded by

$$\|f\|_\infty \int_{\mathbb{R}^n \setminus Q^*} |K(x,y) - K(0,y)|\, dy,$$

provided K satisfies (5.11).

Now let $\bar{Q}$ be some other cube centered at the origin which contains Q. Then we have two definitions of $Tf(x)$ for $x \in Q$. Let $\bar{f}_1 = f\chi_{\bar{Q}^*}$ and $\bar{f}_2 = f\chi_{\mathbb{R}^n \setminus \bar{Q}^*}$; then the difference between the two definitions is

$$T(f_1 - \bar{f}_1)(x) + \int_{\mathbb{R}^n \setminus Q^*} [K(x,y) - K(0,y)] f(y) \, dy$$

$$- \int_{\mathbb{R}^n \setminus \bar{Q}^*} [K(x,y) - K(0,y)] f(y) \, dy = - \int_{\bar{Q}^* \setminus Q^*} K(0,y) f(y) \, dy,$$

and this is independent of x. Hence, the two definitions coincide as functions in BMO since in BMO we identify functions which differ by a constant. We can, therefore, take (6.4) as the definition of the image of f under T. Further, by arguing as we did in Theorem 6.6, we can show that if $f \in L^\infty$ then $Tf \in BMO$. Finally, note that we do not have to take cubes centered at the origin but can take any cube.

If f is a bounded function of compact support, then (6.4) coincides with our original definition since for Q large enough, $f = f_1$. More generally, if $f \in \mathcal{S}$ then the two definitions agree as BMO functions: since

$$\int_{\mathbb{R}^n \setminus Q^*} K(0,y) f(y) \, dy$$

converges absolutely to a value independent of x, the two definitions differ by a constant.

Example 6.7. Let $f(x) = \text{sgn}(x)$; we will find the image of f under the Hilbert transform, whose kernel is $K(x,y) = [\pi(x-y)]^{-1}$. Let $|x| < a/2$; then

$$\pi H f(x) = \text{p.\,v.} \int_{-a}^{a} \frac{\text{sgn}(y)}{x-y} \, dy + \lim_{N \to \infty} \int_{-N}^{-a} + \int_{a}^{N} \left(\frac{1}{x-y} + \frac{1}{y} \right) \text{sgn}(y) \, dy$$

$$= 2 \log |x| - 2 \log(a).$$

Hence, ignoring the constant,

$$H(\text{sgn}(x)) = \frac{2}{\pi} \log |x|.$$

This is an indirect proof that $\log |x|$ is a function in BMO. This result also agrees with our original motivation for the Hilbert transform since there exists an analytic function in the upper half-plane whose real part tends to $\text{sgn}(x)$ and whose imaginary part tends to $\frac{2}{\pi} \log |x|$ as we approach the real axis. We can give such a function explicitly:

$$i \log(iz) = i \log(-y + ix) = i \log(x^2 + y^2)^{1/2} + \arctan(x/y).$$

As $y \to 0$ the limit of this function is

$$\frac{\pi}{2} \text{sgn}(x) + i \log |x|.$$

3. An interpolation result

In applying interpolation theorems (such as the Marcinkiewicz interpolation theorem) we often use the fact that an operator is bounded from L^∞ to L^∞. Here we show that we can replace this with the weaker condition of boundedness from L^∞ to BMO.

Theorem 6.8. *Let T be a linear operator which is bounded on L^{p_0} for some p_0, $1 < p_0 < \infty$, and is bounded from L^∞ to BMO. Then for all p, $p_0 < p < \infty$, T is bounded on L^p.*

The proof of Theorem 6.8 requires two lemmas.

Lemma 6.9. *If $1 \le p_0 \le p < \infty$ and $f \in L^{p_0}$ then*

$$(6.5) \qquad \int_{\mathbb{R}^n} M_d f(x)^p \, dx \le C \int_{\mathbb{R}^n} M^\# f(x)^p \, dx,$$

where M_d is the dyadic maximal operator (2.9).

By Lemma 2.12 we can replace the dyadic maximal function in (6.5) with the Hardy-Littlewood maximal function. Thus, while the reverse of the pointwise inequality $M^\# f(x) \le CMf(x)$ is not true in general, Lemma 6.9 provides a substitute norm inequality.

The proof of Lemma 6.9 uses a technique known as a "good-λ inequality"; more precisely, it depends on the following result.

Lemma 6.10. *If $f \in L^{p_0}$ for some p_0, $1 \le p_0 < \infty$, then for all $\gamma > 0$ and $\lambda > 0$,*

$$|\{x \in \mathbb{R}^n : M_d f(x) > 2\lambda, M^\# f(x) \le \gamma\lambda\}| \le 2^n \gamma |\{x \in \mathbb{R}^n : M_d f(x) > \lambda\}|.$$

Proof. Without loss of generality we may assume that f is non-negative. Fix $\lambda, \gamma > 0$. If we form the Calderón-Zygmund decomposition of f at height λ, then the set $\{x \in \mathbb{R}^n : M_d f(x) > \lambda\}$ can be written as the union of disjoint, maximal dyadic cubes. (See Theorem 2.11; we can substitute $f \in L^{p_0}$ for the hypothesis $f \in L^1$ in the proof.) If Q is one of these cubes, then it will suffice to show that

$$(6.6) \qquad |\{x \in Q : M_d f(x) > 2\lambda, M^\# f(x) \le \gamma\lambda\}| \le 2^n \gamma |Q|.$$

Let $\tilde{Q}$ be the dyadic cube containing Q whose sides are twice as long. Then, since Q is maximal, $f_{\tilde{Q}} \le \lambda$. Furthermore, if $x \in Q$ and $M_d f(x) > 2\lambda$, then $M_d(f\chi_Q)(x) > 2\lambda$, so for those x's,

$$M_d((f - f_{\tilde{Q}})\chi_Q)(x) \ge M_d(f\chi_Q)(x) - f_{\tilde{Q}} > \lambda.$$

By the weak $(1,1)$ inequality for M_d (Theorem 2.10),

$$|\{x \in Q : M_d((f - f_{\tilde{Q}})\chi_Q)(x) > \lambda\}| \leq \frac{1}{\lambda} \int_Q |f(x) - f_{\tilde{Q}}|\,dx$$

$$\leq \frac{2^n|Q|}{\lambda} \frac{1}{|\tilde{Q}|} \int_{\tilde{Q}} |f(x) - f_{\tilde{Q}}|\,dx$$

$$\leq \frac{2^n|Q|}{\lambda} \inf_{x \in Q} M^\# f(x).$$

If the set $\{x \in Q : M_d f(x) > 2\lambda, M^\# f(x) \leq \gamma\lambda\}$ is empty there is nothing to prove. Otherwise, for some $x \in Q$, $M^\# f(x) \leq \gamma\lambda$ and so inequality (6.6) holds. $\qquad\square$

Proof of Lemma 6.9. For $N > 0$ let

$$I_N = \int_0^N p\lambda^{p-1}|\{x \in \mathbb{R}^n : M_d f(x) > \lambda\}|\,d\lambda.$$

I_N is finite since

$$I_N \leq \frac{p}{p_0}N^{p-p_0} \int_0^N p_0\lambda^{p_0-1}|\{x \in \mathbb{R}^n : M_d f(x) > \lambda\}|\,d\lambda,$$

and $M_d f \in L^{p_0}$ since $f \in L^{p_0}$. Furthermore,

$$I_N = 2^p \int_0^{N/2} p\lambda^{p-1}|\{x \in \mathbb{R}^n : M_d f(x) > 2\lambda\}|\,d\lambda$$

$$\leq 2^p \int_0^{N/2} p\lambda^{p-1}\Big(|\{x \in \mathbb{R}^n : M_d f(x) > 2\lambda, M^\# f(x) \leq \gamma\lambda\}|$$

$$+ |\{x \in \mathbb{R}^n : M^\# f(x) > \gamma\lambda\}|\Big)d\lambda$$

$$\leq 2^{p+n}\gamma I_N + \frac{2^p}{\gamma^p} \int_0^{\gamma N/2} p\lambda^{p-1}|\{x \in \mathbb{R}^n : M^\# f(x) > \lambda\}|\,d\lambda.$$

Fix γ such that $2^{p+n}\gamma = 1/2$; then

$$(6.7)\qquad I_N \leq \frac{2^{p+1}}{\gamma^p} \int_0^{\gamma N/2} p\lambda^{p-1}|\{x \in \mathbb{R}^n : M^\# f(x) > \lambda\}|\,d\lambda.$$

If $\int (M^\# f)^p = \infty$ then there is nothing to prove. If it is finite then we can take the limit as $N \to \infty$ in inequality (6.7) to get (6.5). $\qquad\square$

Proof of Theorem 6.8. The composition $M^\# \circ T$ is a sublinear operator. It is bounded on L^{p_0} since both these operators are, and it is bounded on L^∞ since

$$\|M^\#(Tf)\|_\infty = \|Tf\|_* \leq C\|f\|_\infty.$$

Hence, by the Marcinkiewicz interpolation theorem $M^\# \circ T$ is bounded on L^p, $p_0 < p < \infty$.

Now suppose that $f \in L^p$ has compact support. Then $f \in L^{p_0}$ and so $Tf \in L^{p_0}$. Therefore, we can apply Lemma 6.9 to Tf. In particular, since $|Tf(x)| \leq M_d(Tf)(x)$ a.e.,

$$\int_{\mathbb{R}^n} |Tf(x)|^p \, dx \leq \int_{\mathbb{R}^n} M_d(Tf)(x)^p \, dx$$

$$\leq C \int_{\mathbb{R}^n} M^{\#}(Tf)(x)^p \, dx$$

$$\leq C \int_{\mathbb{R}^n} |f(x)|^p \, dx.$$

$\square$

4. The John-Nirenberg inequality

In this section we examine the rate of growth of functions in BMO. We first consider $\log(1/|x|)$, which we gave as an example of an unbounded function in BMO. On the interval $(-a, a)$, its average is $(1 - \log a)$; given $\lambda > 1$, the set where

$$|\log(1/|x|) - (1 - \log a)| > \lambda$$

has measure $2ae^{-\lambda-1}$. The next result shows that in some sense logarithmic growth is the maximum possible for BMO functions.

Theorem 6.11 (John-Nirenberg Inequality). *Let $f \in BMO$. Then there exist constants C_1 and C_2, depending only on the dimension, such that given any cube Q in $\mathbb{R}^n$ and any $\lambda > 0$,*

(6.8) $$|\{x \in Q : |f(x) - f_Q| > \lambda\}| \leq C_1 e^{-C_2\lambda/\|f\|_*}|Q|.$$

Proof. Since (6.8) is homogeneous, we may assume without loss of generality that $\|f\|_* = 1$. Then

(6.9) $$\frac{1}{|Q|} \int_Q |f(x) - f_Q| \, dx \leq 1.$$

Now form the Calderón-Zygmund decomposition of $f - f_Q$ on Q at height 2. (This is done as in Theorem 2.11 except that we begin by bisecting the sides of Q to form 2^n equal cubes and repeating this for all cubes formed. Inequality (6.9) replaces the hypothesis that $f \in L^1$.) This gives us a family of cubes $\{Q_{1,j}\}$ such that

$$2 < \frac{1}{|Q_{1,j}|} \int_{Q_{1,j}} |f(x) - f_Q| \, dx \leq 2^{n+1}$$

and $|f(x) - f_Q| \leq 2$ if $x \notin \bigcup_j Q_{1,j}$. In particular,

$$\sum_j |Q_{1,j}| \leq \frac{1}{2} \int_Q |f(x) - f_Q| \, dx \leq \frac{1}{2}|Q|,$$

and

$$|f_{Q_{1,j}} - f_Q| = \left| \frac{1}{|Q_{1,j}|} \int_{Q_{1,j}} (f(x) - f_Q) \, dx \right| \leq 2^{n+1}.$$

On each cube $Q_{1,j}$ form the Calderón-Zygmund decomposition of $f - f_{Q_{1,j}}$ at height 2. (Again by assumption the average of this function on $Q_{1,j}$ is at most 1.) We then obtain a family of cubes $\{Q_{1,j,k}\}$ which satisfy the following:

$$|f_{Q_{1,j,k}} - f_{Q_{1,j}}| \leq 2^{n+1},$$

$$|f(x) - f_{Q_{1,j}}| \leq 2 \ \text{ if } \ x \in Q_{1,j} \setminus \bigcup_k Q_{1,j,k},$$

$$\sum_k |Q_{1,j,k}| \leq \frac{1}{2}|Q_{1,j}|.$$

Gather the cubes $Q_{1,j,k}$ corresponding to all the $Q_{1,j}$'s and collectively rename them $\{Q_{2,j}\}$. Then

$$\sum_j |Q_{2,j}| \leq \frac{1}{4}|Q|,$$

and if $x \notin \bigcup_j Q_{2,j}$,

$$|f(x) - f_Q| \leq |f(x) - f_{Q_{1,j}}| + |f_{Q_{1,j}} - f_Q| \leq 2 + 2^{n+1} \leq 2 \cdot 2^{n+1}.$$

Repeat this process indefinitely. Then for each N we get a family of disjoint cubes $\{Q_{N,j}\}$ such that

$$|f(x) - f_Q| \leq N \cdot 2^{n+1}$$

if $x \notin \bigcup_j Q_{N,j}$ and

$$\sum_j |Q_{N,j}| \leq \frac{1}{2^N}|Q|.$$

Fix $\lambda \geq 2^{n+1}$ and let N be such that $N2^{n+1} \leq \lambda < (N+1)2^{n+1}$. Then

$$|\{x \in Q : |f(x) - f_Q| > \lambda\}| \leq \sum_j |Q_{N,j}|$$

$$\leq \frac{1}{2^N}|Q|$$

$$= e^{-N \log 2}|Q|$$

$$\leq e^{-C_2 \lambda}|Q|,$$

where $C_2 = \log 2/2^{n+2}$. If $\lambda < 2^{n+1}$ then $C_2\lambda < \log\sqrt{2}$. Hence,

$$|\{x \in Q : |f(x) - f_Q| > \lambda\}| \leq |Q| \leq e^{\log\sqrt{2}-C_2\lambda}|Q| = \sqrt{2}e^{-C_2\lambda}|Q|,$$

so we can take $C_1 = \sqrt{2}$. $\qquad\qquad\qquad\qquad\qquad\qquad\qquad\qquad\square$

Corollary 6.12. *For all p, $1 < p < \infty$,*

$$\|f\|_{*,p} = \sup_Q \left(\frac{1}{|Q|}\int_Q |f(x) - f_Q|^p\, dx\right)^{1/p}$$

is a norm on BMO equivalent to $\|\cdot\|_*$.

Proof. It will suffice to prove that $\|f\|_{*,p} \leq C_p\|f\|_*$ since the reverse inequality is immediate. But by Theorem 6.11

$$\int_Q |f(x) - f_Q|^p\, dx = \int_0^\infty p\lambda^{p-1}|\{x \in Q : |f(x) - f_Q| > \lambda\}|\, d\lambda$$

$$\leq C_1|Q|\int_0^\infty p\lambda^{p-1}e^{-C_2\lambda/\|f\|_*}\, d\lambda.$$

Make the change of variables $s = C_2\lambda/\|f\|_*$; then we get

$$\frac{1}{|Q|}\int_Q |f(x) - f_Q|^p\, dx \leq C_1 p\left(\frac{\|f\|_*}{C_2}\right)^p \int_0^\infty s^{p-1}e^{-s}\, ds$$

$$= C_1 p C_2^{-p}\Gamma(p)\|f\|_*^p,$$

which yields the desired inequality. $\qquad\qquad\qquad\qquad\qquad\qquad\square$

As a consequence of the proof of Corollary 6.12 we get two additional results. Given the size of the constant C_p, if we expand the exponential function as a power series we immediately get the following.

Corollary 6.13. *Given $f \in BMO$, there exists $\lambda > 0$ such that for any cube Q,*

$$\frac{1}{|Q|}\int_Q e^{\lambda|f(x)-f_Q|}\, dx < \infty.$$

Further, the proof of Corollary 6.12 (with $p = 1$) can be readily adapted to show that the converse of the John-Nirenberg inequality (Theorem 6.11) holds.

Corollary 6.14. *Given a function f, suppose there exist constants C_1, C_2 and K such that for any cube Q and $\lambda > 0$,*

$$|\{x \in Q : |f(x) - f_Q| > \lambda\}| \leq C_1 e^{-C_2\lambda/K}|Q|.$$

Then $f \in BMO$.

5. Notes and further results

5.1. References.

For the development of Hardy spaces and in particular the space H^1, see Section 5.2 below. E. M. Stein (*Classes H^p, multiplicateurs et fonctions de Littlewood-Paley*, C. R. Acad. Sci. Paris **263** (1966), 716–719, 780–781) first proved that singular integrals and multipliers are bounded from H^1 to L^1. The space BMO was introduced by F. John and L. Nirenberg while studying PDE's (*On functions of bounded mean oscillation*, Comm. Pure Appl. Math. **14** (1961), 415–426). There they proved Theorem 6.11. That singular integrals take L^∞ into BMO was first observed by S. Spanne (*Sur l'interpolation entre les espaces $\mathcal{L}_k^{p,\Phi}$*, Ann. Scuola Norm. Sup. Pisa **20** (1966), 625–648), J. Peetre (*On convolution operators leaving $L^{p,\lambda}$ spaces invariant*, Ann. Mat. Pura Appl. **72** (1966), 295–304), and E. M. Stein (*Singular integrals, harmonic functions, and differentiability properties of functions of several variables*, Singular Integrals, Proc. Sympos. Pure Math. **X**, pp. 316–335, Amer. Math. Soc., Providence, 1967). The sharp maximal function was introduced by C. Fefferman and E. M. Stein (*H^p spaces of several variables*, Acta Math. **129** (1972), 137–193); in the same paper they proved Theorem 6.8.

5.2. The H^p spaces.

The Hardy spaces were first studied as part of complex analysis by G. H. Hardy (*The mean value of the modulus of an analytic function*, Proc. London Math. Soc. **14** (1914), 269–277). An analytic function F in the unit disk $\mathbb{D} = \{z \in \mathbb{C} : |z| < 1\}$ is in $H^p(\mathbb{D})$, $0 < p < \infty$, if

$$\sup_{0 < r < 1} \int_{-\pi}^{\pi} |F(re^{i\theta})|^p \, d\theta < \infty.$$

A function F which is analytic in the upper half-plane $\mathbb{R}_+^2 = \{z = x + iy : y > 0\}$ is in $H^p(\mathbb{R}_+^2)$ if

$$\sup_{y > 0} \int_{\mathbb{R}} |F(x + iy)|^p \, dx < \infty.$$

When $p > 1$ it can be shown that H^p coincides with the class of analytic functions whose real parts are the Poisson integrals of functions f in $L^p(\mathbb{T})$ or $L^p(\mathbb{R})$, respectively. We can therefore identify $H^p(\mathbb{D})$ with $L^p(\mathbb{T})$ and $H^p(\mathbb{R}_+^2)$ with $L^p(\mathbb{R})$. This identification does not hold, however, for $p \leq 1$. Functions in $H^p(\mathbb{D})$ and $H^p(\mathbb{R}_+^2)$ have a rich structural theory based on "factorization" theorems which allow them to be decomposed into well understood components. For a thorough treatment from this perspective, see Koosis [**11**] or Rudin [**14**].

Unfortunately, these results cannot be extended to higher dimensions using the theory of functions of several complex variables. E. M. Stein and G. Weiss (*On the theory of harmonic functions of several variables, I: The theory of H^p spaces*, Acta Math. **103** (1960), 25–62, also see Stein [**15**, Chapter 7]) defined $H^p(\mathbb{R}^{n+1}_+)$ by considering vector-valued functions which satisfy generalized Cauchy-Riemann equations. This extension is only valid if $p > 1 - 1/n$, which does include H^1. This space H^1 is isomorphic (by passing to boundary values) to the space of functions in $L^1(\mathbb{R}^n)$ whose Riesz transforms are also in $L^1(\mathbb{R}^n)$. (This is the space we called $H^1(\mathbb{R}^n)$ in Section 1.)

D. Burkholder, R. Gundy and M. Silverstein (*A maximal characterization of the class H^p*, Trans. Amer. Math. Soc. **157** (1971), 137–153) proved a crucial result for establishing a strictly real-variable theory of H^p spaces. Given $F = u + iv$, analytic in the upper half-plane, they showed that F is in H^p if and only if the non-tangential maximal function of its real part,

$$u_a^*(x_0) = \sup\{|u(x,y)| : (x,y) \in \Gamma_a(x_0)\},$$

where

$$\Gamma_a(x_0) = \{(x,y) \in \mathbb{R}^2_+ : |x - x_0| < ay\},$$

is in $L^p(\mathbb{R})$. (See Chapter 2, Section 8.7.) Since $u(x,y) = P_y * f(x)$, the Poisson integral of its boundary value f, this characterizes the restriction to $\mathbb{R}$ of the real parts of functions in $H^p(\mathbb{R}^2_+)$. This space of functions on $\mathbb{R}$, which is customarily denoted by $H^p(\mathbb{R})$ (or sometimes by Re $H^p(\mathbb{R})$), is equivalent when $p = 1$ to the space $H^1(\mathbb{R})$ defined in Section 1. The original proof of this result used Brownian motion; a complex analytic proof was given by P. Koosis (*Sommabilité de la fonction maximale et appartenance à H_1*, C. R. Acad. Sci. Paris **28** (1978), 1041–1043, also see [**11**, Chapter 8]).

The key feature of this result is that the fact that u is a harmonic function is irrelevant, in the sense that the same characterization of the boundary values holds if we replace the Poisson kernel by any approximation of the identity defined starting from $\phi \in \mathcal{S}$ with non-zero integral. This leads to an elegant definition of H^p in higher dimensions: given $\phi \in \mathcal{S}(\mathbb{R}^n)$ with non-zero integral, we say a function $f \in H^p(\mathbb{R}^n)$ if

$$M_\phi f(x_0) = \sup\{|\phi_y * f(x)| : (x,y) \in \Gamma_a(x_0)\}$$

is in $L^p(\mathbb{R}^n)$. The resulting space is independent of ϕ: in fact, one can replace M_ϕ by the so-called grand maximal function

$$\mathcal{M}f(x) = \sup_\phi M_\phi f(x),$$

where the supremum is taken over all such ϕ. For $p > 1 - 1/n$ this space is isomorphic (again by taking boundary values) to the H^p spaces of Stein and Weiss above. This approach is developed in the excellent article by Fefferman and Stein cited above. Also see Stein [**17**, Chapter 3].

The atomic decomposition of functions in $H^p(\mathbb{R})$ is due to R. Coifman (*A real variable characterization of H^p*, Studia Math. **51** (1974), 269–274); it was extended to higher dimensions by R. Latter (*A decomposition of $H^p(\mathbb{R}^n)$ in terms of atoms*, Studia Math. **62** (1978), 93–101; also see R. Latter and A. Uchiyama, *The atomic decomposition for parabolic H^p spaces*, Trans. Amer. Math. Soc. **253** (1979), 391–398). For simplicity we used an atomic decomposition as the basis of our definition of $H^1(\mathbb{R}^n)$—the space we called $H_{\mathrm{at}}^1(\mathbb{R}^n)$. Using these methods, R. Coifman and G. Weiss (*Extensions of Hardy spaces and their use in Analysis*, Bull. Amer. Math. Soc. **83** (1977), 569–645) defined H^p spaces on spaces of homogeneous type (see Chapter 5, Section 6.4). Their definition only holds for $p_0 < p \le 1$, where p_0 is a constant which depends on the space being considered.

A monograph on the real theory of H^p spaces with applications to Fourier analysis and approximation theory is due to Shanzhen Lu (*Four Lectures on Real H^p Spaces*, World Scientific, Singapore, 1995).

Finally, we mention another characterization of H^p spaces in terms of the Lusin area integral. If u is a harmonic function on $\mathbb{R}_+^{n+1}$, let

$$S(u)(x_0) = \left(\int_{\Gamma_a^h(x_0)} |\nabla u|^2 y^{1-n} \, dy \, dx \right)^{1/2},$$

where

$$\Gamma_a^h(x_0) = \{(x,y) \in \mathbb{R}_+^{n+1} : |x - x_0| < ay, 0 < y < h\}$$

and

$$|\nabla u|^2 = \left| \frac{\partial u}{\partial y} \right|^2 + \sum_{j=1}^n \left| \frac{\partial u}{\partial x_j} \right|^2.$$

(This is called the area integral since if $n = 1$, $S(u)^2$ is the area of the image of $\Gamma_a^h(x_0)$, counting multiplicities, under the analytic function F whose real part is u.) Then $u \in H^p(\mathbb{R}_+^{n+1})$ if and only if $S(u) \in L^p(\mathbb{R}^n)$ and $u(x,y) \to 0$ as $y \to \infty$. An alternative characterization is gotten by replacing the area integral by a Littlewood-Paley type function which is its radial analogue:

$$g(u)(x) = \left(\int_0^\infty |\nabla u(x,y)|^2 y \, dy \right)^{1/2}.$$

This characterization is due to A. P. Calderón (*Commutators of singular integral operators*, Proc. Nat. Acad. Sci. U.S.A. **53** (1965), 1092–1099). See also García-Cuerva and Rubio de Francia [6], Stein [15], Zygmund [21] and the article by Fefferman and Stein cited above.

5.3. Duality.

The results on boundedness from H^1 to L^1 and from L^∞ to BMO are dual to one another. This is a consequence of a deep result due to C. Fefferman (announced in *Characterizations of bounded mean oscillation*, Bull. Amer. Math. Soc. **77** (1971), 587–588).

Theorem 6.15. *The dual of $H^1(\mathbb{R}^n)$ is BMO.*

The article by Fefferman and Stein cited above gives two proofs of this result. Three appear in García-Cuerva and Rubio de Francia [**6**].

The duals of the H^p spaces, $p < 1$, are Lipschitz spaces. This is due to P. Duren, B. Romberg and A. Shields (*Linear functionals on H^p spaces with $0 < p < 1$*, J. Reine Angew. Math. **238** (1969), 32–60) on the unit circle and to T. Walsh (*The dual of $H^p(\mathbb{R}^{n+1}_+)$ for $p < 1$*, Can. J. Math. **25** (1973), 567–577) in $\mathbb{R}^n$. Also see [**6**, Chapter 3].

5.4. The Hardy-Littlewood maximal function on BMO.

The maximal function is bounded on BMO: if $f \in BMO$ then $Mf \in BMO$. This was first proved by C. Bennett, R. A. DeVore and R. Sharpley (*Weak L^∞ and BMO*, Ann. of Math. **113** (1981), 601–611); simpler proofs were given by F. Chiarenza and M. Frasca (*Morrey spaces and Hardy-Littlewood maximal function*, Rend. Mat. Appl., Series 7, **7** (1981), 273–279) and D. Cruz-Uribe, and C. J. Neugebauer (*The structure of the reverse Hölder classes*, Trans. Amer. Math. Soc. **347** (1995), 2941–2960). See also a proof in Torchinsky [**19**, p. 204].

5.5. Another interpolation result.

In applying the Marcinkiewicz interpolation theorem one often uses that the operator in question is bounded on L^∞ or satisfies a weak $(1,1)$ inequality. In Theorem 6.8 we showed that we can replace the first hypothesis by the assumption that the operator maps L^∞ into BMO. One can also use H^1 to replace the weak $(1,1)$ inequality.

Theorem 6.16. *Given a sublinear operator T, suppose that T maps H^1 into L^1 and for some p_1, $1 < p_1 \leq \infty$, T is weak (p_1, p_1). Then for all p, $1 < p < p_1$, T is bounded on L^p.*

This result can be generalized to the other H^p spaces. For details and references, see García-Cuerva and Rubio de Francia [**6**, Chapter 3].

5.6. Fractional integrals and Sobolev spaces.

For fractional integral operators I_a (see Chapter 4, Section 7.7), the critical index is $p = n/a$: we would expect I_a to map $L^{n/a}$ to L^∞, but it does not. Instead, we have a result analogous to Theorem 6.6.

Theorem 6.17. *If $f \in L^{n/a}$ then $I_a f \in BMO$.*

The proof of this theorem follows at once from an inequality relating the fractional integral, the sharp maximal function and the fractional maximal function.

Theorem 6.18. *There exist positive constants C_1 and C_2 such that for all locally integrable f,*

$$C_1 M_a f(x) \leq M^{\#}(I_a f)(x) \leq C_2 M_a f(x).$$

Both of these results are due to D. R. Adams (*A note on Riesz potentials*, Duke Math. J. **42** (1975), 765–778).

When $p = 1$, besides the weak $(1, n/(n-a))$ inequality in Theorem 4.18, we also have an analogue of Corollary 6.3: $\|I_a f\|_{n/(n-a)} \leq C\|f\|_{H^1}$. This result is due to Stein and Weiss—see the article cited above. Similar inequalities hold for all the H^p spaces: see the article by S. Krantz (*Fractional integration on Hardy Spaces*, Studia Math. **73** (1982), 87–94).

For Sobolev spaces, the corresponding limiting theorem would be that if $f \in L_k^{n/k}$ then $f \in BMO$. However, this is only known when $k = 1$: see the paper by A. Cianchi and L. Pick (*Sobolev embeddings into BMO, VMO and L_∞*, Ark. Mat. **36** (1998), 317–340). In the general case we have as a substitute an exponential integrability result (cf. Corollary 6.13).

Theorem 6.19. *Given $0 < a < n$ and any cube Q, then there exist constants C_1 and C_2 such that if $f \in L^{n/a}(Q)$,*

$$\frac{1}{|Q|} \int_Q \exp\left(\left| \frac{I_a f}{C_1 \|f\|_{L^{n/a}(Q)}} \right|^{p'} \right) \leq C_2.$$

Theorem 6.19 was proved by N. S. Trudinger (*On imbeddings into Orlicz spaces and some applications*, J. Math. Mech. **17** (1967), 473–483) when $a = 1$ and in general by R. S. Strichartz (*A note on Trudinger's extension of Sobolev's inequalities*, Indiana Univ. Math. J. **21** (1972), 841–842). Sharp constants have been found by J. Moser (*A sharp form of an inequality by N. Trudinger*, Indiana Univ. Math. J. **20** (1971), 1077–1092) and D. R. Adams (*A sharp inequality of J. Moser for higher order derivatives*, Ann. of Math. **128** (1988), 385–398). Also see the books by W. Ziemer (*Weakly Differentiable Functions*, Springer-Verlag, New York, 1989) and D. R. Adams and L. Hedberg (*Function Spaces and Potential Theory*, Springer-Verlag, Berlin, 1996).

5.7. Vanishing mean oscillation.

Given a function $f \in BMO$, we say that f has vanishing mean oscillation, and write $f \in VMO$, if

$$\frac{1}{|Q|} \int_Q |f(x) - f_Q|\, dx$$

tends to zero as $|Q|$ tends to either zero or infinity. As in BMO, there are unbounded functions in VMO. For example,

$$f(x) = \begin{cases} \log\log(1/|x|), & |x| \le 1/e, \\ 0, & |x| > 1/e, \end{cases}$$

is in VMO, and in fact it can be shown that in some sense it has the maximum rate of growth possible for functions in VMO. Clearly, if $f \in C_0$ (i.e. the space of continuous functions which vanish at infinity) then $f \in VMO$; further, VMO is the closure in BMO of C_0.

VMO lets us sharpen Theorem 6.6 as follows: given a singular integral operator T, if $f \in C_0$ then $Tf \in VMO$.

The space VMO was introduced by D. Sarason (*Functions of vanishing mean oscillation*, Trans. Amer. Math. Soc. **207** (1975), 391–405). Also see the survey article by R. Coifman and G. Weiss (*Extensions of Hardy spaces and their uses in analysis*, Bull. Amer. Math. Soc. **83** (1977), 569–645).

5.8. Commutators and BMO.

We can give another characterization of BMO in terms of singular integrals. Let T be a singular integral, and for a locally integrable function b, let M_b be the operator given by pointwise multiplication by b: $M_b f(x) = b(x)f(x)$. Define the commutator $[b, T]$ by $M_b T - T M_b$. If $Tf = K * f$ then for $f \in C_c^\infty$

$$[b, T]f(x) = \int_{\mathbb{R}^n} (b(x) - b(y))K(x - y)f(y)\, dy, \quad x \notin \mathrm{supp}(f).$$

Clearly, if $b \in L^\infty$ then $[b, T]$ is bounded on L^p, $1 < p < \infty$. Since both $M_b T$ and $T M_b$ are bounded exactly when b is a bounded function, it would be reasonable to conjecture that this is also the case for $[b, T]$. However, due to cancellation between the two terms, a weaker condition is sufficient.

Theorem 6.20. *Given a singular integral T whose associated kernel is standard, then the commutator $[b, T]$ is bounded on L^p, $1 < p < \infty$, if and only if $b \in BMO$.*

Commutators were introduced by R. Coifman, R. Rochberg and G. Weiss (*Factorization theorems for Hardy spaces in several variables*, Ann. of Math. **103** (1976), 611–635) who used them to extend the classical theory of H^p

spaces to higher dimensions. They proved that $b \in BMO$ is sufficient for $[b, T]$ to be bounded and proved a partial converse. The full converse is due to S. Janson (*Mean oscillation and commutators of singular integral operators*, Ark. Mat. **16** (1978), 263–270). This paper also contains a simpler proof of sufficiency due to J. O. Strömberg which is reproduced in Torchinsky [**19**, p. 418].

The commutator $[b, T]$ is more singular than the associated singular integral; in particular, it does not satisfy the corresponding weak $(1, 1)$ estimate. However, the following weaker result is true.

Theorem 6.21. *Given a singular integral T and $b \in BMO$, then*

$$|\{x \in \mathbb{R}^n : |[b, T]f(x)| > \lambda\}| \leq C\|b\|_* \int_{\mathbb{R}^n} \frac{|f(y)|}{\lambda}\left(1 + \log^+\left(\frac{|f(y)|}{\lambda}\right)\right)\, dy.$$

Theorem 6.21 is due to C. Pérez (*Endpoint estimates for commutators of singular integral operators*, J. Funct. Anal. **128** (1995), 163–185). In this paper he also discusses the boundedness of $[b, T]$ on H^1.

A. Uchiyama (*On the compactness of operators of Hankel type*, Tôhoku Math. J. **30** (1978), 163–171) proved that the commutator $[b, T]$ is a compact operator if and only if $b \in VMO$.

Chapter 7

Weighted Inequalities

1. The A_p condition

In this chapter we are going to find the non-negative, locally integrable functions w such that the operators we have been studying are bounded on the spaces $L^p(w)$. (These are the L^p spaces with Lebesgue measure replaced by the measure $w\,dx$.) We will refer to such functions as weights, and for a measurable set E we define $w(E) = \int_E w$.

Our first step is to assume that the Hardy-Littlewood maximal function satisfies a weighted, weak-type inequality, and deduce from this a necessary condition on the weight w. To simplify our analysis, throughout this chapter we will replace our earlier definition of the Hardy-Littlewood maximal function with

$$Mf(x) = \sup_{Q \ni x} \frac{1}{|Q|} \int_Q |f(y)|\,dy,$$

where the supremum is taken over all cubes Q containing x. This is the non-centered maximal operator we originally denoted by M'' (see (2.6)), but recall that it is pointwise equivalent to our original definition (2.3).

The weighted, weak (p,p) inequality for M with respect to w is

(7.1) $\qquad w(\{x \in \mathbb{R}^n : Mf(x) > \lambda\}) \le \dfrac{C}{\lambda^p} \displaystyle\int_{\mathbb{R}^n} |f(x)|^p w(x)\,dx.$

Let f be a non-negative function and let Q be a cube such that $f(Q) = \int_Q f > 0$. Fix λ such that $0 < \lambda < f(Q)/|Q|$. Then $Q \subset \{x \in \mathbb{R}^n : M(f\chi_Q)(x) > \lambda\}$, so from (7.1) we get that

$$w(Q) \le \frac{C}{\lambda^p} \int_Q |f(x)|^p w(x)\,dx.$$

133

Since this holds for all such λ, it follows that

$$(7.2) \qquad w(Q) \left(\frac{f(Q)}{|Q|} \right)^p \leq C \int_Q |f|^p w.$$

Given a measurable set $S \subset Q$, let $f = \chi_S$. Then (7.2) becomes

$$(7.3) \qquad w(Q) \left(\frac{|S|}{|Q|} \right)^p \leq Cw(S).$$

From (7.3) we can immediately deduce the following:

(1) The weight w is either identically 0 or $w > 0$ a.e. For if $w = 0$ on a set of positive measure S (which we may assume is bounded), then (7.3) implies that for every cube Q that contains S, $w(Q) = 0$.

(2) The weight w is either locally integrable or $w = \infty$ a.e. For if $w(Q) = \infty$ for some cube Q, then the same is true for any larger cube, and so by (7.3), $w(S) = \infty$ for any set S of positive measure.

Note that while we had assumed *a priori* that w was locally integrable, this is actually a consequence of the weighted norm inequality.

To deduce the desired necessary conditions, we will consider two cases.

Case 1: $p = 1$. In this case inequality (7.3) becomes

$$\frac{w(Q)}{|Q|} \leq C \frac{w(S)}{|S|}.$$

Let $a = \inf\{w(x) : x \in Q\}$, where inf is the essential infimum, that is, excluding sets of measure zero. Then for each $\epsilon > 0$ there exists $S_\epsilon \subset Q$ such that $|S_\epsilon| > 0$ and $w(x) \leq a + \epsilon$ for any $x \in S_\epsilon$. Hence, for all $\epsilon > 0$,

$$\frac{w(Q)}{|Q|} \leq C(a + \epsilon),$$

and so

$$\frac{w(Q)}{|Q|} \leq C \inf_{x \in Q} w(x).$$

Therefore, for any cube Q,

$$(7.4) \qquad \frac{w(Q)}{|Q|} \leq Cw(x) \quad \text{a.e. } x \in Q.$$

This is called the A_1 condition, and we refer to the weights which satisfy it as A_1 weights. Condition (7.4) is equivalent to

$$(7.5) \qquad Mw(x) \leq Cw(x) \quad \text{a.e. } x \in \mathbb{R}^n.$$

Clearly, (7.5) implies (7.4). Conversely, suppose that (7.4) holds and let x be such that $Mw(x) > Cw(x)$. Then there exists a cube Q with rational vertices such that $w(Q)/|Q| > Cw(x)$, so x lies in a subset of Q of measure zero. Taking the union over all such cubes we see that $Mw(x) > Cw(x)$ holds only on a set of measure 0 in $\mathbb{R}^n$.

Case 2: $1 < p < \infty$. In (7.2) let $f = w^{1-p'}\chi_Q$; then

$$w(Q) \left(\frac{1}{|Q|} \int_Q w^{1-p'} \right)^p \leq C \int_Q w^{1-p'}.$$

Equivalently,

(7.6) $$\left(\frac{1}{|Q|} \int_Q w \right) \left(\frac{1}{|Q|} \int_Q w^{1-p'} \right)^{p-1} \leq C,$$

where C is independent of Q. (Note that to derive (7.6) we have assumed that $w^{1-p'}$ is locally integrable. To avoid this assumption we can replace it by $\min(w^{1-p'}, n)$ and take the limit as n tends to infinity. However, since $w > 0$ a.e., (7.6) implies that $w^{1-p'}$ is locally integrable.)

Condition (7.6) is called the A_p condition, and the weights which satisfy it are called A_p weights.

Theorem 7.1. *For $1 \leq p < \infty$, the weak (p,p) inequality*

$$w(\{x \in \mathbb{R}^n : Mf(x) > \lambda\}) \leq \frac{C}{\lambda^p} \int_{\mathbb{R}^n} |f(x)|^p w(x)\, dx$$

holds if and only if $w \in A_p$.

Proof. We proved the necessity of the A_p condition above.

To prove sufficiency, we first consider the case $p = 1$. This case is a corollary to Theorem 2.16. The right-hand side of the weak $(1,1)$ inequality (2.11) contains Mw, and since $w \in A_1$, by (7.5) we can replace Mw by Cw.

Now suppose that $p > 1$ and $w \in A_p$. Given a function f, we first show that inequality (7.2) holds, and so inequality (7.3) also holds. By Hölder's inequality

$$\left(\frac{1}{|Q|} \int_Q |f| \right)^p = \left(\frac{1}{|Q|} \int_Q |f| w^{1/p} w^{-1/p} \right)^p$$

$$\leq \left(\frac{1}{|Q|} \int_Q |f|^p w \right) \left(\frac{1}{|Q|} \int_Q w^{1-p'} \right)^{p-1}$$

$$\leq C \left(\frac{1}{|Q|} \int_Q |f|^p w \right) \left(\frac{|Q|}{w(Q)} \right).$$

Now fix $f \in L^p(w)$; we may assume without loss of generality that f is non-negative. We may also assume that $f \in L^1$ since otherwise we can replace f by $f\chi_{B(0,k)}$ and the following argument will yield constants independent of k. (Note that the previous argument shows that f is locally integrable.) Form the Calderón-Zygmund decomposition of f at height $4^{-n}\lambda$ to get a collection of disjoint cubes $\{Q_j\}$ such that $f(Q_j) > 4^{-n}\lambda|Q_j|$. (See Theorem 2.11.) Then by the same argument as in the proof of Lemma 2.12, we can show that

$$\{x \in \mathbb{R}^n : Mf(x) > \lambda\} \subset \bigcup_j 3Q_j.$$

(Here we dilate the cubes by a factor of 3 instead of 2 because M is the non-centered maximal operator.)

Therefore,

$$w(\{x \in \mathbb{R}^n : Mf(x) > \lambda\}) \leq \sum_j w(3Q_j)$$

$$\leq C3^{np} \sum_j w(Q_j)$$

$$\leq C3^{np} \sum_j \left(\frac{|Q_j|}{f(Q_j)}\right)^p \int_{Q_j} |f|^p w$$

$$\leq C3^{np} \left(\frac{4^n}{\lambda}\right)^p \int_{\mathbb{R}^n} |f|^p w,$$

where the second inequality follows from (7.3), the third from (7.2) and the fourth from the properties of the Q_j's. $\square$

The following properties of A_p weights are consequences of the definition.

Proposition 7.2.

(1) $A_p \subset A_q$, $1 \leq p < q$.

(2) $w \in A_p$ if and only if $w^{1-p'} \in A_{p'}$.

(3) If $w_0, w_1 \in A_1$ then $w_0 w_1^{1-p} \in A_p$.

Proof. (1) If $p = 1$ then

$$\left(\frac{1}{|Q|}\int_Q w^{1-q'}\right)^{q-1} \leq \sup_{x \in Q} w(x)^{-1} = \left(\inf_{x \in Q} w(x)\right)^{-1} \leq C\left(\frac{w(Q)}{|Q|}\right)^{-1}.$$

If $p > 1$ then this follows immediately from Hölder's inequality.

(2) The $A_{p'}$ condition for $w^{1-p'}$ is

$$\left(\frac{1}{|Q|}\int_Q w^{1-p'}\right)\left(\frac{1}{|Q|}\int_Q w^{(1-p')(1-p)}\right)^{p'-1} \leq C,$$

and since $(p'-1)(p-1) = 1$, the left-hand side is the A_p condition raised to the power $p'-1$.

(3) We need to prove that

$$(7.7) \qquad \left(\frac{1}{|Q|} \int_Q w_0 w_1^{1-p} \right) \left(\frac{1}{|Q|} \int_Q w_0^{1-p'} w_1 \right)^{p'-1} \le C.$$

By the A_1 condition, for $x \in Q$ and $i = 0, 1$,

$$w_i(x)^{-1} \le \sup_{x \in Q} w_i(x)^{-1} = \left(\inf_{x \in Q} w_i(x) \right)^{-1} \le C \left(\frac{w_i(Q)}{|Q|} \right)^{-1}.$$

If we substitute this into the left-hand side of (7.7) for the negative exponents we get the desired inequality. □

2. Strong-type inequalities with weights

Using the Marcinkiewicz interpolation theorem, we can immediately derive a strong (p, p) inequality from Theorem 7.1. Let $w \in A_q$, $1 < q < p$. Then $L^\infty(w) = L^\infty$ with equality of norms since by (7.3), $w(E) = 0$ if and only if $|E| = 0$. Therefore, we have the inequality

$$\|Mf\|_{L^\infty(w)} \le \|f\|_{L^\infty(w)}.$$

If we interpolate between this and the weak (q, q) inequality we get

$$(7.8) \qquad \int_{\mathbb{R}^n} |Mf|^p w \le C_p \int_{\mathbb{R}^n} |f|^p w$$

for all $p > q$.

A much deeper result is that this inequality remains true when $p = q$.

Theorem 7.3. *If $1 < p < \infty$ then M is bounded on $L^p(w)$ if and only if $w \in A_p$.*

Since the strong (p, p) inequality implies the weak (p, p) inequality, necessity follows from Theorem 7.1. Sufficiency would follow from the above interpolation argument if we could show that given $w \in A_p$, there exists q, $1 < q < p$, such that $w \in A_q$. The existence of such a q comes from the following key result.

Theorem 7.4 (Reverse Hölder Inequality). *Let $w \in A_p$, $1 \le p < \infty$. Then there exist constants C and $\epsilon > 0$, depending only on p and the A_p constant of w, such that for any cube Q,*

$$(7.9) \qquad \left(\frac{1}{|Q|} \int_Q w^{1+\epsilon} \right)^{1/(1+\epsilon)} \le \frac{C}{|Q|} \int_Q w.$$

The name of Theorem 7.4 comes from the fact that the reverse of inequality (7.9) is an immediate consequence of Hölder's inequality.

To prove this result we first need to prove a lemma.

Lemma 7.5. *Let $w \in A_p$, $1 \le p < \infty$. Then for every α, $0 < \alpha < 1$, there exists β, $0 < \beta < 1$, such that given a cube Q and $S \subset Q$ with $|S| \le \alpha|Q|$, $w(S) \le \beta w(Q)$.*

Proof. If we replace S by $Q \setminus S$ in inequality (7.3) we get

$$w(Q)\left(1 - \frac{|S|}{|Q|}\right)^p \le C(w(Q) - w(S)).$$

If $|S| \le \alpha|Q|$ then

$$w(S) \le \frac{C - (1 - \alpha)^p}{C} w(Q),$$

which gives us the desired result with $\beta = 1 - C^{-1}(1 - \alpha)^p$. $\qquad\square$

Proof of Theorem 7.4. Fix a cube Q and form Calderón-Zygmund decompositions of w with respect to Q at heights given by the increasing sequence $w(Q)/|Q| = \lambda_0 < \lambda_1 < \cdots < \lambda_k < \cdots$; we will fix the λ_k's below. (The decomposition is formed by repeatedly bisecting the sides of Q; cf. the proof of Theorem 6.11.)

For each λ_k we get a family of disjoint cubes $\{Q_{k,j}\}$ such that

$$w(x) \le \lambda_k \ \text{ if } \ x \notin \Omega_k = \bigcup_j Q_{k,j},$$

$$\lambda_k < \frac{1}{|Q_{k,j}|} \int_{Q_{k,j}} w \le 2^n \lambda_k.$$

It is clear from their construction that $\Omega_{k+1} \subset \Omega_k$. If we fix Q_{k,j_0} from the Calderón-Zygmund decomposition at height λ_k, then $Q_{k,j_0} \cap \Omega_{k+1}$ is the union of cubes $Q_{k+1,i}$ from the decomposition at height λ_{k+1}. Therefore,

$$|Q_{k,j_0} \cap \Omega_{k+1}| = \sum_i |Q_{k+1,i}|$$

$$\le \frac{1}{\lambda_{k+1}} \sum_i \int_{Q_{k+1,i}} w$$

$$\le \frac{1}{\lambda_{k+1}} \int_{Q_{k,j_0}} w$$

$$\le \frac{2^n \lambda_k}{\lambda_{k+1}} |Q_{k,j_0}|.$$

Fix $\alpha < 1$ and choose the λ_k's so that $2^n \lambda_k / \lambda_{k+1} = \alpha$; that is, $\lambda_k = (2^n \alpha^{-1})^k w(Q)/|Q|$. Then

$$|Q_{k,j_0} \cap \Omega_{k+1}| \le \alpha |Q_{k,j_0}|,$$

so by Lemma 7.5 there exists $\beta < 1$ such that

$$w(Q_{k,j_0} \cap \Omega_{k+1}) \le \beta w(Q_{k,j_0}).$$

Now sum over all the cubes in the decomposition at height λ_k; we then get $w(\Omega_{k+1}) \leq \beta w(\Omega_k)$. If we iterate this inequality we get $w(\Omega_k) \leq \beta^k w(\Omega_0)$. Similarly, $|\Omega_k| \leq \alpha^k |\Omega_0|$; hence,

$$\left| \bigcap_k \Omega_k \right| = \lim_{k \to \infty} |\Omega_k| = 0.$$

Therefore,

$$\frac{1}{|Q|} \int_Q w^{1+\epsilon} = \frac{1}{|Q|} \int_{Q \setminus \Omega_0} w^{1+\epsilon} + \frac{1}{|Q|} \sum_{k=0}^{\infty} \int_{\Omega_k \setminus \Omega_{k+1}} w^{1+\epsilon}$$

$$\leq \lambda_0^\epsilon \frac{w(Q)}{|Q|} + \frac{1}{|Q|} \sum_{k=0}^{\infty} \lambda_{k+1}^\epsilon w(\Omega_k)$$

$$= \lambda_0^\epsilon \frac{w(Q)}{|Q|} + \frac{1}{|Q|} \sum_{k=0}^{\infty} (2^n \alpha^{-1})^{(k+1)\epsilon} \lambda_0^\epsilon \beta^k w(\Omega_0).$$

Fix $\epsilon > 0$ such that $(2^n \alpha^{-1})^\epsilon \beta < 1$; then the series converges and the last term is bounded by $C\lambda_0^\epsilon w(Q)/|Q|$. Since $\lambda_0 = w(Q)/|Q|$ we have shown the desired inequality. □

As a corollary to the reverse Hölder inequality we get the property of A_p weights needed to complete the proof of Theorem 7.3.

Corollary 7.6.

(1) $A_p = \bigcup_{q<p} A_q$, $1 < p < \infty$.

(2) If $w \in A_p$, $1 \leq p < \infty$, then there exists $\epsilon > 0$ such that $w^{1+\epsilon} \in A_p$.

(3) If $w \in A_p$, $1 \leq p < \infty$, then there exists $\delta > 0$ such that given a cube Q and $S \subset Q$,

(7.10) $$\frac{w(S)}{w(Q)} \leq C \left(\frac{|S|}{|Q|} \right)^\delta.$$

If a weight w satisfies (7.10) then we say that $w \in A_\infty$. We use this notation since then (1) holds with $p = \infty$. See Section 5.3 below.

Proof. (1) If $w \in A_p$ then by Proposition 7.2, $w^{1-p'} \in A_{p'}$. Therefore, it also satisfies the reverse Hölder inequality for some $\epsilon > 0$:

(7.11) $$\left(\frac{1}{|Q|} \int_Q w^{(1-p')(1+\epsilon)} \right)^{1/(1+\epsilon)} \leq \frac{C}{|Q|} \int_Q w^{1-p'}.$$

Fix q such that $(q'-1) = (p'-1)(1+\epsilon)$; then $q < p$ and inequality (7.11) together with the A_p condition implies that $w \in A_q$.

(2) If $p > 1$ then this follows immediately if we choose $\epsilon > 0$ small enough so that both w and $w^{1-p'}$ satisfy the reverse Hölder inequality with exponent $1 + \epsilon$. If $p = 1$ then for any cube Q and almost every $x \in Q$,

$$\frac{1}{|Q|} \int_Q w^{1+\epsilon} \leq C \left(\frac{1}{|Q|} \int_Q w \right)^{1+\epsilon} \leq Cw(x)^{1+\epsilon}.$$

(3) Fix $S \subset Q$ and suppose w satisfies the reverse Hölder inequality with exponent $1 + \epsilon$. Then

$$w(S) = \int_Q \chi_S w \leq \left(\int_Q w^{1+\epsilon} \right)^{1/(1+\epsilon)} |S|^{\epsilon/(1+\epsilon)} \leq Cw(Q) \left(\frac{|S|}{|Q|} \right)^{\epsilon/(1+\epsilon)}.$$

This gives (7.10) with $\delta = \epsilon/(1 + \epsilon)$. $\qquad\qquad\qquad\qquad\qquad\qquad\square$

3. A_1 weights and an extrapolation theorem

In this section we first give a constructive characterization of A_1 using the Hardy-Littlewood maximal function. This, combined with Proposition 7.2, lets us construct A_p weights for all p. We will then use this construction to prove a powerful extrapolation theorem: if an operator is bounded on $L^r(w)$ for a fixed index r and all weights w in A_r, then for any p the operator is bounded on $L^p(w)$, $w \in A_p$.

Theorem 7.7.

   (1) *Let $f \in L^1_{\text{loc}}(\mathbb{R}^n)$ be such that $Mf(x) < \infty$ a.e. If $0 \leq \delta < 1$, then $w(x) = Mf(x)^\delta$ is an A_1 weight whose A_1 constant depends only on δ.*

   (2) *Conversely, if $w \in A_1$ then there exist $f \in L^1_{\text{loc}}(\mathbb{R}^n)$, $\delta < 1$, and K with $K, K^{-1} \in L^\infty$, such that $w(x) = K(x)Mf(x)^\delta$.*

Proof. (1) It will suffice to show that there exists a constant C such that for every f, every cube Q and almost every $x \in Q$,

$$\frac{1}{|Q|} \int_Q (Mf)^\delta \leq CMf(x)^\delta.$$

Fix Q and decompose f as $f = f_1 + f_2$, where $f_1 = f\chi_{2Q}$. Then $Mf(x) \leq Mf_1(x) + Mf_2(x)$, and so for $0 \leq \delta < 1$,

$$Mf(x)^\delta \leq Mf_1(x)^\delta + Mf_2(x)^\delta.$$

Since M is weak $(1,1)$, by Kolmogorov's inequality (Lemma 5.16)

$$\frac{1}{|Q|} \int_Q (Mf_1)^\delta \leq \frac{C_\delta}{|Q|} |Q|^{1-\delta} \|f_1\|_1^\delta \leq C_\delta \left(\frac{1}{|Q|} \int_{2Q} f \right)^\delta \leq 2^{n\delta} C_\delta Mf(x)^\delta.$$

To estimate Mf_2, note that if $y \in Q$ and R is a cube such that $y \in R$ and $\int_R |f_2| > 0$, then we must have that $l(R) > \frac{1}{2}l(Q)$, where $l(\cdot)$ denotes the side length of a cube. Hence, there exists a constant c_n, depending only on n, such that if $x \in Q$ then $x \in c_n R$. Therefore,

$$\frac{1}{|R|} \int_R |f_2| \leq \frac{c_n^n}{|c_n R|} \int_{c_n R} |f_2| \leq c_n^n Mf(x),$$

and so $Mf_2(y) \leq c_n^n Mf(x)$ for any $y \in Q$. Thus

$$\frac{1}{|Q|} \int_Q Mf_2(y)^\delta \, dy \leq c_n^{n\delta} Mf(x)^\delta.$$

(2) If $w \in A_1$ then by the reverse Hölder inequality there exists $\epsilon > 0$ such that

$$\left(\frac{1}{|Q|} \int_Q w^{1+\epsilon} \right)^{1/(1+\epsilon)} \leq \frac{C}{|Q|} \int_Q w.$$

This, together with the A_1 condition, implies that

$$M(w^{1+\epsilon})(x)^{1/(1+\epsilon)} \leq C w(x) \quad \text{a.e. } x \in \mathbb{R}^n.$$

By the Lebesgue differentiation theorem (Corollary 2.13), the reverse inequality holds with constant 1, so if we let $f = w^{1+\epsilon}$ and $\delta = 1/(1+\epsilon)$ we get

$$w(x) \leq Mf(x)^\delta \leq C w(x).$$

The desired equality now follows if we let $K(x) = w(x)/Mf(x)^\delta$. $\qquad \square$

In part (1) of Theorem 7.7 we can replace $f \in L^1_{\text{loc}}(\mathbb{R}^n)$ by a finite Borel measure μ such that $M\mu(x) < \infty$ a.e. since the weak $(1,1)$ inequality also holds for such measures. (This is readily shown using the covering lemmas described in Chapter 2, Section 8.6.) In particular, if δ is the Dirac measure at the origin then $M\delta(x) = C|x|^{-n}$. Thus $|x|^a \in A_1$ if $-n < a \leq 0$, and by Proposition 7.2, $|x|^a \in A_p$ if $-n < a < n(p-1)$. This range is sharp since outside of it, $|x|^a$ and $|x|^{a(1-p')}$ are not both locally integrable.

Using Theorem 7.7 we can now prove our extrapolation theorem.

Theorem 7.8. *Fix r, $1 < r < \infty$. If T is a bounded operator on $L^r(w)$ for any $w \in A_r$, with operator norm depending only on the A_r constant of w, then T is bounded on $L^p(w)$, $1 < p < \infty$, for any $w \in A_p$.*

Proof. We first show that if $1 < q < r$ and $w \in A_1$ then T is bounded on $L^q(w)$. By Theorem 7.7 the function $(Mf)^{(r-q)/(r-1)}$ is in A_1 since $r - q < r - 1$, and by Proposition 7.2, $w(Mf)^{q-r}$ is an A_r weight. Therefore,

$$\int_{\mathbb{R}^n} |Tf|^q w = \int_{\mathbb{R}^n} |Tf|^q (Mf)^{-(r-q)q/r} (Mf)^{(r-q)q/r} w$$

$$\leq \left(\int_{\mathbb{R}^n} |Tf|^r w (Mf)^{q-r} \right)^{q/r} \left(\int_{\mathbb{R}^n} (Mf)^q w \right)^{(r-q)/r}$$

$$\leq C \left(\int_{\mathbb{R}^n} |f|^r w (Mf)^{q-r} \right)^{q/r} \left(\int_{\mathbb{R}^n} |f|^q w \right)^{(r-q)/r}$$

$$\leq C \int_{\mathbb{R}^n} |f|^q w;$$

the second inequality holds by our hypothesis on T and by Theorem 7.3 (since by Proposition 7.2, $w \in A_q$), and the third inequality holds since $|f(x)| \leq Mf(x)$ a.e. and $q - r < 0$, so $Mf(x)^{q-r} \leq |f(x)|^{q-r}$ a.e.

We will now show that given any p, $1 < p < \infty$, and q, $1 < q < \min(p, r)$, T is bounded on $L^p(w)$ if $w \in A_{p/q}$. The desired result follows at once from this: given $w \in A_p$, by Corollary 7.6 there exists $q > 1$ such that $w \in A_{p/q}$ and so T is bounded on $L^p(w)$.

Fix $w \in A_{p/q}$. Then by duality there exists $u \in L^{(p/q)'}(w)$ with norm 1 such that

$$\left(\int_{\mathbb{R}^n} |Tf|^p w \right)^{q/p} = \int_{\mathbb{R}^n} |Tf|^q wu.$$

For any $s > 1$, $wu \leq M((wu)^s)^{1/s}$ and $M((wu)^s)^{1/s} \in A_1$. Therefore, by the first part of the proof,

$$\int_{\mathbb{R}^n} |Tf|^q wu \leq \int_{\mathbb{R}^n} |Tf|^q M((wu)^s)^{1/s}$$

$$\leq C \int_{\mathbb{R}^n} |f|^q M((wu)^s)^{1/s}$$

$$= C \int_{\mathbb{R}^n} |f|^q w^{q/p} M((wu)^s)^{1/s} w^{-q/p}$$

$$\leq C \left(\int_{\mathbb{R}^n} |f|^p w \right)^{q/p} \left(\int_{\mathbb{R}^n} M((wu)^s)^{(p/q)'/s} w^{1-(p/q)'} \right)^{1/(p/q)'}.$$

Since $w \in A_{p/q}$, by Proposition 7.2, $w^{1-(p/q)'} \in A_{(p/q)'}$. Therefore, if we take s sufficiently close to 1, $w^{1-(p/q)'} \in A_{(p/q)'/s}$. Hence, by Theorem 7.3 the second integral is bounded by

$$C \int_{\mathbb{R}^n} (wu)^{(p/q)'} w^{1-(p/q)'} = C.$$

This completes the proof. $\square$

A similar argument yields the following variation: given $s \geq 1$, if T is bounded on $L^r(w)$ for all $w \in A_{r/s}$, then for $p > s$ it is bounded on $L^p(w)$ for all $w \in A_{p/s}$.

4. Weighted inequalities for singular integrals

In this section we prove weighted norm inequalities for Calderón-Zygmund operators. Recall (see Definition 5.11) that a Calderón-Zygmund operator is an operator which is bounded on L^2, and for $f \in \mathcal{S}$ can be represented by

$$Tf(x) = \int_{\mathbb{R}^n} K(x,y)f(y)\,dy, \quad x \notin \operatorname{supp}(f),$$

where K is a standard kernel (i.e. one which satisfies (5.12), (5.13) and (5.14)).

We begin with two lemmas.

Lemma 7.9. *If T is a Calderón-Zygmund operator, then for each $s > 1$,*

$$M^{\#}(Tf)(x) \le C_s M(|f|^s)(x)^{1/s},$$

where $M^{\#}$ is the sharp maximal operator (6.1).

Proof. Fix $s > 1$. Given x and a cube Q containing it, by Proposition 6.5 it will suffice to find a constant a such that

$$\frac{1}{|Q|} \int_Q |Tf(y) - a|\,dy \le C M(|f|^s)(x)^{1/s}.$$

As in the proof of Theorem 7.7, decompose f as $f = f_1 + f_2$, where $f_1 = f\chi_{2Q}$. Now let $a = Tf_2(x)$; then

$$(7.12) \quad \frac{1}{|Q|} \int_Q |Tf(y) - a|\,dy$$

$$\le \frac{1}{|Q|} \int_Q |Tf_1(y)|\,dy + \frac{1}{|Q|} \int_Q |Tf_2(y) - Tf_2(x)|\,dy.$$

Since $s > 1$, T is bounded on $L^s(\mathbb{R}^n)$. Therefore,

$$\frac{1}{|Q|} \int_Q |Tf_1(y)|\,dy \le \left(\frac{1}{|Q|} \int_Q |Tf_1(y)|^s\,dy \right)^{1/s}$$

$$\le C \left(\frac{1}{|Q|} \int_{2Q} |f(y)|^s\,dy \right)^{1/s}$$

$$\le 2^{n/s} C M(|f|^s)(x)^{1/s}.$$

We estimate the second half of the right-hand side of (7.12) using (5.14); as before $l(Q)$ denotes the side length of Q.

$$\frac{1}{|Q|} \int_Q |Tf_2(y) - Tf_2(x)|\,dy$$

$$\le \frac{1}{|Q|} \int_Q \left| \int_{\mathbb{R}^n \setminus 2Q} [K(y,z) - K(x,z)]f(z)\,dz \right| dy$$

$$\leq \frac{C}{|Q|} \int_Q \int_{\mathbb{R}^n \setminus 2Q} \frac{|y-x|^\delta}{|x-z|^{n+\delta}} |f(z)| \, dz \, dy$$

$$\leq \frac{C}{|Q|} \int_Q l(Q)^\delta \sum_{k=-1}^\infty \int_{2^k l(Q) < |x-z| < 2^{k+1} l(Q)} \frac{|f(z)|}{|x-z|^{n+\delta}} \, dz \, dy$$

$$\leq C l(Q)^\delta \sum_{k=-1}^\infty \frac{1}{(2^k l(Q))^{n+\delta}} \int_{|x-z| < 2^{k+1} l(Q)} |f(z)| \, dz$$

$$\leq C M f(x)$$

$$\leq C M(|f|^s)(x)^{1/s}.$$

$\square$

Lemma 7.10. *Let $w \in A_p$, $1 \leq p_0 \leq p < \infty$. If f is such that $M_d f \in L^{p_0}(w)$, then*

$$\int_{\mathbb{R}^n} |M_d f|^p w \leq C \int_{\mathbb{R}^n} |M^\# f|^p w,$$

where M_d is the dyadic maximal operator (2.9) and $M^\#$ is the sharp maximal operator (6.1), whenever the left-hand side is finite.

Proof. This is a weighted version of Lemma 6.9, and the proof is almost exactly the same. It will suffice to prove a good-λ inequality which is a weighted analogue of Lemma 6.10: for some $\delta > 0$,

$$w(\{x \in \mathbb{R}^n : M_d f(x) > 2\lambda, M^\# f(x) \leq \gamma\lambda\})$$
$$\leq C\gamma^\delta w(\{x \in \mathbb{R}^n : M_d f(x) > \lambda\}).$$

Since $\{x \in \mathbb{R}^n : M_d f(x) > \lambda\}$ can be decomposed into disjoint dyadic cubes, it is enough to show that for each such cube Q,

$$w(\{x \in Q : M_d f(x) > 2\lambda, M^\# f(x) \leq \gamma\lambda\}) \leq C\gamma^\delta w(Q).$$

However, this is an immediate consequence of inequality (6.6) (the same inequality with Lebesgue measure and with $C\gamma$ on the right-hand side) and the A_∞ condition (7.10). $\square$

Theorem 7.11. *If T is a Calderón-Zygmund operator, then for any $w \in A_p$, $1 < p < \infty$, T is bounded on $L^p(w)$.*

Proof. Fix $w \in A_p$. We may assume that f is a bounded function of compact support since the set of such functions is dense in $L^p(w)$. By Corollary 7.6, we can find $s > 1$ such that $w \in A_{p/s}$. Therefore, since $Tf(x) \leq M_d(Tf)(x)$ a.e., by Lemmas 7.9 and 7.10,

$$\int_{\mathbb{R}^n} |Tf|^p w \leq \int_{\mathbb{R}^n} M_d(Tf)^p w$$

$$\leq C \int_{\mathbb{R}^n} M^\#(Tf)^p w$$

$$\leq C \int_{\mathbb{R}^n} M(|f|^s)^{p/s} w$$

$$\leq C \int_{\mathbb{R}^n} |f|^p w,$$

provided the second integral is finite. To show this it will suffice to show that $Tf \in L^p(w)$. If the support of f is contained in $B(0, R)$, then for $\epsilon > 0$

$$\int_{|x|<2R} |Tf(x)|^p w(x)\, dx$$

$$\leq \left(\int_{|x|<2R} w(x)^{1+\epsilon}\, dx \right)^{1/(1+\epsilon)} \left(\int_{|x|<2R} |Tf(x)|^{p(1+\epsilon)/\epsilon}\, dx \right)^{\epsilon/(1+\epsilon)}.$$

By the reverse Hölder inequality we can choose ϵ such that the first integral is finite; the second is finite since $Tf \in L^q$, $1 < q < \infty$.

To complete our estimate, note that for $|x| > 2R$,

$$|Tf(x)| = \left| \int_{\mathbb{R}^n} f(y) K(x, y)\, dy \right| \leq C \int_{|y|<R} \frac{|f(y)|}{|x-y|^n}\, dy \leq \frac{C\|f\|_\infty}{|x|^n}.$$

Therefore,

$$\int_{|x|>2R} |Tf(x)|^p w(x)\, dx \leq C \sum_{k=1}^\infty \int_{2^k R<|x|<2^{k+1}R} \frac{w(x)}{|x|^{np}}\, dx$$

$$\leq C \sum_{k=1}^\infty (2^k R)^{-np} w(B(0, 2^{k+1}R)).$$

Since $w \in A_p$, by Corollary 7.6 there exists $q < p$ such that $w \in A_q$. Then by (7.3), which holds for balls as well as for cubes,

$$w(B(0, 2^{k+1}R)) \leq C(n, R, w) 2^{knq}.$$

If we substitute this into the above expression we get a convergent series. Hence, $Tf \in L^p(w)$ and our proof is complete. $\square$

Theorem 7.12. *Let T be a Calderón-Zygmund operator and let $w \in A_1$. Then*

$$w(\{x \in \mathbb{R}^n : |Tf(x)| > \lambda\}) \leq \frac{C}{\lambda} \int_{\mathbb{R}^n} |f| w.$$

Proof. The proof is very similar to the proof of Theorem 5.1, the corresponding result without weights, and we use the same notation. Form the Calderón-Zygmund decomposition of f at height λ and decompose f

as $f = g + b$. It will suffice to estimate $w(\{x \in \mathbb{R}^n : |Tg(x)| > \lambda\})$ and $w(\{x \in \mathbb{R}^n : |Tb(x)| > \lambda\})$. To estimate the first, note that by Proposition 7.2, $w \in A_2$. Hence, by Theorem 7.11

$$w(\{x \in \mathbb{R}^n : |Tg(x)| > \lambda\}) \leq \frac{1}{\lambda^2} \int_{\mathbb{R}^n} |Tg|^2 w$$

$$\leq \frac{C}{\lambda^2} \int_{\mathbb{R}^n} |g|^2 w$$

$$\leq \frac{2^n C}{\lambda} \int_{\mathbb{R}^n} |g| w.$$

To complete this estimate we must show that $\int |g| w \leq C \int |f| w$. On the set $\mathbb{R}^n \setminus \bigcup_j Q_j$, $g = f$; on each Q_j, since $w \in A_1$,

$$\int_{Q_j} |g| w \leq \int_{Q_j} \frac{1}{|Q_j|} \int_{Q_j} |f(y)| \, dy \, w(x) \, dx$$

$$= \int_{Q_j} |f(y)| \frac{w(Q_j)}{|Q_j|} \, dy$$

$$\leq C \int_{Q_j} f(y) w(y) \, dy.$$

For our second estimate, by (7.3) we have that

$$w\left(\bigcup_j Q_j^*\right) \leq \sum_j w(Q_j^*) \leq C \sum_j w(Q_j) \leq C \sum_j \frac{w(Q_j)}{|Q_j|} |Q_j|.$$

By our choice of the Q_j's,

$$|Q_j| < \frac{1}{\lambda} \int_{Q_j} |f|,$$

so by the same argument as above we can bound this sum.

Now let c_j be the center of Q_j. Then, since b_j has zero average on Q_j,

$$w\left(\left\{x \in \mathbb{R}^n \setminus \bigcup_j Q_j^* : |Tb(x)| > \lambda\right\}\right)$$

$$\leq \frac{C}{\lambda} \sum_j \int_{\mathbb{R}^n \setminus Q_j^*} |Tb_j(x)| w(x) \, dx$$

$$= \frac{C}{\lambda} \sum_j \int_{\mathbb{R}^n \setminus Q_j^*} \left| \int_{Q_j} [K(x,y) - K(x,c_j)] b_j(y) \, dy \right| w(x) \, dx.$$

By inequality (5.13), the last term is bounded by

$$(7.13) \qquad \frac{C}{\lambda} \sum_j \int_{Q_j} |b_j(y)| \left(\int_{\mathbb{R}^n \setminus Q_j^*} \frac{|y - c_j|^\delta}{|x - c_j|^{n+\delta}} w(x) \, dx \right) dy.$$

Arguing as in the proof of Lemma 7.9, we see that the term in parentheses is bounded by $CMw(y)$; since $w \in A_1$, this in turn is bounded by $Cw(y)$. Hence, (7.13) is bounded by

$$\frac{C}{\lambda} \int_{\mathbb{R}^n} |b|w \le \frac{C}{\lambda} \int_{\mathbb{R}^n} (|f| + |g|)w \le \frac{C}{\lambda} \int_{\mathbb{R}^n} |f|w,$$

where the last inequality follows from our previous argument. □

Finally, recall that T is a Calderón-Zygmund singular integral if it is a Calderón-Zygmund operator such that

(7.14) $$Tf(x) = \lim_{\epsilon \to 0} T_\epsilon f(x),$$

where

$$T_\epsilon f(x) = \int_{|x-y|>\epsilon} K(x,y)f(y) \, dy.$$

(See Chapter 5, Section 4.) To determine when the limit (7.14) exists almost everywhere for $f \in L^p(w)$, we need to consider weighted norm inequalities for the associated maximal operator,

$$T^* f(x) = \sup_{\epsilon > 0} |T_\epsilon f(x)|.$$

Corollary 7.13. *If T is a Calderón-Zygmund operator, then for $1 < p < \infty$, T^* is bounded on $L^p(w)$ if $w \in A_p$, and T^* is weak $(1,1)$ with respect to w if $w \in A_1$.*

Proof. Corollary 7.13 is a weighted version of Theorem 5.14 and its proof depends on Cotlar's inequality (5.18): for $0 < \nu \le 1$,

$$T^* f(x) \le C_\nu \left(M(|Tf|^\nu)(x)^{1/\nu} + Mf(x) \right).$$

When $1 < p < \infty$ the desired result follows at once from Theorems 7.3 and 7.11. When $p = 1$ the proof proceeds as in the proof of Theorem 5.14, given the following: Kolmogorov's inequality (Lemma 5.16) is true when Lebesgue measure is replaced by any positive Borel measure; Lemma 2.12 is true with Lebesgue measure replaced by $w \, dx$, when $w \in A_1$; and M is weak $(1,1)$ with respect to w (by Theorem 7.1). □

5. Notes and further results

5.1. References.

The A_p condition first appeared, in a somewhat different form, in a paper by M. Rosenblum (*Summability of Fourier series in $L^p(\mu)$*, Trans. Amer. Math. Soc. **105** (1962), 32–42). The characterization of A_p when $n = 1$ is due to B. Muckenhoupt (*Weighted norm inequalities for the Hardy maximal function*, Trans. Amer. Math. Soc. **165** (1972), 207–226). B. Muckenhoupt,

R. Hunt and R. Wheeden (*Weighted norm inequalities for the conjugate function and the Hilbert transform*, Trans. Amer. Math. Soc. **176** (1973), 227–251) proved that $w \in A_p$ is necessary and sufficient for the Hilbert transform to be bounded on $L^p(w)$. For $p = 2$ there is a different characterization due to H. Helson and G. Szegö. (See Section 5.2 for more details.) R. Coifman and C. Fefferman (*Weighted norm inequalities for maximal functions and singular integrals*, Studia Math. **51** (1974), 241–250) extended these results to higher dimensions. (See Section 5.7 for more details.) Our proof is due to Journé [**8**]. In the same paper, Coifman and Fefferman also proved that A_p weights satisfy the crucial reverse Hölder inequality. This inequality first appeared in a paper by F. W. Gehring (*The L^p-integrability of the partial derivatives of a quasiconformal mapping*, Acta Math. **130** (1973), 3–4, 265–277). The strong (p, p) norm inequality for the maximal function can be proved without the reverse Hölder inequality: see the paper by M. Christ and R. Fefferman (*A note on weighted norm inequalities for the Hardy-Littlewood maximal operator*, Proc. Amer. Math. Soc. **87** (1983), 447–448). Also see Section 5.9 below. The characterization of A_1 weights in Theorem 7.7 is due to R. Coifman and R. Rochberg (*Another characterization of BMO*, Proc. Amer. Math. Soc. **79** (1980), 249–254). The extrapolation theorem is due to J. L. Rubio de Francia (*Factorization theory and A_p weights*, Amer. J. Math. **106** (1984), 533–547), who proved it using the connection between weighted norm inequalities and vector-valued inequalities; J. García-Cuerva (*An extrapolation theorem in the theory of A_p-weights*, Proc. Amer. Math. Soc. **87** (1983), 422–426) gave a direct proof without using vector-valued inequalities; our proof is simpler and seems to be new, at least in organization, although it follows the standard approach. The book by García-Cuerva and Rubio de Francia [**6**] contains an excellent exposition of the results related to weighted norm inequalities. See also the survey articles by B. Muckenhoupt (*Weighted norm inequalities for classical operators*, Harmonic Analysis in Euclidean Spaces, G. Weiss and S. Wainger, eds., vol. 1, pp. 69–84, Proc. Sympos. Pure Math. **35**, Amer. Math. Soc., Providence, 1979) and E. M. Dynkin and B. P. Osilenker (*Weighted estimates for singular integrals and their applications*, J. Soviet Math. **30** (1985), 2094–2154; translated from Itogi Nauki i Tekhniki, Akad. Nauk SSSR, Moscow, 1983).

5.2. The Helson-Szegö condition.

The first result characterizing weights for the Hilbert transform is due to H. Helson and G. Szegö (*A problem in prediction theory*, Ann. Math. Pura Appl. **51** (1960), 107–138): the Hilbert transform is bounded on $L^2(w)$ if and only if $\log w = u + Hv$, where $u, v \in L^\infty$ and $\|v\|_\infty < \pi/2$. Their proof uses complex analysis; while it is straightforward to prove that their condition implies the A_2 condition, no direct proof of the converse is known.

The best that can be shown is that the above decomposition holds with $\|v\|_\infty < \pi$. This was first shown by R. Coifman, P. Jones and J. L. Rubio de Francia (*Constructive decomposition of BMO functions and factorization of A_p weights*, Proc. Amer. Math. Soc. **87** (1983), 675–676). A higher dimensional analogue of this result was proved by J. Garnett and P. Jones (*The distance in BMO to L^∞*, Ann. of Math. **108** (1978), 373–393).

The Helson-Szegö theorem condition has been generalized to $L^p(w)$ by M. Cotlar and C. Sadosky (*On some L^p versions of the Helson-Szegö theorem*, Conference on Harmonic Analysis in Honor of Antoni Zygmund, W. Beckner et al., eds., vol. 1, pp. 306–317, Wadsworth, Belmont, 1983).

5.3. The A_∞ condition.

As we already remarked, inequality (7.10) is called the A_∞ condition since

$$A_\infty = \bigcup_{p < \infty} A_p.$$

This was proved independently by B. Muckenhoupt (*The equivalence of two conditions for weight functions*, Studia Math. **49** (1974), 101–106) and by Coifman and Fefferman in the article cited above. We have already shown that $A_p \subset A_\infty$, so to prove this it will suffice to show that if $w \in A_\infty$ there exists p such that $w \in A_p$. The key step in the proof is to show that w^{-1} satisfies a reverse Hölder inequality with Lebesgue measure replaced by the measure $w\,dx$; that is, there exist positive constants ϵ and C such that for every cube Q

$$(7.15) \qquad \left(\frac{1}{w(Q)} \int_Q w^{-1-\epsilon} w \right)^{1/(1+\epsilon)} \leq \frac{C}{w(Q)} \int_Q w^{-1} w.$$

This is equivalent to

$$\frac{1}{|Q|} \int_Q w^{-\epsilon} \leq C \left(\frac{|Q|}{w(Q)} \right)^\epsilon,$$

which is the A_p condition with $\epsilon = p' - 1$.

The proof of (7.15) is similar to the proof of Theorem 7.4. Starting from the A_∞ condition we can prove a result analogous to Lemma 7.5 but interchanging the measures: there exist $\alpha' < 1$, $\beta' < 1$ such that if $S \subset Q$ and $w(S) \leq \alpha' w(Q)$ then $|S| \leq \beta'|Q|$. (Note that in the proof of Theorem 7.4 we did not use the full strength of Lemma 7.5 but only the existence of some α and β.)

To complete the proof, we use the fact that if $w \in A_\infty$ then w is a doubling measure: there exists $C > 0$ such that for any cube Q, $w(2Q) \leq Cw(Q)$. This property is sufficient to let us form the Calderón-Zygmund decomposition of a function f at height λ with respect to the measure $w\,dx$. This yields a collection of disjoint cubes such that

$$f(x) \leq \lambda \quad w \text{ a.e. } x \notin \bigcup_j Q_j,$$

$$\lambda < \frac{1}{w(Q_j)} \int_{Q_j} f\,w \leq C\lambda.$$

The proof is essentially the same as the proof for Lebesgue measure (see Theorem 2.11). With this, we can complete the proof of (7.15) as in the proof of Theorem 7.4 by forming Calderón-Zygmund decompositions of w^{-1}.

If $w \in A_\infty$ then by the above argument and by Proposition 7.2 there exists $p > 1$ such that for any $q > p$, w satisfies the A_q condition with uniform constant. Therefore, if we take the limit as q tends to infinity we get

(7.16) $$\left(\frac{1}{|Q|} \int_Q w \right) \leq C \exp \left(\frac{1}{|Q|} \int_Q \log w \right).$$

(Inequality (7.16) is called the reverse Jensen inequality.) Conversely, if w satisfies (7.16) for all cubes Q, then $w \in A_\infty$. This was proved independently by García-Cuerva and Rubio de Francia [**6**, p. 405] and S. V. Hruščev (*A description of weights satisfying the A_∞ condition of Muckenhoupt*, Proc. Amer. Math. Soc. **90** (1984), 253–257).

5.4. The necessity of the A_p condition for singular integrals.

The A_p condition is necessary and sufficient for the Hardy-Littlewood maximal function to be bounded on $L^p(w)$, $1 < p < \infty$, and to be weak $(1, 1)$ with respect to w, but we only showed that it is a sufficient condition for Calderón-Zygmund operators. The A_p condition is also necessary in the following sense: if w is a weight on $\mathbb{R}^n$ such that each of the Riesz transforms is weak (p, p) with respect to w, $1 \leq p < \infty$, then $w \in A_p$. In particular, the Hilbert transform is weak (p, p) with respect to w if and only if $w \in A_p$. This is proved for the Hilbert transform in the article by Hunt, Muckenhoupt and Wheeden cited above, and their argument can be adapted to the case of Riesz transforms in $\mathbb{R}^n$. Further, Stein [**17**, p. 210] has shown that if any of the Riesz transforms is bounded on $L^p(w)$, $1 < p < \infty$, then $w \in A_p$.

5.5. Factorization of A_p weights.

Proposition 7.2, part (3), lets us construct A_p weights from A_1 weights. It is a very deep fact that the converse is also true, so that $w \in A_p$ if and only if $w = w_0 w_1^{1-p}$, where $w_0, w_1 \in A_1$. This is referred to as the factorization theorem and was first conjectured by Muckenhoupt. It was proved by P. Jones (*Factorization of A_p weights*, Ann. of Math. **111** (1980),

511–530). A very simple proof was later given by R. Coifman, P. Jones and J. L. Rubio de Francia: see the article cited above or Stein [**17**, Chapter 5]. J. L. Rubio de Francia (in the paper cited above) studied factorization in a much more general setting and was able to prove a general factorization principle relating the factorization of operators with weighted inequalities. (Also see [**6**, Chapter 6].) The factorization theorem can be generalized to include information about the size of the exponent in the reverse Hölder inequality. See the paper by D. Cruz-Uribe and C. J. Neugebauer (*The structure of the reverse Hölder classes*, Trans. Amer. Math. Soc. **347** (1995), 2941–2960).

5.6. A_p weights and BMO.

Let f be a locally integrable function such that $\exp(f) \in A_2$. Given a cube Q, let f_Q be the average of f on Q. Then the A_2 condition implies that

$$\left(\frac{1}{|Q|} \int_Q \exp(f) \right) \left(\frac{1}{|Q|} \int_Q \exp(-f) \right) \leq C;$$

equivalently,

$$\left(\frac{1}{|Q|} \int_Q \exp(f - f_Q) \right) \left(\frac{1}{|Q|} \int_Q \exp(f_Q - f) \right) \leq C.$$

By Jensen's inequality, each factor is at least 1 and at most C. Therefore, this inequality implies that

$$\frac{1}{|Q|} \int_Q \exp(|f - f_Q|) \leq 2C,$$

and so

$$\frac{1}{|Q|} \int_Q |f - f_Q| \leq 2C.$$

Hence, $f \in BMO$. We have proved that if $\exp(f) \in A_2$ then $f \in BMO$; equivalently, if $w \in A_2$, $\log w \in BMO$.

From the John-Nirenberg inequality one can prove that if $f \in BMO$ then for all $\lambda > 0$ sufficiently small, $\exp(\lambda f) \in A_2$. (Cf. Corollary 6.13.) In other words,

$$BMO = \{\lambda \log w : \lambda \in \mathbb{R}, \ w \in A_2\}.$$

In fact, by Proposition 7.2 it follows that one can take A_p, $1 < p \leq \infty$, in place of A_2.

5.7. The Coifman-Fefferman inequality.

The original proof of Theorem 7.11 by Coifman and Fefferman (see the reference given above) depended on the following inequality, which they proved for singular integrals T which satisfy the gradient condition (5.3): if $w \in A_\infty$ then for $0 < p < \infty$,

$$(7.17) \qquad \int_{\mathbb{R}^n} |T^* f|^p w \leq C_p \int_{\mathbb{R}^n} (Mf)^p w.$$

(T^* is the maximal operator associated with T.) The heart of the proof is a good-λ inequality relating M and T^*: there exists $\delta > 0$ such that for all $\gamma > 0$,

$$w(\{x \in \mathbb{R}^n : |T^* f(x)| > 2\lambda, Mf(x) \leq \gamma\lambda\})$$
$$\leq C\gamma^\delta w(\{x \in \mathbb{R}^n : |T^* f(x)| > \lambda\}).$$

R. Bagby and D. Kurtz (*A rearranged good λ inequality*, Trans. Amer. Math. Soc. **293** (1986), 71–81) gave another proof of (7.17) with an asymptotically sharp constant; they did so by replacing the good-λ inequality with a rearrangement inequality:

$$(T^* f)^*_w(t) \leq C(Mf)^*_w(t/2) + (Tf)^*_w(2t),$$

where $(g)^*_w$ denotes the decreasing rearrangement of g with respect to the measure $w\,dx$. (Cf. Chapter 2, Section 8.2.) J. Alvarez and C. Pérez (*Estimates with A_∞ weights for various singular integral operators*, Boll. Unione Mat. Ital. (7) **8-A** (1994), 123–133) extended inequality (7.17) to Calderón-Zygmund operators, but with T^* replaced by T on the left-hand side. They did this by proving a sharper form of Lemma 7.9: for $0 < \delta < 1$,

$$M^\#(|Tf|^\delta)(x)^{1/\delta} \leq C_\delta Mf(x).$$

Inequality (7.17) then follows from Lemma 7.10.

5.8. The strong maximal function.

In Chapter 2, Section 8.8, we introduced the strong maximal operator M_s as the average of a function over rectangles with sides parallel to the coordinate axes. This operator satisfies weighted norm inequalities with weights analogous to A_p weights. The "strong" A_p condition is the following: $w \in A_p^*$, $1 < p < \infty$, if for any rectangle R with sides parallel to the coordinate axes,

$$\left(\frac{1}{|R|} \int_R w\right) \left(\frac{1}{|R|} \int_R w^{1-p'}\right)^{p-1} \leq C.$$

Theorem 7.14. *For $1 < p < \infty$, M_s is bounded on $L^p(w)$ if and only if $w \in A_p^*$.*

Theorem 7.14 is a consequence of the corresponding result for the Hardy-Littlewood maximal function. For $1 \leq i \leq n$, define M_i to be the maximal operator restricted to the i-th variable:

$$M_i f(x_1, \ldots, x_n) = M f(x_1, \ldots, x_{i-1}, \cdot, x_{i+1}, \ldots, x_n)(x_i).$$

Then by Fubini's theorem, $M_s f(x) \leq (M_1 \circ \cdots \circ M_n) f(x)$. By a limiting argument, if $w \in A_p^*$ then for each i, $w(x_1, \ldots, x_{i-1}, \cdot, x_{i+1}, \ldots, x_n)$ satisfies the one-dimensional A_p condition with a uniform constant. Theorem 7.14 now follows at once from Theorem 7.3.

If we define $A_1^* = \{w : M_s w \leq Cw \text{ a.e.}\}$, then A_p^* weights can be factored in terms of A_1^* weights.

Theorem 7.15. *Let* $1 < p < \infty$. *Then* $w \in A_p^*$ *if and only if there exist* $w_0, w_1 \in A_1^*$ *such that* $w = w_0 w_1^{1-p}$.

This theorem was first proved by J. L. Rubio de Francia; see the paper cited in Section 5.1.

However, the analogue of Theorem 7.7 is false and $(M_s f)^\delta$, $0 < \delta < 1$, need not be in A_1^*. This was proved by F. Soria (*A remark on A_1-weights for the strong maximal function*, Proc. Amer. Math. Soc. **100** (1987), 46–48).

B. Jawerth (*Weighted inequalities for maximal operators: linearization, localization and factorization*, Amer. J. Math. **108** (1986), 361–414) gave a different proof of Theorem 7.14 as a corollary to a much more general result. Let $\mathcal{B}$ be a basis, that is, a collection of open sets. Given a weight w, we define the weighted maximal function with respect to $\mathcal{B}$ and w by

$$M_{\mathcal{B},w} f(x) = \sup_{x \in B \in \mathcal{B}} \frac{1}{w(B)} \int_B |f| w$$

if $x \in \bigcup_{B \in \mathcal{B}} B$ and 0 otherwise. If $w = 1$ we simply write $M_{\mathcal{B}}$. Note that if $\mathcal{B}$ is the collection of all rectangles R with sides parallel to the coordinate axes, then $M_{\mathcal{B}} = M_s$. We say that a weight w satisfies the A_p condition with respect to $\mathcal{B}$, $1 < p < \infty$, and write $w \in A_{p,\mathcal{B}}$, if for every $B \in \mathcal{B}$,

$$\left(\frac{1}{|B|} \int_B w \right) \left(\frac{1}{|B|} \int_B w^{1-p'} \right)^{p-1} \leq C.$$

Theorem 7.16. *Given a basis* $\mathcal{B}$, *a weight* w *and* p, $1 < p < \infty$, *let* $\sigma = w^{1-p'}$. *Then the following are equivalent:*

(1) $M_{\mathcal{B}}$ *is bounded on both* $L^p(w)$ *and* $L^{p'}(\sigma)$;

(2) $w \in A_{p,\mathcal{B}}$, $M_{\mathcal{B},w}$ *is bounded on* $L^{p'}(w)$ *and* $M_{\mathcal{B},\sigma}$ *is bounded on* $L^p(\sigma)$.

The boundedness of $M_{\mathcal{B},w}$ and $M_{\mathcal{B},\sigma}$ depends on the geometry of the basis $\mathcal{B}$. If $\mathcal{B}$ is the basis of rectangles then the boundedness of these two operators was proved by R. Fefferman (*Strong differentiation with respect to measures*, Amer. J. Math. **103** (1981), 33–40) and by B. Jawerth and A. Torchinsky (*The strong maximal function with respect to measures*, Studia Math. **80** (1984), 261–285). For more general bases, $M_{\mathcal{B},w}$ is bounded on $L^{p'}(w)$ if and only if the basis satisfies a covering property closely related to problems of differentiation of the integral. For further details see the article by Jawerth cited above.

5.9. Norm inequalities with two weights.

A very difficult problem is to generalize the results in this chapter to L^p spaces with different weights; more precisely, given an operator T, to determine necessary and sufficient conditions on a pair of weights (u, v) for the operator to be bounded from $L^p(v)$ to $L^p(u)$, or to satisfy the weak (p, p) inequality

$$u(\{x \in \mathbb{R}^n : |Tf(x)| > \lambda\}) \le \frac{C}{\lambda^p} \int_{\mathbb{R}^n} |f|^p v.$$

Complete answers to these questions are known for the Hardy-Littlewood maximal function. We generalize the A_p condition as follows: a pair of weights (u, v) is in A_p, $1 < p < \infty$, if

$$\left(\frac{1}{|Q|} \int_Q u \right) \left(\frac{1}{|Q|} \int_Q v^{1-p'} \right)^{p-1} \le C,$$

and in A_1 if

$$Mu(x) \le Cv(x) \quad \text{a.e. } x \in \mathbb{R}^n.$$

(When $u = v$ this is exactly the A_p condition defined in Section 1.) With only minor changes we can adapt the proof of Theorem 7.1 to get the following result.

Theorem 7.17. *Given p, $1 \le p < \infty$, the weak-type inequality*

$$u(\{x \in \mathbb{R}^n : Mf(x) > \lambda\}) \le \frac{C}{\lambda^p} \int_{\mathbb{R}^n} |f|^p v$$

holds if and only if $(u, v) \in A_p$.

For the strong (p, p) inequality, however, the A_p condition is necessary but is not sufficient: there exist pairs (u, v) in A_p for which the strong (p, p) inequality is false. This can be seen as follows: since the pair (u, Mu) is in $A_1 \subset A_p$, the pair $((Mu)^{1-p'}, u^{1-p'})$ is in $A_{p'}$ (arguing as in the proof of Proposition 7.2, we have that $(u, v) \in A_p$ and $(v^{1-p'}, u^{1-p'}) \in A_{p'}$ are equivalent conditions). Then the strong (p', p') inequality for the pair $((Mu)^{1-p'}, u^{1-p'})$ with $u = |f|$ would imply that M is bounded on L^1, a contradiction. (See Proposition 2.14.)

Nevertheless, there is a characterization for the strong (p, p) inequality.

Theorem 7.18. *Given a pair of weights (u,v) and p, $1 < p < \infty$, the following are equivalent:*

(1) *M is a bounded operator from $L^p(v)$ to $L^p(u)$;*

(2) *given any cube Q,*

$$(7.18) \qquad \int_Q M(v^{1-p'}\chi_Q)^p u \le C \int_Q v^{1-p'} < \infty.$$

Inequality (7.18) is equivalent to saying that M is bounded on the family of "test functions" $v^{1-p'}\chi_Q$.

Theorem 7.18 was first proved by E. Sawyer (*A characterization of a two-weight norm inequality for maximal operators*, Studia Math. **75** (1982), 1–11). A simpler version of this proof was given by D. Cruz-Uribe (*New proofs of two-weight norm inequalities for the maximal operator*, Georgian Math. J. **7** (2000), 33–42). A very different proof was given by Jawerth in the article cited in the previous section. When $u = v$, (7.18) is equivalent to the A_p condition, so this result gives another proof of Theorem 7.3. This was proved by R. Hunt, D. Kurtz and C. J. Neugebauer (*A note on the equivalence of A_p and Sawyer's condition for equal weights*, Conference on Harmonic Analysis in Honor of Antoni Zygmund, W. Beckner et al., eds., vol. 1, pp. 156–158, Wadsworth, Belmont, 1983).

For singular integral operators, almost nothing is known except for the Hilbert transform. The A_p condition is necessary but not sufficient for the weak (p,p) inequality, $1 < p < \infty$; see the article by B. Muckenhoupt and R. Wheeden (*Two weight function norm inequalities for the Hardy-Littlewood maximal function and the Hilbert transform*, Studia Math. **60** (1976), 279–294). For $p = 1$, Muckenhoupt has conjectured that the A_1 condition is necessary and sufficient for the weak $(1,1)$ inequality for the Hilbert transform. (Also see the next section.) A necessary and sufficient condition is known for the strong $(2,2)$ inequality for the Hilbert transform, or, more precisely, for the conjugate function $\tilde{f}$ on the unit circle. (See Chapter 3, Section 6.2.) This is due to M. Cotlar and C. Sadosky (*On the Helson-Szegö theorem and a related class of modified Toeplitz kernels*, Harmonic Analysis in Euclidean Spaces, G. Weiss and S. Wainger, eds., vol. 1, pp. 383–407, Proc. Sympos. Pure Math. **35**, Amer. Math. Soc., Providence, 1979).

5.10. More on two weight inequalities.

A general technique for applying weighted inequalities can be summarized as follows: given an operator T, first find a positive operator S such that T is bounded from $L^p(Su)$ to $L^p(u)$. Then deduce boundedness properties for T from those of S. (We will use this technique in Chapter 8, Section 3 below.)

To apply this technique we need to find such two weight inequalities. Theorem 2.16 above is a result of this kind: the Hardy-Littlewood maximal function is bounded from $L^p(Mu)$ to $L^p(u)$. The first attempt to generalize this result to other operators was due to A. Córdoba and C. Fefferman (*A weighted norm inequality for singular integrals*, Studia Math. **57** (1976), 97–101). They showed that if T is a singular integral satisfying the gradient condition (5.3), then T is a bounded map from $L^p(M(u^s)^{1/s})$ into $L^p(u)$. By Theorem 7.7, $M(u^s)^{1/s} \in A_1 \subset A_p$, so this result now follows from Theorem 7.3.

The next theorem gives a sharper result.

Theorem 7.19. *Let T be a singular integral satisfying the hypotheses of Theorem 5.1. Given a weight u, for $1 < p < \infty$,*

$$\int_{\mathbb{R}^n} |Tf|^p u \le C_p \int_{\mathbb{R}^n} |f|^p M^{[p]+1} u,$$

where $[p]$ is the integer part of p and $M^k = M \circ \cdots \circ M$ is the k-th iterate of the maximal operator. Further, this inequality is sharp since $[p] + 1$ cannot be replaced by $[p]$.

Note in particular that singular integral operators are not in general bounded from $L^p(Mu)$ to $L^p(u)$. Since $M(u^s)^{1/s} \in A_1$,

$$M^k u(x) \le M^k (M(u^s)^{1/s})(x) \le C_k M(u^s)(x)^{1/s},$$

so Theorem 7.19 is stronger than the result of Córdoba and Fefferman. It was first proved by J. M. Wilson (*Weighted norm inequalities for the continuous square function*, Trans. Amer. Math. Soc. **314** (1989), 661–692) for $1 < p < 2$, and for all $p > 1$ by C. Pérez (*Weighted norm inequalities for singular integral operators*, J. London Math. Soc. **49** (1994), 296–308). In the same paper Pérez also proved the corresponding weak $(1,1)$ inequality:

$$u(\{x \in \mathbb{R}^n : |Tf(x)| > \lambda\}) \le \frac{C}{\lambda} \int_{\mathbb{R}^n} |f| M^2 u.$$

It is unknown if this inequality is true with M^2 replaced with M.

Chapter 8

Littlewood-Paley Theory and Multipliers

1. Some vector-valued inequalities

Our approach to the study of Littlewood-Paley theory will be through the theory of vector-valued singular integrals introduced in Chapter 5. In this section we prove some additional vector-valued inequalities which we will need in later sections using those ideas as well as the weighted norm inequalities in Chapter 7.

Theorem 8.1. *If T is a convolution operator which is bounded on $L^2(\mathbb{R}^n)$ and whose associated kernel K satisfies the Hörmander condition (5.2), then for any r, $1 < r < \infty$, and p, $1 < p < \infty$,*

$$\left\| \left(\sum_j |Tf_j|^r \right)^{1/r} \right\|_p \leq C_{p,r} \left\| \left(\sum_j |f_j|^r \right)^{1/r} \right\|_p,$$

and for $p = 1$,

$$\left| \left\{ x \in \mathbb{R}^n : \left(\sum_j |Tf_j(x)|^r \right)^{1/r} > \lambda \right\} \right| \leq \frac{C_r}{\lambda} \left\| \left(\sum_j |f_j|^r \right)^{1/r} \right\|_1.$$

Proof. We use Theorem 5.17 with $A = B = \ell^r$. The first inequality is immediate when $p = r$ since T is bounded on $L^r(\mathbb{R}^n)$, $1 < r < \infty$. Now consider the vector-valued operator which associates to each sequence $\{f_j\}$ the sequence $\{Tf_j\}$. The kernel associated with this operator is $K(x)I$, where I is the identity operator on ℓ^r. For a convolution operator, conditions

(5.20) and (5.21) reduce to

$$\int_{|x|>2|y|} \|(K(x-y) - K(x))I\|_{\ell^r}\, dx \le C,$$

which in turn is equivalent to the Hörmander condition since

$$\|(K(x-y) - K(x))I\|_{\ell^r} = |K(x-y) - K(x)|.$$

$\square$

A natural problem is to generalize Theorem 8.1 to a sequence of operators $\{T_j\}$ to get an inequality of the form

$$(8.1) \qquad \left\|\left(\sum_j |T_j f_j|^r\right)^{1/r}\right\|_p \le C_{p,r} \left\|\left(\sum_j |f_j|^r\right)^{1/r}\right\|_p, \qquad 1 < p,r < \infty.$$

It seems reasonable to conjecture that if the operators T_j are uniformly bounded on L^2 and the Hörmander condition holds uniformly for their kernels K_j then (8.1) holds. However, if $p \ne r$ this can still be false. The vector-valued operator which sends $\{f_j\}$ to $\{T_j f_j\}$ has as kernel the operator in $\mathcal{L}(\ell^r, \ell^r)$ which maps the sequence $\{\lambda_j\}$ to $\{K_j(x)\lambda_j\}$. For this operator the Hörmander condition becomes

$$\int_{|x|>2|y|} \sup_j |K_j(x-y) - K_j(x)|\, dx \le C,$$

and this condition is sufficient for (8.1) to hold.

Nevertheless, we can use Theorem 8.1 to show that an inequality like (8.1) holds in particular cases. For example, we have the following result.

Corollary 8.2. *Let $\{I_j\}$ be a sequence of intervals on the real line, finite or infinite, and let $\{S_j\}$ be the sequence of operators defined by $(S_j f)^{\widehat{}}(\xi) = \chi_{I_j}(\xi)\hat{f}(\xi)$. Then for $1 < r, p < \infty$,*

$$\left\|\left(\sum_j |S_j f_j|^r\right)^{1/r}\right\|_p \le C_{p,r} \left\|\left(\sum_j |f_j|^r\right)^{1/r}\right\|_p.$$

Proof. If $I_j = (a_j, b_j)$ then by (3.9) we have the formula

$$S_j f_j = \frac{i}{2}\left(M_{a_j} H M_{-a_j} f_j - M_{b_j} H M_{-b_j} f_j\right),$$

with the obvious modifications if the interval is unbounded. The desired result now follows if we apply Theorem 8.1 to the Hilbert transform. $\square$

A common technique for proving vector-valued inequalities like (8.1) involves weighted norm inequalities. The following result is an example of this approach.

Theorem 8.3. *Let $\{T_j\}$ be a sequence of linear operators which are bounded on $L^2(w)$ for any $w \in A_2$ with constants that are uniform in j and which depend only on the A_2 constant of w. Then for all p, $1 < p < \infty$,*

(8.2)
$$\left\| \left(\sum_j |T_j f_j|^2 \right)^{1/2} \right\|_p \leq C \left\| \left(\sum_j |f_j|^2 \right)^{1/2} \right\|_p.$$

Proof. When $p = 2$ this result is immediate. Now suppose that $p > 2$. Then there exists a function $u \in L^{(p/2)'}$ with norm 1 such that

$$\left\| \left(\sum_j |T_j f_j|^2 \right)^{1/2} \right\|_p^2 = \int_{\mathbb{R}^n} \sum_j |T_j f_j|^2 u.$$

By Theorem 7.7, if $0 < \delta < 1$ then $M(u^{1/\delta})^\delta$ is an A_1 weight (and so is in A_2) with a constant that depends only on δ. Since $u(x) \leq M(u^{1/\delta})(x)^\delta$ a.e., it follows that

$$\left\| \left(\sum_j |T_j f_j|^2 \right)^{1/2} \right\|_p^2 \leq C_\delta \int_{\mathbb{R}^n} \left(\sum_j |f_j|^2 \right) M(u^{1/\delta})^\delta.$$

Fix δ such that $\delta(p/2)' > 1$ and then apply Hölder's inequality with exponents $p/2$ and $(p/2)'$ to get inequality (8.2).

Finally, if $p < 2$ then, since the adjoint operators T_j^* are also bounded on $L^2(w)$, $w \in A_2$, we get (8.2) by duality. $\qquad\square$

2. Littlewood-Paley theory

From the Plancherel theorem we know that if we multiply the Fourier transform of a function in L^2 by a function of modulus 1, the result is again a function in L^2. Similarly, if we multiply the terms of the Fourier series of an L^2 function by ± 1, we get another function in L^2. However, neither of these properties holds for functions in L^p, $p \neq 2$. Thus, whether a function is in L^p depends on more than the size of its Fourier transform or Fourier coefficients.

Littlewood-Paley theory provides a partial substitute in L^p for the results derived from the Plancherel theorem. It shows that membership in L^p is preserved if the Fourier transform or Fourier coefficients are modified by ± 1 in dyadic blocks. For example, in the case of the Fourier series of an L^p function, if we assign the same factor 1 or -1 to all the coefficients whose indices lie between 2^k and 2^{k+1}, we get the Fourier series of another L^p function.

We will first prove the corresponding result for the Fourier transform for functions defined on $\mathbb{R}$. Let

$$\Delta_j = (-2^{j+1}, -2^j] \cup [2^j, 2^{j+1}),$$

and define the operator S_j by

$$(S_j f)\widehat{}(\xi) = \chi_{\Delta_j}(\xi)\hat{f}(\xi), \qquad j \in \mathbb{Z}.$$

(The intervals $[2^j, 2^{j+1})$ are called dyadic intervals.) If $f \in L^2$ then by the Plancherel theorem

$$(8.3) \qquad \left\| \left(\sum_j |S_j f|^2 \right)^{1/2} \right\|_2 = \|f\|_2;$$

by the Littlewood-Paley theorem these two quantities are comparable in L^p.

Theorem 8.4 (Littlewood-Paley). *Let $f \in L^p(\mathbb{R})$, $1 < p < \infty$. Then there exist positive constants c_p and C_p such that*

$$(8.4) \qquad c_p \|f\|_p \leq \left\| \left(\sum_j |S_j f|^2 \right)^{1/2} \right\|_p \leq C_p \|f\|_p.$$

We will prove Theorem 8.4 as a consequence of a similar result, but one where the operators are defined using smooth functions instead of characteristic functions of intervals. Let $\psi \in \mathcal{S}(\mathbb{R})$ be non-negative, have support in $1/2 \leq |\xi| \leq 4$ and be equal to 1 on $1 \leq |\xi| \leq 2$. Define

$$\psi_j(\xi) = \psi(2^{-j}\xi) \quad \text{and} \quad (\tilde{S}_j f)\widehat{}(\xi) = \psi_j(\xi)\hat{f}(\xi).$$

It follows immediately that $S_j \tilde{S}_j = S_j$.

The next result is the analogue of Theorem 8.4 for the $\tilde{S}_j$'s. We will use it to prove Theorem 8.4; it is also important in its own right.

Theorem 8.5. *Let $f \in L^p(\mathbb{R})$, $1 < p < \infty$. Then there exists a constant C_p such that*

$$(8.5) \qquad \left\| \left(\sum_j |\tilde{S}_j f|^2 \right)^{1/2} \right\|_p \leq C_p \|f\|_p.$$

Proof. If $\hat{\Psi} = \psi$ and $\Psi_j(x) = 2^j \Psi(2^j x)$, then $\hat{\Psi}_j = \psi_j$ and $\tilde{S}_j f = \Psi_j * f$. Therefore, given the vector-valued operator which maps f to the sequence $\{\tilde{S}_j f\}$, it will suffice to prove that it is a bounded operator from L^p to $L^p(\ell^2)$. When $p = 2$, by the Plancherel theorem

$$\left\| \left(\sum_j |\tilde{S}_j f|^2 \right)^{1/2} \right\|_2^2 = \int_{\mathbb{R}} \sum_j |\psi_j(\xi)|^2 |\hat{f}(\xi)|^2 \, d\xi \leq 3\|f\|_2^2$$

since at any value of ξ at most 3 of the ψ_j's are non-zero.

To prove inequality (8.5) we need to show that the kernel $\{\Psi_j\}$ of the vector-valued operator satisfies the Hörmander condition; to do this it suffices to show that $\|\Psi'_j(x)\|_{\ell^2} \leq C|x|^{-2}$. (This follows from Proposition 5.2, which also holds in the vector-valued case.) But

$$\left(\sum_j |\Psi'_j(x)|^2\right)^{1/2} \leq \sum_j |\Psi'_j(x)| = \sum_j 2^{2j}|\Psi'(2^j x)|;$$

further, since $\Psi \in \mathcal{S}$, $|\Psi'(x)| \leq C\min(1, |x|^{-3})$. Fix i so that $2^{-i} \leq |x| < 2^{-i+1}$. Then the left-hand side is bounded by

$$C\sum_{j \leq i} 2^{2j} + C|x|^{-3}\sum_{j > i} 2^{-j} \leq C|x|^{-2}.$$

$\square$

Proof of Theorem 8.4. By Corollary 8.2 and the identity $S_j \tilde{S}_j = S_j$,

$$\left\|\left(\sum_j |S_j f|^2\right)^{1/2}\right\|_p = \left\|\left(\sum_j |S_j \tilde{S}_j f|^2\right)^{1/2}\right\|_p \leq C\left\|\left(\sum_j |\tilde{S}_j f|^2\right)^{1/2}\right\|_p.$$

Therefore, by Theorem 8.5 we immediately get the right-hand inequality in (8.4).

From the polarization identity and (8.3) we get

$$\int_{\mathbb{R}} \sum_j S_j f \cdot \overline{S_j g} = \int_{\mathbb{R}} f\bar{g}.$$

Hence,

$$\|f\|_p = \sup\left\{\left|\int_{\mathbb{R}} f\bar{g}\right| : \|g\|_{p'} \leq 1\right\}$$

$$= \sup\left\{\left|\int_{\mathbb{R}} \sum_j S_j f \cdot \overline{S_j g}\right| : \|g\|_{p'} \leq 1\right\}$$

$$\leq \sup\left\{\left\|\left(\sum_j |S_j f|^2\right)^{1/2}\right\|_p \cdot \left\|\left(\sum_j |S_j g|^2\right)^{1/2}\right\|_{p'} : \|g\|_{p'} \leq 1\right\}$$

$$\leq C_p\left\|\left(\sum_j |S_j f|^2\right)^{1/2}\right\|_p.$$

$\square$

These results can be extended to $\mathbb{R}^n$ in two different ways. One analogue of Theorem 8.5 cuts the Fourier transform with smooth functions supported on the annuli $2^{j-1} \leq |\xi| \leq 2^{j+1}$; the other generalizes Theorem 8.4 with the cuts made by characteristic functions of products of dyadic intervals on the coordinate axes. We cannot generalize it by using characteristic functions of annuli: this follows from Theorem 8.32 in Section 8.3 below.

Theorem 8.6. *Given* $\psi \in \mathcal{S}(\mathbb{R}^n)$ *with* $\psi(0) = 0$, *let* S_j, $j \in \mathbb{Z}$, *be the operator defined by* $(S_j f)\hat{}(\xi) = \psi(2^{-j}\xi)\hat{f}(\xi)$. *Then for* $1 < p < \infty$,

$$(8.6) \qquad \left\| \left(\sum_j |S_j f|^2 \right)^{1/2} \right\|_p \leq C_p \|f\|_p.$$

Furthermore, if for all $\xi \neq 0$

$$(8.7) \qquad \sum_j |\psi(2^{-j}\xi)|^2 = C,$$

then we also have

$$(8.8) \qquad \|f\|_p \leq C_p' \left\| \left(\sum_j |S_j f|^2 \right)^{1/2} \right\|_p.$$

Since $\psi \in \mathcal{S}$ and $\psi(0) = 0$, it satisfies

$$\sum_j |\psi(2^{-j}\xi)|^2 \leq C.$$

Therefore, the proof of the first part of Theorem 8.6 is exactly the same as the proof of Theorem 8.5, while the proof of the second part is the same as the proof of the corresponding part of Theorem 8.4 since it follows from (8.7) that when $p = 2$ we have equality (up to a constant).

There is a simple method for constructing functions which satisfy (8.7). Fix $\phi \in \mathcal{S}(\mathbb{R}^n)$, non-negative, radial, decreasing and such that $\phi(\xi) = 1$ if $|\xi| \leq 1/2$ and $\phi(\xi) = 0$ if $|\xi| \geq 1$. Then define

$$\psi^2(\xi) = \phi(\xi/2) - \phi(\xi).$$

It follows immediately that

$$\sum_j |\psi(2^{-j}\xi)|^2 = 1, \quad \xi \neq 0.$$

We will state and prove the next result only for $\mathbb{R}^2$; its extension to higher dimensions follows at once by induction. Dyadic rectangles in the plane are the Cartesian product of dyadic intervals in $\mathbb{R}$. The associated operators are then defined as the composition $S_j^1 S_k^2$, where

$$(S_j^1 f)\hat{}(\xi_1, \xi_2) = \chi_{\Delta_j}(\xi_1)\hat{f}(\xi_1, \xi_2)$$

and

$$(S_k^2 f)\hat{}(\xi_1, \xi_2) = \chi_{\Delta_k}(\xi_2)\hat{f}(\xi_1, \xi_2).$$

Theorem 8.7. *Let $f \in L^p(\mathbb{R}^2)$, $1 < p < \infty$. Then there exist positive constants c_p and C_p such that*

$$c_p \|f\|_p \leq \left\| \left(\sum_{j,k} |S_j^1 S_k^2 f|^2 \right)^{1/2} \right\|_p \leq C_p \|f\|_p.$$

Proof. By the same argument as in the proof of Theorem 8.5, and with the same notation as there, we have that

$$(8.9) \qquad \left\| \left(\sum_{j,k} |\tilde{S}_j f_k|^2 \right)^{1/2} \right\|_p \leq C_p \left\| \left(\sum_{k} |f_k|^2 \right)^{1/2} \right\|_p.$$

By Fubini's theorem, inequality (8.9) is true even if f_k is a function of two variables and $\tilde{S}_j$ acts only on one of them. Furthermore, arguing as in the proof of Theorem 8.4 (Corollary 8.2 readily adapts to this case) we can also replace $\tilde{S}_j$ by S_j since $S_j \tilde{S}_j = S_j$. But then we can first apply (8.9) and then Theorem 8.4 (along with Fubini's theorem since f is a function of two variables) to get

$$\left\| \left(\sum_{j,k} |S_j^1 S_k^2 f|^2 \right)^{1/2} \right\|_p \leq C_p \left\| \left(\sum_{k} |S_k^2 f|^2 \right)^{1/2} \right\|_p \leq C_p' \|f\|_p.$$

$\square$

3. The Hörmander multiplier theorem

We are now going to give some applications of Littlewood-Paley theory. In the next three sections we will consider the problem of characterizing multipliers on L^p. More precisely, given a function m, when is the operator T_m defined by $(T_m f)\widehat{} = m\hat{f}$ bounded on L^p, $1 \leq p \leq \infty$? (We first considered multipliers on $L^p(\mathbb{R})$ in Chapter 3, Section 5; also see Chapter 3, Section 6.7.)

The Sobolev space $L_a^2(\mathbb{R}^n)$ is defined to be the set of functions g such that $(1 + |\xi|^2)^{a/2} \hat{g}(\xi) \in L^2$ and the norm of this function is the norm of g in L_a^2. (When a is a positive integer this definition is equivalent to that given in Chapter 4, Section 7.7.) Note that if $a' < a$, $L_a^2(\mathbb{R}^n) \subset L_{a'}^2(\mathbb{R}^n)$.

Proposition 8.8. *If $a > n/2$ and $g \in L_a^2(\mathbb{R}^n)$ then $\hat{g} \in L^1$; in particular, g is continuous and bounded.*

Proof. Since $(1 + |\xi|^2)^{a/2} \hat{g}(\xi) = h(\xi) \in L^2$,

$$\int_{\mathbb{R}^n} |\hat{g}(\xi)| \, d\xi \leq \left(\int_{\mathbb{R}^n} |h(\xi)|^2 \, d\xi \right)^{1/2} \left(\int_{\mathbb{R}^n} \frac{d\xi}{(1 + |\xi|^2)^a} \right)^{1/2} \leq C_a \|g\|_{L_a^2}.$$

$\square$

It follows from this result that if $m \in L_a^2$ with $a > n/2$ then m is a multiplier on L^p, $1 \le p \le \infty$. In fact, if $(Tf)\hat{} = m\hat{f}$ then $Tf = K * f$ with $K \in L^1$. Hörmander's theorem shows that m is a multiplier on L^p under much weaker hypotheses. To prove it we first need to prove a weighted norm inequality.

Lemma 8.9. *Let $m \in L_a^2$, $a > n/2$, and let $\lambda > 0$. Define the operator T_λ by $(T_\lambda f)\hat{}(\xi) = m(\lambda\xi)\hat{f}(\xi)$. Then*

$$\int_{\mathbb{R}^n} |T_\lambda f(x)|^2 u(x)\, dx \le C \int_{\mathbb{R}^n} |f(x)|^2 Mu(x)\, dx,$$

where the constant C is independent of u and λ, and M is the Hardy-Littlewood maximal operator.

Proof. If $\hat{K} = m$ then by our hypothesis, $(1 + |x|^2)^{a/2}K(x) = R(x) \in L^2$, and the kernel of T_λ is $\lambda^{-n}K(\lambda^{-1}x)$. Hence,

$$\int_{\mathbb{R}^n} |T_\lambda f|^2 u = \int_{\mathbb{R}^n} \left| \int_{\mathbb{R}^n} \frac{\lambda^{-n}R(\lambda^{-1}(x-y))}{(1 + |\lambda^{-1}(x-y)|^2)^{a/2}} f(y)\, dy \right|^2 u(x)\, dx$$

$$\le \|m\|_{L_a^2}^2 \int_{\mathbb{R}^n} \int_{\mathbb{R}^n} \frac{\lambda^{-n}|f(y)|^2}{(1 + |\lambda^{-1}(x-y)|^2)^a} u(x)\, dy\, dx$$

$$\le C_a \|m\|_{L_a^2}^2 \int_{\mathbb{R}^n} |f(y)|^2 Mu(y)\, dy;$$

the second inequality follows by applying the Cauchy-Schwarz inequality and using the fact that $\|R\|_2 = \|m\|_{L_a^2}$, and the third inequality follows if we integrate in x because $(1 + |x|^2)^{-a}$ is radial, decreasing and integrable since $a > n/2$. (See Proposition 2.7 and Theorem 2.16.) $\qquad\square$

To state Hörmander's theorem, let $\psi \in C^\infty$ be a radial function supported on $1/2 \le |\xi| \le 2$ and such that

$$\sum_{j=-\infty}^{\infty} |\psi(2^{-j}\xi)|^2 = 1, \quad \xi \ne 0.$$

Theorem 8.10 (Hörmander). *Let m be such that for some $a > n/2$,*

$$\sup_j \|m(2^j\cdot)\psi\|_{L_a^2} < \infty.$$

Then the operator T associated with the multiplier m is bounded on $L^p(\mathbb{R}^n)$, $1 < p < \infty$.

Proof. We apply Theorem 8.6. First, define the family of operators $\{S_j\}$ by $(S_j f)\hat{}(\xi) = \psi(2^{-j}\xi)\hat{f}(\xi)$. Then inequality (8.8) holds by our choice of ψ. Now let $\tilde{\psi}$ be another C^∞ function supported on $1/4 \le |\xi| \le 4$ and equal to 1 on $1/2 \le |\xi| \le 2$. If we define $\tilde{S}_j$ by $(\tilde{S}_j f)\hat{}(\xi) = \tilde{\psi}(2^{-j}\xi)\hat{f}(\xi)$, then $S_j \tilde{S}_j = S_j$ and the family $\{\tilde{S}_j\}$ satisfies inequality (8.6). (Note that (8.7) does not necessarily hold for $\tilde{\psi}$.) Therefore,

$$\|Tf\|_p \le C\left\|\left(\sum_j |S_j Tf|^2\right)^{1/2}\right\|_p = C\left\|\left(\sum_j |S_j T\tilde{S}_j f|^2\right)^{1/2}\right\|_p.$$

The multiplier associated with $S_j T$ is $\psi(2^{-j}\xi)m(\xi)$, so by our hypothesis and by Lemma 8.9,

$$\int_{\mathbb{R}^n} |S_j Tf|^2 u \le C \int_{\mathbb{R}^n} |f|^2 Mu,$$

where C is independent of j. Using this inequality, by an argument analogous to that in the proof of Theorem 8.3 we can prove that for $p > 2$

$$\left\|\left(\sum_j |S_j T g_j|^2\right)^{1/2}\right\|_p \le C\left\|\left(\sum_j |g_j|^2\right)^{1/2}\right\|_p.$$

Therefore, if we combine this with inequality (8.6) for $\{\tilde{S}_j\}$ we get

$$\|Tf\|_p \le C\left\|\left(\sum_j |\tilde{S}_j f|^2\right)^{1/2}\right\|_p \le C\|f\|_p, \qquad p > 2.$$

Finally, for $p < 2$ this inequality follows by duality. (See Chapter 3, Section 6.7.) $\qquad\square$

Hörmander's theorem is usually stated in the following way.

Corollary 8.11. *If for $k = [n/2] + 1$, $m \in C^k$ away from the origin, and if for $|\beta| \le k$*

$$(8.10) \qquad \sup_R R^{|\beta|}\left(\frac{1}{R^n}\int_{R<|\xi|<2R} |D^\beta m(\xi)|^2\, d\xi\right)^{1/2} < \infty,$$

then m is a multiplier on L^p, $1 < p < \infty$. In particular, m is a multiplier if

$$|D^\beta m(\xi)| \le C|\xi|^{-|\beta|}, \qquad |\beta| \le k.$$

Proof. If we make the change of variables $\xi \mapsto R\xi$ in inequality (8.10) and use the fact that $D^\beta m(R\cdot)(\xi) = R^{|\beta|}(D^\beta m)(R\xi)$, we get

$$\sup_R \left(\int_{1<|\xi|<2} |D^\beta m(R\cdot)(\xi)|^2\, d\xi\right)^{1/2} \le C.$$

Since

$$D^\beta(m(2^j \cdot)\psi)(\xi) = \sum_{|\gamma| \leq |\beta|} C_{\gamma,\beta} D^\gamma m(2^j \cdot) D^{\beta-\gamma}\psi,$$

and since $|D^\beta \psi| \leq C$, it follows that $\sup \|m(2^j \cdot)\psi\|_{L_k^2} < \infty$ and so we can apply Theorem 8.10. $\square$

Example 8.12.

(1) $m(\xi) = |\xi|^{it}$ satisfies the last hypothesis of Corollary 8.11. In fact, it is easy to see that $|D^\beta m(\xi)| \leq C_t |\xi|^{-|\beta|}$.

(2) If m is homogeneous of degree 0 and of class C^k on the unit sphere for some $k > [n/2]$ then m is a multiplier on $L^p(\mathbb{R}^n)$, $1 < p < \infty$.

4. The Marcinkiewicz multiplier theorem

By Corollary 3.8 we know that if m is of bounded variation on $\mathbb{R}$ then it is a multiplier on L^p. The Marcinkiewicz multiplier theorem shows that we can weaken this hypothesis to a condition on dyadic intervals.

Theorem 8.13. *Let m be a bounded function which has uniformly bounded variation on each dyadic interval in $\mathbb{R}$. Then m is a multiplier on $L^p(\mathbb{R})$, $1 < p < \infty$.*

Proof. The proof is similar to the proof of Corollary 3.8. Given a dyadic interval I_j, let T_j be the operator associated with the multiplier $m\chi_{I_j}$. We will consider the case $I_j = (2^j, 2^{j+1})$; the other case is handled in exactly the same way. For $\xi \in I_j$

$$(m\chi_{I_j})(\xi) = m(2^j) + \int_{2^j}^\xi dm(t);$$

without loss of generality we may assume that m is right continuous on $\mathbb{R} \setminus \{0\}$. But then

$$T_j f(x) = m(2^j) S_j f(x) + \int_{2^j}^{2^{j+1}} S_{t,2^{j+1}} f(x) \, dm(t),$$

where $S_{t,2^{j+1}}$ is the operator associated with the multiplier $\chi_{[t,2^{j+1}]}$. By (3.9) and Theorem 7.11, the operators S_j and $S_{t,2^{j+1}}$ are uniformly bounded on $L^2(w)$ if $w \in A_2$. Therefore, by Minkowski's inequality and our hypotheses, the operators T_j are also bounded on $L^2(w)$ with a constant depending only on the L^∞ norm of m and the total variation of m on I_j. Hence, by Theorems 8.4 and 8.3, if T is the operator associated with m then

$$\|Tf\|_p \leq C \left\| \left(\sum_j |S_j Tf|^2 \right)^{1/2} \right\|_p$$

$$= C \left\| \left(\sum_j |T_j S_j f|^2 \right)^{1/2} \right\|_p$$

$$\leq C \left\| \left(\sum_j |S_j f|^2 \right)^{1/2} \right\|_p$$

$$\leq C \|f\|_p.$$

$\square$

We can extend Theorem 8.13 to higher dimensions; we first do so in $\mathbb{R}^2$.

Theorem 8.14. *Suppose m is a bounded function in the plane, twice differentiable in each quadrant of $\mathbb{R}^2$ and such that*

$$\sup_j \int_{I_j} \left| \frac{\partial m}{\partial t_1}(t_1, t_2) \right| dt_1 < \infty,$$

$$\sup_j \int_{I_j} \left| \frac{\partial m}{\partial t_2}(t_1, t_2) \right| dt_2 < \infty,$$

$$\sup_{i,j} \int_{I_i \times I_j} \left| \frac{\partial^2 m}{\partial t_1 \partial t_2}(t_1, t_2) \right| dt_1 dt_2 < \infty,$$

where I_i and I_j are dyadic intervals in $\mathbb{R}$. Then m is a multiplier on $L^p(\mathbb{R}^2)$, $1 < p < \infty$.

Proof. As before, we restrict our attention to dyadic intervals in $\mathbb{R}_+$. Let $I_i = (2^i, 2^{i+1})$, $I_j = (2^j, 2^{j+1})$, and fix $(\xi_1, \xi_2) \in I_i \times I_j$. Then

$$m(\xi_1, \xi_2) = \int_{2^i}^{\xi_1} \int_{2^j}^{\xi_2} \frac{\partial^2 m}{\partial t_1 \partial t_2}(t_1, t_2) \, dt_1 dt_2$$

$$+ \int_{2^i}^{\xi_1} \frac{\partial m}{\partial t_1}(t_1, 2^j) \, dt_1 + \int_{2^j}^{\xi_2} \frac{\partial m}{\partial t_2}(2^i, t_2) \, dt_2$$

$$+ m(2^i, 2^j).$$

If $T_{i,j}$ is the operator associated with the multiplier $m\chi_{I_i \times I_j}$ then

$$T_{i,j} f(x) = \int_{I_i \times I_j} \frac{\partial^2 m}{\partial t_1 \partial t_2}(t_1, t_2) S^1_{t_1, 2^{i+1}} S^2_{t_2, 2^{j+1}} f(x) \, dt_1 dt_2$$

$$+ \int_{I_i} \frac{\partial m}{\partial t_1}(t_1, 2^j) S^1_{t_1, 2^{i+1}} f(x) \, dt_1 + \int_{I_j} \frac{\partial m}{\partial t_2}(2^i, t_2) S^2_{t_2, 2^{j+1}} f(x) \, dt_2$$

$$+ m(2^i, 2^j) S^1_i S^2_j f(x),$$

where the superscripts denote the variable on which the operator is acting. Therefore, $T_{i,j}$ is bounded on $L^2(w)$ where w is any weight which satisfies the A_2 condition uniformly in each variable (i.e. if $w \in A_2^*$; see Chapter 7,

Section 5.8). We can now argue as we did in the proof of Theorem 8.13 to get the desired result.   □

The proof of Theorem 8.14 extends immediately to higher dimensions; the only problem is that the notation quickly becomes unwieldy. In $\mathbb{R}^n$ the hypotheses become

$$\sup_{j_1,\dots,j_k} \int_{I_{j_1} \times \cdots \times I_{j_k}} \left| \frac{\partial^k m}{\partial \xi_{i_1} \cdots \partial \xi_{i_k}}(\xi) \right| d\xi_{i_1} \cdots d\xi_{i_k} < \infty,$$

where the I_j's are dyadic intervals in $\mathbb{R}$ and the set $\{i_1,\dots,i_k\}$ runs over all the subsets of $\{1,\dots,n\}$ containing k elements, $1 \leq k \leq n$.

5. Bochner-Riesz multipliers

As we discussed in Chapter 1, Section 9, the spherical convergence of Fourier integrals consists in studying when

$$S_R f(x) = \int_{|\xi| \leq R} \hat{f}(\xi) e^{2\pi i \xi \cdot x} \, d\xi$$

converges to f (either in L^p norm or pointwise almost everywhere) as $R \to \infty$ for $f \in L^p$. The multiplier of this partial sum operator is $\chi_{\{|\xi| \leq R\}}$:

$$(S_R f)\hat{\ }(\xi) = \chi_{\{|\xi| \leq R\}} \hat{f}(\xi).$$

When $n = 1$ we already showed (Proposition 3.6) that this multiplier is bounded on $L^p(\mathbb{R})$, $1 < p < \infty$. For $n \geq 2$ this multiplier is not well behaved; see Section 8.3 below. In higher dimensions, the problem is simpler if we consider multipliers which are more regular than the characteristic function of a ball. For example, if we take the Cesàro means of the operators S_t for $0 < t \leq R$, we get the operator

$$\sigma_R f(x) = \frac{1}{R} \int_0^R S_t f(x) \, dt = \int_{|\xi| \leq R} \left(1 - \frac{|\xi|}{R} \right) \hat{f}(\xi) e^{2\pi i \xi \cdot x} \, d\xi.$$

This example leads us to consider the following family of operators:

$$(S_R^a f)\hat{\ }(\xi) = \left(1 - \frac{|\xi|}{R} \right)_+^a \hat{f}(\xi), \quad a > 0,$$

where $A_+ = \max(A, 0)$. For a fixed value of a the operators $\{S_R^a\}$ are all dilations of the operator S_1^a, so to prove that these operators are uniformly bounded on L^p it suffices to consider the case $R = 1$. When $n = 1$, the Fourier transform of the function $m(\xi) = (1 - |\xi|)_+^a$ is in L^1. (This can be shown directly by applying integration by parts and then arguing as in the proof of the Riemann-Lebesgue lemma (Lemma 1.4) to show that $|\hat{m}(x)| \leq C(1 + |x|)^{-1-a}$.) Therefore, by Young's inequality (Corollary 1.21)

m is a multiplier on L^p, $1 \leq p \leq \infty$. However, in higher dimensions this is no longer true.

Rather than considering these operators directly, it is customary to replace them with the Bochner-Riesz multipliers:

$$(T^a f)\hat{\ }(\xi) = (1 - |\xi|^2)^a_+ \hat{f}(\xi), \quad a > 0.$$

For if ψ_1 and ψ_2 are C^∞ functions on $\mathbb{R}$ with compact support such that $\psi_1(|\xi|) = \psi_2(|\xi|) = 1$ if $|\xi| \leq 1$, then we can write

$$(1 - |\xi|^2)^a_+ = (1 - |\xi|)^a_+ [(1 + |\xi|)^a \psi_1(|\xi|)],$$
$$(1 - |\xi|)^a_+ = (1 - |\xi|^2)^a_+ [(1 + |\xi|)^{-a} \psi_2(|\xi|)].$$

Since each term in square brackets is a Hörmander multiplier, it follows that T^a is a bounded operator on some L^p, $1 < p < \infty$, if and only if S^a_1 is.

Our main result is the following.

Theorem 8.15. *The Bochner-Riesz multipliers T^a satisfy the following:*

(1) *If $a > \dfrac{n-1}{2}$ then T^a is bounded on $L^p(\mathbb{R}^n)$, $1 \leq p \leq \infty$.*

(2) *If $0 < a \leq \dfrac{n-1}{2}$ then T^a is bounded on $L^p(\mathbb{R}^n)$ if*

$$\left| \frac{1}{p} - \frac{1}{2} \right| < \frac{a}{n-1},$$

and is not bounded if

$$\left| \frac{1}{p} - \frac{1}{2} \right| \geq \frac{2a+1}{2n}.$$

For the values of p not considered in Theorem 8.15, see Section 8.3 below. The value $(n-1)/2$ is called the critical index.

The singularity of the Bochner-Riesz multipliers is on the circle $|\xi| = 1$; therefore, to prove Theorem 8.15 we are going to decompose the multipliers on dyadic annuli whose widths are approximately their distances to the unit sphere. To be precise: choose functions $\phi_k \in C^\infty(\mathbb{R})$ which are supported on $1 - 2^{-k+1} < t < 1 - 2^{-k-1}$ and are such that $0 \leq \phi_k \leq 1$, $|D^\beta \phi_k| \leq C_\beta 2^{k|\beta|}$ for all multi-indices β (where C_β is independent of k), and for $1/2 \leq t \leq 1$

$$\sum_{k=1}^{\infty} \phi_k(t) = 1.$$

Now define

$$\phi_0(t) = 1 - \sum_{k=1}^{\infty} \phi_k(t), \quad 0 \leq t < 1/2,$$

and let $\phi_0(t) = 0$ if $t \geq 1/2$. Then

$$(1 - |\xi|^2)_+^a = \sum_{k=0}^{\infty} (1 - |\xi|^2)^a \phi_k(|\xi|).$$

On the support of ϕ_k the size of $1 - |\xi|^2$ is approximately 2^{-k}, so we define

$$\tilde{\phi}_k(|\xi|) = 2^{ka}(1 - |\xi|^2)^a \phi_k(|\xi|)$$

in order to write

$$(1 - |\xi|^2)_+^a = \sum_{k=0}^{\infty} 2^{-ka} \tilde{\phi}_k(|\xi|).$$

This allows us to decompose the operator T^a as

$$T^a f = \sum_{k=0}^{\infty} 2^{-ka} T_k f,$$

where

$$(T_k f)\hat{}(\xi) = \tilde{\phi}_k(|\xi|) \hat{f}(\xi).$$

The behavior of operators like the T_k's is given by the next lemma, which will yield the positive part of Theorem 8.15.

Lemma 8.16. *Given $0 < \delta < 1$, let ϕ be a function on $\mathbb{R}$ which is supported on $1 - 4\delta < t < 1 - \delta$ and is such that $0 \leq \phi \leq 1$ and $|D^\beta \phi| \leq C\delta^{-|\beta|}$ for any β. Then for any $\epsilon > 0$ the operator T_δ associated with the multiplier $\phi(|\xi|)$ satisfies*

(8.11)
$$\|T_\delta f\|_p \leq C_\epsilon \delta^{-\left(\frac{n-1}{2} + \epsilon\right)\left|\frac{2}{p} - 1\right|} \|f\|_p.$$

Proof. Fix K so that $\hat{K}(\xi) = \phi(|\xi|)$ and let a be a positive even integer. Then by inequality (1.20) and the Plancherel theorem,

$$\|(1 + |x|^a)K\|_2 \leq C\|(I + (-\Delta)^{a/2})\phi\|_2 \leq C\delta^{1/2}(1 + \delta^{-a}) \leq C\delta^{-a+1/2};$$

the second inequality follows by our hypotheses on the support of ϕ and the size of $D^a \phi$. By Hölder's inequality this holds for arbitrary $a > 0$. Given a, fix $s > 1$ such that as is an even integer. Then

$$\|(1 + |x|^a)K\|_2 \leq C\|(1 + |x|^{as})^{1/s}K\|_2 \leq \|(1 + |x|^{as})K\|_2^{1/s} \|K\|_2^{1/s'},$$

and the desired inequality now follows from the previous argument.

Now let $a = n/2 + \epsilon$. Then by Hölder's inequality

$$\|K\|_1 \leq \|(1 + |x|^a)K\|_2 \|(1 + |x|^a)^{-1}\|_2 \leq C_\epsilon \delta^{-\left(\frac{n-1}{2} + \epsilon\right)}.$$

Therefore, by Young's inequality (Corollary 1.21) with $q = 1, \infty$,

$$\|T_\delta f\|_q \leq C_\epsilon \delta^{-\left(\frac{n-1}{2}+\epsilon\right)} \|f\|_q.$$

If we interpolate between these two inequalities and the trivial inequality when $q = 2$ we get (8.11). □

To prove the negative part of Theorem 8.15 we need two lemmas.

Lemma 8.17. *If m is a function with compact support which is a multiplier on L^p for some p, then $\hat{m} \in L^p$.*

Proof. Let $f \in \mathcal{S}$ be such that $\hat{f} = 1$ on the support of m. Then $f \in L^p$ and so $T_m f \in L^p$, but $(T_m f)\hat{} = m\hat{f} = m$. □

Lemma 8.18. *The Fourier transform of $(1 - |\xi|^2)_+^a$ is*

$$(8.12) \qquad K^a(x) = \pi^{-a}\Gamma(a+1)|x|^{-\frac{n}{2}-a}J_{\frac{n}{2}+a}(2\pi|x|),$$

where J_μ is the Bessel function

$$J_\mu(t) = \frac{\left(\frac{t}{2}\right)^\mu}{\Gamma\left(\mu + \frac{1}{2}\right)\Gamma\left(\frac{1}{2}\right)} \int_{-1}^{1} e^{its}(1 - s^2)^{\mu-\frac{1}{2}}\, ds.$$

Proof. Inequality (8.12) follows immediately from two results:

(1) If $f(x) = f_0(|x|) \in L^1(\mathbb{R}^n)$ is radial then $\hat{f}$ is radial and

$$\hat{f}(\xi) = 2\pi|\xi|^{1-\frac{n}{2}} \int_0^\infty f_0(s)J_{\frac{n}{2}-1}(2\pi|\xi|s)s^{n/2}\, ds.$$

(2) If $j > -1/2$, $k > -1$ and $t > 0$ then

$$J_{j+k+1}(t) = \frac{t^{k+1}}{2^k\Gamma(k+1)} \int_0^1 J_j(ts)s^{j+1}(1 - s^2)^k\, ds.$$

The proofs of these can be found in Stein and Weiss [**18**, pp. 155, 170]. □

Proof of Theorem 8.15. By Lemma 8.16, for each k

$$\|T_k f\|_p \leq C_\epsilon 2^{k\left(\frac{n-1}{2}+\epsilon\right)\left|\frac{2}{p}-1\right|} \|f\|_p.$$

Therefore, by Minkowski's inequality

$$\|T^a f\|_p \leq C_\epsilon \sum_{k=0}^{\infty} 2^{k\left(\frac{n-1}{2}+\epsilon\right)\left|\frac{2}{p}-1\right|-ka} \|f\|_p.$$

The positive results now follow immediately.

To prove the negative results, note that from the definition of the Bessel function we have that $J_\mu(t) = O(t^\mu)$ as $t \to 0$. Further, as $t \to \infty$, $J_\mu(t) \approx t^{-1/2}$ (see Stein [**17**, p. 338]). Hence, by Lemma 8.18

$$|K^a(x)| \leq C \quad \text{as} \quad |x| \to 0,$$

and

$$|K^a(x)| \approx |x|^{-\left(\frac{n+1}{2}+a\right)} \quad \text{as} \quad |x| \to \infty.$$

Therefore, $K^a \in L^p$ only if

$$p > \frac{2n}{n+1+2a},$$

and so if we combine Lemma 8.17 with a duality argument (see Chapter 3, Section 6.7) we get that T^a cannot be bounded if

$$\left|\frac{1}{p} - \frac{1}{2}\right| \geq \frac{2a+1}{2n}.$$

$\square$

6. Return to singular integrals

In this section we apply Littlewood-Paley theory to singular integral operators. Our main result is the following.

Theorem 8.19. *Let $K \in L^1(\mathbb{R}^n)$ be a function of compact support such that for some $a > 0$*

$$|\hat{K}(\xi)| \leq C|\xi|^{-a},$$

and such that

$$\int_{\mathbb{R}^n} K(x)\,dx = 0.$$

For each integer j let $K_j(x) = 2^{-jn}K(2^{-j}x)$. Then the operator

$$Tf(x) = \sum_{j=-\infty}^{\infty} K_j * f(x)$$

satisfies

$$\|Tf\|_p \leq C_p \|f\|_p, \quad 1 < p < \infty.$$

The L^2 norm inequality for the operator T follows at once from the Plancherel theorem and our hypotheses. Since K has compact support we also have that $|\hat{K}(\xi)| \le C|\xi|$, so

$$\int_{\mathbb{R}^n} |Tf(x)|^2 \, dx = \int_{\mathbb{R}^n} \left| \sum_j \hat{K}_j(\xi) \right|^2 |\hat{f}(\xi)|^2 \, d\xi$$

$$\le \int_{\mathbb{R}^n} \left(\sum_j |\hat{K}(2^j \xi)| \right)^2 |\hat{f}(\xi)|^2 \, d\xi$$

$$\le C \int_{\mathbb{R}^n} \left(\sum_j \min(|2^j \xi|^{-a}, |2^j \xi|) \right)^2 |\hat{f}(\xi)|^2 \, d\xi$$

$$\le C\|f\|_2^2.$$

To prove Theorem 8.19 for arbitrary $p > 1$ we will decompose the operator as

$$Tf = \sum_{k=-\infty}^{\infty} \tilde{T}_k f,$$

where each $\tilde{T}_k$ is gotten by cutting up each multiplier $\hat{K}_j$ into pieces supported on the annuli $2^{-j-k-1} < |\xi| < 2^{-j-k+1}$ (which we will denote by $|\xi| \approx 2^{-j-k}$) and summing in j. For each k the corresponding pieces have supports which are almost disjoint and whose size depends only on k. Because of this, the sum of the norms of the $\tilde{T}_k$'s will be dominated by a convergent geometric series.

Proof. Let $\psi \in \mathcal{S}(\mathbb{R}^n)$ be a radial function whose Fourier transform is supported on $1/2 < |\xi| < 2$ and which satisfies

$$\sum_{k=-\infty}^{\infty} \hat{\psi}(2^k \xi) = 1, \quad \xi \ne 0.$$

Let $\psi_k(x) = 2^{-kn} \psi(2^{-k} x)$; then by the Plancherel theorem

$$K_j = \sum_{k=-\infty}^{\infty} K_j * \psi_{j+k}.$$

Now define

$$\tilde{T}_k f = \sum_{j=-\infty}^{\infty} K_j * \psi_{j+k} * f = \sum_{j=-\infty}^{\infty} (K * \psi_k)_j * f.$$

Then we have that

$$Tf = \sum_j K_j * f = \sum_{j,k} K_j * \psi_{j+k} * f = \sum_k \tilde{T}_k f.$$

Suppose the following inequalities were true:

(8.13) $$\|\tilde{T}_k f\|_2 \le C 2^{-a|k|} \|f\|_2,$$

(8.14) $$|\{x \in \mathbb{R}^n : |\tilde{T}_k f(x)| > \lambda\}| \le \frac{C(1+|k|)}{\lambda} \|f\|_1.$$

(In fact, we will show (8.13) provided $0 < a \le 1$. If $a > 1$ then the constant will be $2^{-|k|}$ but this will not affect the proof.) If we apply the Marcinkiewicz interpolation theorem (cf. (2.2)) to (8.13) and (8.14), then for $1 < p < 2$ we get that

$$\|\tilde{T}_k f\|_p \le C_p 2^{-a\theta|k|} (1+|k|)^{1-\theta} \|f\|_p,$$

where $1/p = \theta/2 + (1-\theta)$. The desired result follows if we sum in k for $1 < p < 2$; by a duality argument we get it for $2 < p < \infty$.

It remains, therefore, to prove (8.13) and (8.14). The first follows from the definition: since $\hat{\psi}_j \hat{\psi}_m$ is non-zero only if $m = j, j \pm 1$, by the Plancherel theorem

$$\|\tilde{T}_k f\|_2^2 \le \sum_j \sum_{m=j-1}^{j+1} \int_{\mathbb{R}^n} |\hat{K}_j(\xi)\hat{K}_m(\xi)||\hat{\psi}_{j+k}(\xi)\hat{\psi}_{m+k}(\xi)||\hat{f}(\xi)|^2 \, d\xi$$

$$\le C \sum_j \int_{|\xi| \approx 2^{-j-k}} 2^{-2a|k|} |\hat{f}(\xi)|^2 \, d\xi$$

$$\le C 2^{-2a|k|} \|f\|_2^2.$$

The second inequality follows since $|\hat{K}_j(\xi)| \le \min(|2^j \xi|^{-a}, |2^j \xi|)$.

To prove (8.14) we will apply Theorem 5.1; it will suffice to show that the constant in the Hörmander condition (5.2) for $\tilde{T}_k$ is $C(1+|k|)$. Fix $y \ne 0$; then

$$\int_{|x|>2|y|} \left| \sum_{j=-\infty}^{\infty} (K * \psi_k)_j (x-y) - (K * \psi_k)_j(x) \right| dx$$

$$\le \sum_{j=-\infty}^{\infty} \int_{|x|>2|y|} 2^{-jn} |(K * \psi_k)(2^{-j}x - 2^{-j}y) - (K * \psi_k)(2^{-j}x)| \, dx$$

$$= \sum_j \int_{|x|>2^{1-j}|y|} |(K * \psi_k)(x - 2^{-j}y) - (K * \psi_k)(x)| \, dx$$

$$= \sum_j I_j,$$

where I_j denotes the j-th summand. If we make the change of variables $y \mapsto 2y$ then I_j becomes I_{j-1}. Since this does not affect the sum, we may assume that $1 \le |y| \le 2$.

We have several different estimates for the I_j's. First, by the mean value theorem,

$$I_j \le \int_{\mathbb{R}^n} \int_{\mathbb{R}^n} |K(z)||\psi_k(x - 2^{-j}y - z) - \psi_k(x - z)| \, dz \, dx$$

$$\le \int_{\mathbb{R}^n} |K(z)| \int_{\mathbb{R}^n} |\psi_k(x - 2^{-j}y) - \psi_k(x)| \, dx \, dz$$

$$\le C\|K\|_1 2^{-j-k}.$$

We will use this estimate if $k + j \ge 0$; if $k + j < 0$ then from the first inequality we get the better estimate $I_j \le C$.

To get the third estimate we may assume without loss of generality that the support of K is contained in $B(0, 1)$. But then

$$I_j \le 2 \int_{|x|>2^{-j}} |(K * \psi_k)(x)| \, dx$$

$$\le 2 \int_{|z|\le 1} |K(z)| \int_{|x|>2^{-j-k}} |\psi(x - 2^{-k}z)| \, dx \, dz.$$

If $j < 0$ then $|x| > 2|2^{-k}z|$, so that $|x - 2^{-k}z| > |x|/2$. Hence,

$$I_j \le 2\|K\|_1 \int_{|x|>2^{-j-k-1}} |\psi(x)| \, dx \le C2^{j+k}.$$

From these estimates we get the following: if $k \ge 0$,

$$\sum_{j=-\infty}^{\infty} I_j \le C \left(\sum_{j=-k}^{\infty} 2^{-j-k} + \sum_{j=-\infty}^{-k-1} 2^{j+k} \right) \le C;$$

if $k < 0$,

$$\sum_{j=-\infty}^{\infty} I_j \le C \left(\sum_{j=|k|}^{\infty} 2^{-j-k} + \sum_{j=0}^{|k|-1} 1 + \sum_{j=-\infty}^{-1} 2^{j+k} \right) \le C(1 + |k|).$$

This completes the proof. $\qquad\square$

Theorem 8.19 has several applications. The first is a simpler proof of Theorem 4.12; it requires the following lemma.

Lemma 8.20. *If* $\Omega \in L^q(S^{n-1})$, $q > 1$, *and*

$$K(x) = \frac{\Omega(x')}{|x|^n} \chi_{\{1<|x|\le 2\}},$$

then for $a < 1/q'$

$$|\hat{K}(\xi)| \leq C|\xi|^{-a}.$$

Proof. If we rewrite the Fourier transform in polar coordinates we get

$$\hat{K}(\xi) = \int_{S^{n-1}} \Omega(u) \int_1^2 e^{-2\pi i r(u\cdot\xi)} \frac{dr}{r} d\sigma(u) = \int_{S^{n-1}} \Omega(u) I(u\cdot\xi) \, d\sigma(u),$$

where

$$I(t) = \int_1^2 e^{-2\pi i r t} \frac{dr}{r}.$$

Since $|I(t)| \leq \min(1, |t|^{-1})$, we have that $|I(t)| \leq |t|^{-a}$, $0 \leq a \leq 1$. Hence,

$$|\hat{K}(\xi)| \leq |\xi|^{-a} \int_{S^{n-1}} |\Omega(u)||u\cdot\xi'|^{-a} \, d\sigma(u)$$

$$\leq |\xi|^{-a} \|\Omega\|_q \left(\int_{S^{n-1}} |u\cdot\xi|^{-aq'} \, d\sigma(u) \right)^{1/q'}.$$

The last integral does not depend on ξ' and is convergent if $aq' < 1$. □

Corollary 8.21. *If* $\Omega \in L^q(S^{n-1})$, $q > 1$, *and* $\int \Omega(u) \, d\sigma(u) = 0$, *then the singular integral*

$$Tf(x) = \text{p.\,v.} \int_{\mathbb{R}^n} \frac{\Omega(y')}{|y|^n} f(x-y) \, dy$$

is bounded on L^p, $1 < p < \infty$.

If we define K as in Lemma 8.20 then

$$Tf = \sum_{j=-\infty}^{\infty} K_j * f$$

and the desired result follows immediately from Theorem 8.19.

Our second application is to a family of square functions.

Corollary 8.22. *If* K *and* K_j *are defined as in Theorem 8.19 then the square function*

$$g(f) = \left(\sum_{j=-\infty}^{\infty} |K_j * f|^2 \right)^{1/2}$$

is bounded on L^p, $1 < p < \infty$.

Proof. First note that given a sequence $\epsilon = \{\epsilon_j\}$ such that for each j, $\epsilon_j = \pm 1$, if we define the operator

$$T_\epsilon f = \sum_j \epsilon_j K_j * f,$$

then it follows from the proof of Theorem 8.19 that $\|T_\epsilon f\|_p \leq C_p \|f\|_p$ with the constant C_p independent of ϵ.

Recall that the Rademacher functions are defined as follows:

$$r_0(t) = \begin{cases} -1, & 0 \leq t < 1/2, \\ 1, & 1/2 \leq t < 1, \end{cases}$$

and for $j \geq 1$, $r_j(t) = r_0(2^j t)$. (We extend r_0 to all of $\mathbb{R}$ as a periodic function.) The Rademacher functions form an orthonormal system in $L^2([0,1])$; furthermore, if

$$F(t) = \sum_{j=0}^{\infty} a_j r_j(t) \in L^2([0,1])$$

then $F \in L^p([0,1])$, $1 < p < \infty$, and there exist positive constants A_p and B_p such that

$$A_p \|F\|_p \leq \|F\|_2 = \left(\sum_{j=0}^{\infty} |a_j|^2 \right)^{1/2} \leq B_p \|F\|_p.$$

(See Stein [**15**, p. 104].) Therefore,

$$g(f)(x)^p = \left(\sum_j |K_j * f(x)|^2 \right)^{p/2} \leq B_p^p \int_0^1 \left| \sum_j r_j(t) K_j * f(x) \right|^p dt.$$

If we integrate with respect to x and apply Fubini's theorem, then for each t we have an operator like T_ϵ, so the desired inequality follows by the above observation. $\square$

For our final application, note that in the statement of Theorem 8.19 and Corollary 8.22 we can replace $K \in L^1$ by a finite Borel measure with compact support whose Fourier transform decays quickly enough.

Corollary 8.23. *If μ is a finite Borel measure with compact support and such that for some $a > 0$,*

$$|\hat{\mu}(\xi)| \leq C|\xi|^{-a},$$

then the maximal function

$$\mathcal{M}f(x) = \sup_j \left| \int_{\mathbb{R}^n} f(x - 2^j y) \, d\mu(y) \right|$$

is bounded on L^p, $1 < p \leq \infty$.

Proof. Let $\phi \in \mathcal{S}(\mathbb{R}^n)$ have compact support and be such that $\hat{\phi}(0) = 1$. Define the measure $\sigma = \mu - \hat{\mu}(0)\phi$; then σ satisfies the hypotheses of Theorem 8.19. Therefore, from the definition of $\mathcal{M}$ and from Proposition 2.7 we have that

$$\mathcal{M}f(x) \leq \sup_j |\sigma_j * f(x)| + |\hat{\mu}(0)| \sup_j \left| \int_{\mathbb{R}^n} f(x - 2^j y)\phi(y)\, dy \right|$$

$$\leq \left(\sum_j |\sigma_j * f(x)|^2 \right)^{1/2} + |\hat{\mu}(0)| M f(x),$$

where M is the Hardy-Littlewood maximal operator. By Corollary 8.22 the square function in the last term is bounded on L^p, so we are done. $\square$

If μ is Lebesgue measure on the unit sphere S^{n-1} then the integral

$$\int_{\mathbb{R}^n} f(x - 2^j y)\, d\mu(y)$$

is the average of f on the sphere centered at x with radius 2^{-j}. In this case the corresponding maximal function is called the dyadic spherical maximal function. Since

$$|\hat{\mu}(\xi)| \leq C|\xi|^{(-n+1)/2}$$

(apply Lemma 8.18 with f_0 replaced by the Dirac delta at 1), Corollary 8.23 immediately implies the following result.

Corollary 8.24. *If $n \geq 2$ then the dyadic spherical maximal function is bounded on L^p, $1 < p \leq \infty$.*

7. The maximal function and the Hilbert transform along a parabola

Let L be the parabolic operator

$$Lu = \frac{\partial u}{\partial x_2} - \frac{\partial^2 u}{\partial x_1^2}.$$

If we take the Fourier transform then, arguing as in Chapter 4, Section 5, we get

$$\frac{\partial u}{\partial x_2} = T_1(Lu), \qquad \frac{\partial^2 u}{\partial x_1^2} = T_2(Lu),$$

where

$$(T_1 f)\hat{\ }(\xi_1, \xi_2) = \frac{2\pi i \xi_2}{2\pi i \xi_2 + 4\pi^2 |\xi_1|^2} \hat{f}(\xi_1, \xi_2),$$

$$(T_2 f)\hat{\ }(\xi_1, \xi_2) = \frac{4\pi^2 |\xi_1|^2}{2\pi i \xi_2 + 4\pi^2 |\xi_1|^2} \hat{f}(\xi_1, \xi_2).$$

Unlike the multipliers we considered in Chapter 4, these multipliers are not homogeneous of degree 0. However, they do satisfy the following condition:

$$m(\lambda \xi_1, \lambda^2 \xi_2) = m(\xi_1, \xi_2), \quad \lambda > 0.$$

By an argument analogous to the proof of Proposition 4.3, we can show that if $K(x_1, x_2)$ is the Fourier transform of m then K satisfies the homogeneity condition

$$K(\lambda x_1, \lambda^2 x_2) = \lambda^{-3} K(x_1, x_2), \quad \lambda > 0.$$

This example leads us to consider operators of the following type. Given $(x_1, x_2) \in \mathbb{R}^2 \setminus \{(0,0)\}$, there exist unique values $r > 0$ and $\theta \in S^1$ such that $x_1 = r \cos(\theta)$ and $x_2 = r^2 \sin(\theta)$. Define $\Omega(\theta) = K(\cos(\theta), \sin(\theta))$; then $K(x_1, x_2) = r^{-3} \Omega(\theta)$. Define the operator T by

$$Tf(x_1, x_2)$$

$$= \mathrm{p.\,v.} \int_{\mathbb{R}^2} K(y_1, y_2) f(x_1 - y_1, x_2 - y_2)\, dy_1 dy_2$$

$$= \mathrm{p.\,v.} \int_0^\infty \int_0^{2\pi} \frac{\Omega(\theta)}{r} f(x_1 - r\cos(\theta), x_2 - r^2 \sin(\theta))(1 + \sin^2(\theta))\, dr d\theta.$$

If $\Omega(\theta + \pi) = -\Omega(\theta)$ (i.e. if K is odd), then by the same argument as we used in the method of rotations (see Corollary 4.8),

$$Tf(x_1, x_2) = \int_0^\pi \Omega(\theta) H_\theta(x_1, x_2)(1 + \sin^2(\theta))\, d\theta,$$

where

$$H_\theta f(x_1, x_2) = \mathrm{p.\,v.} \int_{\mathbb{R}} f(x_1 - r\cos(\theta), x_2 - r^2 \,\mathrm{sgn}(r) \sin(\theta)) \frac{dr}{r}.$$

The operator H_θ is the Hilbert transform along the (odd) parabola $(r\cos(\theta), r^2 \,\mathrm{sgn}(r) \sin(\theta))$, $r \in \mathbb{R}$. (When $\theta = 0$ or $\pi/2$ this is a line and we get the usual Hilbert transform.) By the proof of Proposition 4.6, if $\Omega \in L^1(S^1)$ and if the operators H_θ were uniformly bounded on L^p, then T would also be bounded.

For simplicity, the remainder of this section is devoted to proving that the Hilbert transform and the maximal function along the parabola $\Gamma(t) = (t, t^2)$ are bounded on $L^p(\mathbb{R}^2)$, $1 < p < \infty$. More precisely, we will consider

$$H_\Gamma(x_1, x_2) = \mathrm{p.\,v.} \int_{\mathbb{R}} f(x_1 - t, x_2 - t^2) \frac{dt}{t},$$

$$M_\Gamma(x_1, x_2) = \sup_{h>0} \left| \frac{1}{2h} \int_{-h}^{h} f(x_1 - t, x_2 - t^2)\, dt \right|.$$

A similar argument shows that the operators H_θ are uniformly bounded.

Our approach will be to decompose the operators H_Γ and M_Γ in a way similar to the decomposition done in the previous section. For $j \in \mathbb{Z}$, let σ_j and μ_j be finite measures which act on a continuous function g by

$$(8.15) \qquad \sigma_j(g) = \int_{2^j < |t| < 2^{j+1}} g(t, t^2) \frac{dt}{t},$$

$$(8.16) \qquad \mu_j(g) = \frac{1}{2^{j+1}} \int_{2^j < |t| < 2^{j+1}} g(t, t^2) \, dt.$$

Then

$$(8.17) \qquad H_\Gamma f = \sum_{-\infty}^{\infty} \sigma_j * f,$$

and

$$(8.18) \qquad M_\Gamma f \le 2 \sup_j \mu_j * |f|;$$

the latter inequality holds since if $2^j \le h < 2^{j+1}$ then

$$\left| \frac{1}{2h} \int_{-h}^{h} f(x_1 - t, x_2 - t^2) \, dt \right| \le \frac{1}{2^{j+1}} \sum_{i=-\infty}^{j} 2^{i+1} \mu_i * |f|.$$

Using these decompositions, we will derive the boundedness of H_Γ and M_Γ from two more general results. Hereafter, given a measure σ, let $|\sigma|$ denote its total variation measure and let $\|\sigma\|$ denote its total variation.

Theorem 8.25. *Let $\{\sigma_j\}_{j \in \mathbb{Z}}$ be a sequence of finite Borel measures with $\|\sigma_j\| \le C$ and such that for some $a > 0$*

$$(8.19) \qquad |\hat{\sigma}_j(\xi)| \le C \min(|2^j \xi_1|^a, |2^j \xi_1|^{-a}).$$

If the operator

$$\sigma^*(f) = \sup_j \||\sigma_j| * f|$$

is a bounded operator on L^q for some $q > 1$, then the operators

$$T f = \sum_{j=-\infty}^{\infty} \sigma_j * f \quad and \quad g(f) = \left(\sum_{j=-\infty}^{\infty} |\sigma_j * f|^2 \right)^2$$

are bounded on L^p provided $|1/p - 1/2| < 1/2q$.

Proof. Define the operator S_j by $(S_j)^{\hat{}}(\xi) = \chi_{\Delta_j}(\xi_1) \hat{f}(\xi)$, where

$$\Delta_j = (-2^{j+1}, -2^j] \cup [2^j, 2^{j+1}).$$

Then

$$Tf = \sum_{k=-\infty}^{\infty} T_k f,$$

where

$$T_k f = \sum_{j=-\infty}^{\infty} \sigma_j * S_{j+k} f.$$

We can now argue as we did in proving (8.13) in Theorem 8.19: by applying the Plancherel theorem and (8.19) we get

$$(8.20) \qquad \|T_k f\|_2 \leq C 2^{-a|k|} \|f\|_2.$$

Define p_0 by $1/2 - 1/p_0 = 1/2q$; equivalently, $q = (p_0/2)'$. We will first prove that

$$(8.21) \qquad \left\| \left(\sum_j |\sigma_j * g_j|^2 \right)^{1/2} \right\|_{p_0} \leq C \left\| \left(\sum_j |g_j|^2 \right)^{1/2} \right\|_{p_0}.$$

Since $|\sigma_j * g|^2 \leq \|\sigma_j\|(|\sigma_j| * |g_j|^2)$, and since the square of the left-hand side of (8.21) is the $p_0/2$ norm of $\sum |\sigma_j * g|^2$, by duality there exists $u \in L^q$, $\|u\|_q = 1$, such that the left-hand side equals

$$\int_{\mathbb{R}^2} \sum_j |\sigma_j * g_j|^2 u \leq C \sum_j \int_{\mathbb{R}^2} (|\sigma_j| * |g_j|^2) u \leq C \sum_j \int_{\mathbb{R}^2} |g_j|^2 \sigma^*(u).$$

Inequality (8.21) now follows by Hölder's inequality and our hypothesis on σ^*. Therefore, since $S_i S_j f = 0$ unless $i = j$, by Theorem 8.4 and inequality (8.21),

$$\|T_k f\|_{p_0} \leq C \left\| \left(\sum_{j=-\infty}^{\infty} |\sigma_j * S_{j+k} f|^2 \right)^{1/2} \right\|_{p_0}$$

$$\leq C \left\| \left(\sum_{j=-\infty}^{\infty} |S_{j+k} f|^2 \right)^{1/2} \right\|_{p_0}$$

$$\leq C \|f\|_{p_0}.$$

If we interpolate between this and inequality (8.20) and sum in k we get that T is bounded on L^p for $2 \leq p < p_0$. Then by duality we get the desired result.

Finally, the boundedness of $g(f)$ follows by the same argument as in the proof of Corollary 8.22. $\qquad \square$

Theorem 8.26. *Let $\{\mu_j\}$ be a sequence of positive Borel measures on $\mathbb{R}^2$ with $\|\mu_j\| \leq C$ and such that for some $a > 0$*

$$(8.22) \qquad\qquad |\hat{\mu}_j(\xi)| \leq C|2^j\xi_1|^{-a},$$

$$(8.23) \qquad\qquad |\hat{\mu}_j(\xi) - \hat{\mu}_j(0,\xi_2)| \leq C|2^j\xi_1|^a.$$

Let

$$\mathcal{M}_2 f = \sup_j |\mu_j^2 * f|$$

be a maximal operator in the variable x_2, where the measures μ_j^2 have Fourier transforms $\hat{\mu}_j(0,\xi_2)$. If $\mathcal{M}_2$ is bounded on $L^p(\mathbb{R})$, $1 < p \leq \infty$, then the maximal operator

$$\mathcal{M}f(x) = \sup_j |\mu_j * f(x)|$$

is also bounded on $L^p(\mathbb{R}^2)$, $1 < p \leq \infty$.

Proof. Fix $\phi \in \mathcal{S}(\mathbb{R})$ such that $\hat{\phi}(0) = 1$, and for each j define the measure $\tilde{\sigma}_j$ by

$$\widehat{\tilde{\sigma}_j}(\xi) = \hat{\mu}_j(\xi) - \hat{\mu}_j(0,\xi_2)\hat{\phi}(2^j\xi_1).$$

Then the $\tilde{\sigma}_j$'s satisfy the hypotheses of Theorem 8.25: for the estimate with negative exponent in (8.19) use (8.22) and bound $|\hat{\phi}(t)|$ by Ct^{-a}; for the estimate with positive exponent, add and subtract $\hat{\mu}_j(0,\xi_2)$ and apply the mean value theorem. Let $\tilde{g}$ and $\tilde{\sigma}^*$ be the associated operators. Then if we argue exactly as we did in the proof of Corollary 8.23 we get that

$$(8.24) \qquad\qquad \mathcal{M}f(x) \leq \tilde{g}(f)(x) + C\mathcal{M}_2 M_1 f(x),$$

$$(8.25) \qquad\qquad \tilde{\sigma}^*(f)(x) \leq \mathcal{M}f(x) + C\mathcal{M}_2 M_1 f(x),$$

where M_1 is the Hardy-Littlewood maximal operator in the first variable.

By the Plancherel theorem, $\tilde{g}(f)$ is bounded on L^2. Therefore, by (8.24) and our hypothesis on $\mathcal{M}_2$, $\mathcal{M}$ is also bounded on L^2, so by (8.25), $\tilde{\sigma}^*(f)$ is bounded on L^2. Hence, by Theorem 8.25, $\tilde{g}(f)$ is bounded on L^p for $4/3 < p < 4$. But then from (8.24) and (8.25) we have that $\mathcal{M}$ and $\tilde{\sigma}^*$ are also bounded on this range. Theorem 8.25 then gives us that $\tilde{g}$ is bounded on $8/7 < p < 8$. If we apply this "boot-strapping" argument repeatedly, we get that $\mathcal{M}$, $\tilde{\sigma}^*$ and $\tilde{g}$ are bounded on L^p, $1 < p < \infty$. $\qquad\square$

In order to apply these theorems to the operators H_Γ and M_Γ, we need to estimate the Fourier transforms of the measures σ_j and μ_j defined in (8.17) and (8.18). We can estimate these oscillatory integrals using Van der Corput's lemma; because this result is of independent interest we give its proof.

Lemma 8.27 (Van der Corput's Lemma). *Let*

$$I(a,b) = \int_a^b e^{ih(t)}\,dt.$$

Then

(1) *if* $|h'(t)| \geq \lambda > 0$ *and* h' *is monotonic,*

$$|I(a,b)| \leq C\lambda^{-1};$$

(2) *if* $h \in C^k([a,b])$ *and* $|h^{(k)}(t)| \geq \lambda > 0,$

$$|I(a,b)| \leq C\lambda^{-1/k}.$$

In either case the constants are independent of a *and* b.

Proof. (1) If we integrate by parts we get

$$I(a,b) = \int_a^b ih'(t)e^{ih(t)} \cdot \frac{dt}{ih'(t)} = \frac{e^{ih(b)}}{ih'(b)} - \frac{e^{ih(a)}}{ih'(a)} + i\int_a^b e^{ih(t)}d\left(\frac{1}{h'(t)}\right).$$

Therefore, since h' is monotonic,

$$|I(a,b)| \leq \frac{2}{\lambda} + \int_a^b \left| d\left(\frac{1}{h'(t)}\right)\right| = \frac{2}{\lambda} + \left|\int_a^b d\left(\frac{1}{h'(t)}\right)\right| \leq \frac{4}{\lambda}.$$

(2) We will prove this for $k = 2$; for $k > 2$ the result follows by induction. First, without loss of generality we may assume that $h''(t) \geq \lambda > 0$. Then $h'(t)$ is increasing and $h'(t_0) = 0$ for at most one $t_0 \in (a,b)$. If such a t_0 exists, for $\delta > 0$ define

$$J_1 = \{t \in (a,b) : t < t_0 - \delta\},$$
$$J_2 = (t_0 - \delta, t_0 + \delta) \cap (a,b),$$
$$J_3 = \{t \in (a,b) : t > t_0 + \delta\}.$$

(Some of these may be empty.) On J_1 and J_3, $|h'(t)| \geq \lambda\delta$, so arguing as in (1) we get

$$\left|\int_{J_1 \cup J_3} e^{ih(t)}\,dt\right| \leq 8(\lambda\delta)^{-1}.$$

The integral on J_2 is less than 2δ, so if we let $\delta = \lambda^{-1/2}$ we get the desired result.

If h' is never 0 on (a,b) then we can apply a similar argument with a or b in place of t_0, depending on whether h' is positive or negative. $\square$

Lemma 8.28. *Let*

$$I(b) = \int_1^b e^{i(t\xi_1 + t^2\xi_2)}\,dt.$$

Then for $1 < b < 2$ *and* $|\xi_1| > 1$, $|I(b)| \leq C|\xi_1|^{-1/2}.$

Proof. Let $h(t) = t\xi_1 + t^2\xi_2$. When $|\xi_1| \geq 8|\xi_2|$, $|h'(t)| = |\xi_1 + 2t\xi_2| \geq |\xi_1|/2$, so by Van der Corput's lemma, $|I(b)| \leq C|\xi_1|^{-1} \leq C|\xi_1|^{-1/2}$, where the second inequality follows from our assumption on ξ_1.

By the same lemma, since $h''(t) = 2\xi_2$, $|I(b)| \leq C|\xi_2|^{-1/2}$ for any ξ_1 and ξ_2. When $|\xi_1| \leq 8|\xi_2|$, this implies that $|I(b)| \leq C|\xi_1|^{-1/2}$. $\qquad\square$

We can now use Theorems 8.25 and 8.26 to prove the desired result.

Corollary 8.29. *The operators H_Γ and M_Γ are bounded on $L^p(\mathbb{R}^2)$ for $1 < p < \infty$ and $1 < p \leq \infty$ respectively.*

Proof. Let σ_j, μ_j be as in (8.15) and (8.16). Then by Lemma 8.28, for $|\xi_1| > 1$ we have that

$$|\hat{\mu}_0(\xi)|, \ |\hat{\sigma}_0(\xi)| \leq C|\xi_1|^{-1/2}.$$

(To get the estimate for $\hat{\sigma}_0$ use integration by parts.) Then from the relations

$$\hat{\mu}_j(\xi) = \hat{\mu}_0(2^j\xi_1, 2^{2j}\xi_2), \quad \hat{\sigma}_j(\xi) = \hat{\sigma}_0(2^j\xi_1, 2^{2j}\xi_2),$$

we get

$$|\hat{\mu}_j(\xi)|, \ |\hat{\sigma}_j(\xi)| \leq C|2^j\xi_1|^{-1/2}, \quad |2^j\xi_1| > 1.$$

The estimates

$$|\hat{\sigma}_j(\xi)|, \ |\hat{\mu}_j(\xi) - \hat{\mu}_j(0, \xi_2)| \leq C|2^j\xi_1|$$

follow immediately from the definition.

The maximal operator $\mathcal{M}_2$ of Theorem 8.26 here becomes

$$\sup_j \frac{1}{2^{j+1}} \left| \int_{2^j \leq |t| \leq 2^{j+1}} g(x_2 - t^2)\, dt \right|.$$

If we make the change of variables $s = t^2$ we see that $\mathcal{M}_2$ is dominated by the one-dimensional Hardy-Littlewood maximal function and so is bounded on $L^p(\mathbb{R})$, $1 < p < \infty$. Therefore, by Theorem 8.26, M_Γ is bounded on $L^p(\mathbb{R}^2)$, $1 < p \leq \infty$.

Finally, the maximal operator σ^* in Theorem 8.25 satisfies $\sigma^*(f) \leq M_\Gamma f$, so by that result it follows that H_Γ is bounded on $L^p(\mathbb{R}^2)$, $1 < p < \infty$. $\quad\square$

8. Notes and further results

8.1. References.

The original results of J. E. Littlewood and R. A. E. C. Paley are found in *Theorems on Fourier series and power series, I* (J. London Math. Soc. **6** (1931), 230–233) and *Theorems on Fourier series and power series, II* (Proc. London Math. Soc. **42** (1936), 52–89). They used techniques from complex variables. (See Zygmund [**21**].) The approach taken here is derived from A. Benedek, A. P. Calderón and R. Panzone (*Convolution operators with Banach-space valued functions*, Proc. Nat. Acad. Sci. U.S.A. **48** (1962), 356–365). Also see J. L. Rubio de Francia, F. J. Ruiz and J. L. Torrea (*Calderón-Zygmund theory for operator-valued kernels*, Adv. in Math. **62** (1986), 7–48.) The Hörmander multiplier theorem first appeared in *Estimates for translation invariant operators in L^p-spaces* (Acta Math. **104** (1960), 93–139). The Marcinkiewicz multiplier theorem can be found in *Sur les multiplicateurs des séries de Fourier* (Studia Math. **8** (1939), 78–91). The proofs given in the text are different from the originals. In Hörmander's theorem it can also be shown that the multiplier is weak $(1, 1)$. Bochner-Riesz multipliers were introduced by S. Bochner (*Summation of multiple Fourier series by spherical means*, Trans. Amer. Math. Soc. **40** (1936), 175–207). The methods in Sections 6 and 7 are adapted from J. Duoandikoetxea and J. L. Rubio de Francia (*Maximal and singular integral operators via Fourier transform estimates*, Invent. Math. **84** (1986), 541–561). For references on singular integrals and maximal functions on curves, see Section 8.8 below. Van der Corput's lemma originally appeared in *Zahlentheoretische Abschätzungen* (Math. Ann. **84** (1921), 53–79).

There are other versions of the Littlewood-Paley theory (with different square functions and with continuous parameter) which can be found, for example, in Stein [**15**, Chapter 4].

Theorem 8.6 can be thought of as a characterization of L^p spaces via the Littlewood-Paley decomposition given by $\{S_j f\}$. In a similar way many other spaces—including Besov spaces and Triebel-Lizorkin spaces—can be characterized using different mixed norm inequalities for the Littlewood-Paley decomposition. For more information see, for instance, the books by M. Frazier, B. Jawerth and G. Weiss (*Littlewood-Paley theory and the study of function spaces*, CBMS Regional Conference Series in Mathematics **79**, Amer. Math. Soc., Providence, 1991) and H. Triebel (*Theory of function spaces II*, Birkhäuser, Basel, 1992).

8.2. Other Littlewood-Paley inequalities.

Theorem 8.30. *Let $\{I_j\}$ be any sequence of disjoint intervals in $\mathbb{R}$, and define the operator S_j by $(S_j f)\hat{}(\xi) = \chi_{I_j}(\xi)\hat{f}(\xi)$. Then for $2 \leq p < \infty$,*

$$\left\| \left(\sum_j |S_j f|^2 \right)^{1/2} \right\|_p \leq C_p \|f\|_p.$$

When $I_j = (j, j + 1)$ this theorem was first proved by L. Carleson (*On the Littlewood-Paley theorem*, Report, Mittag-Leffler Inst., Djursholm,

1967); new proofs were later given by A. Córdoba (*Some remarks on the Littlewood-Paley theory*, Rend. Circ. Mat. Palermo **1** (1981), suppl., 75–80) and J. L. Rubio de Francia (*Estimates for some square functions of Littlewood-Paley type*, Publ. Mat. **27** (1983), 81–108). The general result is due to J. L. Rubio de Francia (*A Littlewood-Paley inequality for arbitrary intervals*, Rev. Mat. Iberoamericana **1** (1985), 1–14), and another proof is due to J. Bourgain (*On square functions on the trigonometric system*, Bull. Soc. Math. Belg. Sér. B **37** (1985), 20–26). By taking $\hat{f}_N = \chi_{[0,N]}$ one can see that this result is false if $1 < p < 2$.

A generalization of Theorem 8.30 in $\mathbb{R}^n$ is due to J. L. Journé (*Calderón-Zygmund operators on product spaces*, Rev. Mat. Iberoamericana **1** (1985), 55–91). His proof is quite difficult, especially when compared to the proof for $n = 1$. Simpler proofs were later given by P. Sjölin (*A note on Littlewood-Paley decompositions with arbitrary intervals*, J. Approx. Theory **48** (1986), 328–334), F. Soria (*A note on a Littlewood-Paley inequality for arbitrary intervals in $\mathbb{R}^2$*, J. London Math. Soc. **36** (1987), 137–142), and S. Sato (*Note on a Littlewood-Paley operator in higher dimensions*, J. London Math. Soc. **42** (1990), 527–534).

Theorem 8.30 can be used to improve the Marcinkiewicz multiplier theorem (Theorem 8.13).

Theorem 8.31. *If m is bounded and m^2 is of bounded variation on each dyadic interval in $\mathbb{R}$, then m is a multiplier on L^p, $1 < p < \infty$.*

This result is due to R. Coifman, J. L. Rubio de Francia and S. Semmes (*Multiplicateurs de Fourier de $L^p(\mathbb{R})$ et estimations quadratiques*, C. R. Acad. Sci. Paris **306** (1988), 351–354).

In $\mathbb{R}^2$ one can prove an "angular" Littlewood-Paley theorem: let Δ_j be the region bounded by the lines with slopes 2^j and 2^{j+1}, and define S_j by $(S_j f)\hat{\ }(\xi) = \chi_{\Delta_j}(\xi)\hat{f}(\xi)$. Then for $1 < p < \infty$,

$$\left\| \left(\sum_j |S_j f|^2 \right)^{1/2} \right\|_p \le C_p \|f\|_p.$$

This result is due to A. Nagel, E. M. Stein and S. Wainger (*Differentiation in lacunary directions*, Proc. Nat. Acad. Sci. U.S.A. **75** (1978), 1060–1062).

There are also weighted versions of the Littlewood-Paley inequalities. Theorem 8.6 is true in $L^p(w)$ when $w \in A_p$. This was proved by D. Kurtz (*Littlewood-Paley and multiplier theorems on weighted L^p spaces*, Trans. Amer. Math. Soc. **259** (1980), 235–254) for ψ supported in an annulus, but his result can be extended to ψ as in Theorem 8.6. The proof of Theorem 8.30 by Rubio de Francia actually gives a weighted version with $A_{p/2}$ weights when $p > 2$; the proof is based on techniques introduced in his paper with Ruiz and Torrea cited in Section 8.1. The same result in higher dimensions was proved by H. Lin (*Some weighted inequalities on product domains,* Trans. Amer. Math. Soc. **318** (1990), 69–85). It is not known whether the weighted version of Theorem 8.30 is true in $L^2(w)$ with $w \in A_1$; however, it is true in the special case of equally spaced intervals (see the paper by Rubio de Francia in Publ. Mat. cited above.)

8.3. The multiplier of the ball and Bochner-Riesz multipliers.

In dimension $n \geq 2$, the multiplier of the ball exhibits the worst possible behavior.

Theorem 8.32. *The characteristic function of a (Euclidean) ball in $\mathbb{R}^n$, $n \geq 2$, is not a multiplier on L^p if $p \neq 2$.*

This negative result was proved by C. Fefferman (*The multiplier problem for the ball,* Ann. of Math. **94** (1972), 330–336). This is much stronger than what can be proved using Lemmas 8.17 and 8.18: this approach only shows that it is not a multiplier if $|1/p - 1/2| \geq 1/2n$. However, it is a multiplier when restricted to radial functions in L^p if $|1/p - 1/2| < 1/2n$. This is due to C. S. Herz (*On the mean inversion of Fourier and Hankel transforms,* Proc. Nat. Acad. Sci. U.S.A. **40** (1954), 996–999).

For $a > 0$, the sufficient condition in Theorem 8.14 was first proved by E. M. Stein (*Interpolation of linear operators,* Trans. Amer. Math. Soc. **83** (1956), 482–492) using Theorem 1.22. In this result we omit a range of values for p when $0 < a < (n-1)/2$. Despite the negative result for $a = 0$ (the multiplier of the ball), it is conjectured that T^a is a bounded operator on L^p when

$$(8.26) \qquad \left| \frac{1}{p} - \frac{1}{2} \right| < \frac{2a+1}{2n}.$$

This has only been fully proved in $\mathbb{R}^2$. The first proof was given by L. Carleson and P. Sjölin (*Oscillatory integrals and a multiplier problem for the disc,* Studia Math. **44** (1972), 287–299). Additional proofs were given by L. Hörmander (*Oscillatory integrals and multipliers on FL^p,* Ark. Mat. **11** (1973), 1–11), C. Fefferman (*A note on spherical summation multipliers,* Israel J. Math. **15** (1973), 44–52) and A. Córdoba (*A note on Bochner-Riesz operators,* Duke Math. J. **46** (1979), 505–511).

In higher dimensions, the first result proving the boundedness of T^a for the full range of values of p given by (8.26) for some values of $a < (n-1)/2$ is due to C. Fefferman (*Inequalities for strongly singular convolution operators,* Acta Math. **124** (1970), 9–36). He showed it for $a > (n-1)/4$. An important aspect of his proof is that it introduced the connection between Bochner-Riesz multipliers and the restriction of the Fourier transform to spheres. In the next section we give stronger results derived using this connection.

All of these results can be found in the book by K. M. Davis and Y. C. Chang [**3**].

Bochner-Riesz multipliers give rise to a family of summability methods for the Fourier transform. Besides norm convergence, we can also consider pointwise convergence, that is, whether

$$(8.27) \qquad \lim_{R \to \infty} T_R^a f(x) = f(x) \quad \text{a.e.},$$

where

$$(T_R^a f)\widehat{\;}(\xi) = \left(1 - \frac{|\xi^2|}{R^2}\right)_+^a \hat{f}(\xi).$$

The usual way to study pointwise convergence is via the associated maximal operator $(T^a)^* f(x) = \sup_{R>0} |T_R^a f(x)|$ (see Chapter 2, Section 2). For a greater than the critical index $(n-1)/2$, $(T^a)^*$ is bounded by the Hardy-Littlewood maximal operator and pointwise convergence follows immediately. For $a < (n-1)/2$ partial results are known. When $n = 2$ and $p \geq 2$, (8.27) holds in the range given by (8.26). See the paper by A. Carbery (*The boundedness of the maximal Bochner-Riesz operator on $L^4(\mathbb{R}^2)$*), Duke Math. J. **50** (1983), 409–416). The same result for $n \geq 3$, $p \geq 2$, and $a \geq (n-1)/2(n+1)$ is due to M. Christ (*On almost everywhere convergence of Bochner-Riesz means in higher dimensions*, Proc. Amer. Math. Soc. **95** (1985), 16–20). Both results were proved by showing that $(T^a)^*$ is bounded on L^p for the corresponding values of p. A. Carbery, J. L. Rubio de Francia and L. Vega (*Almost everywhere summability of Fourier integrals*, J. London Math. Soc. **38** (1988), 513–524) proved that $(T^a)^*$ is bounded on the weighted space $L^2(|x|^{-\beta})$ if $0 \leq \beta < 1 + 2a \leq n$, and deduced almost everywhere convergence in these spaces. For those $p \geq 2$ such that (8.26) holds, there exist $\beta < 1 + 2a$ for which $L^p \subset L^2 + L^2(|x|^{-\beta})$, so (8.27) holds for all such p. Note that this gives us the almost everywhere convergence of Bochner-Riesz means on a larger range of values of p than that for which we know the boundedness of T^a (and *a fortiori* of $(T^a)^*$).

8.4. Restriction theorems.

If $f \in L^1$ then $\hat{f}$ is continuous and bounded, so for any $S \subset \mathbb{R}^n$, $\|\hat{f}\|_{L^\infty(S)} \leq \|f\|_{L^1(\mathbb{R}^n)}$. In general, however, if $f \in L^p(\mathbb{R}^n)$ for some $p > 1$ and S has measure 0 we cannot, *a priori*, define $\hat{f}$ on S since it is only defined almost everywhere. But if for, say, $f \in C_c^\infty$ we have the estimate $\|\hat{f}\|_{L^q(S)} \leq C_{p,q}\|f\|_{L^p(\mathbb{R}^n)}$, then by continuity, if $f \in L^p$ we can define the restriction of $\hat{f}$ to S as an L^q function. If S is contained in a hyperplane then this estimate only holds for $p = 1$. Surprisingly, it is possible to get nontrivial restriction estimates for some S with non-zero curvature.

The case $S = S^{n-1}$, the unit sphere in $\mathbb{R}^n$, is of particular interest because it is related to Bochner-Riesz multipliers as the following theorem of C. Fefferman shows (see the Acta paper cited above).

Theorem 8.33. *If for some $p > 1$,*

$$\|\hat{f}\|_{L^2(S^{n-1})} \leq C_{p,2}\|f\|_{L^p(\mathbb{R}^n)}, \tag{8.28}$$

then T^a is bounded on L^p for all a such that (8.26) holds.

C. Fefferman proved the restriction inequality for $1 < p < 4n/(3n + 1)$, which gives the condition $a > (n - 1)/4$ mentioned above. This result was improved by P. Tomas (*A restriction theorem for the Fourier transform*, Bull. Amer. Math. Soc. **81** (1975), 477–478), developing earlier work of E. M. Stein.

Theorem 8.34 (Tomas-Stein). *Inequality (8.28) holds for all p such that*

$$1 \leq p \leq \frac{2n + 2}{n + 3}.$$

As an immediate consequence we have the boundedness of Bochner-Riesz multipliers in the full range (8.26) if $a > (n - 1)/(2n + 2)$.

It is conjectured that, in general,

$$\|\hat{f}\|_{L^q(S^{n-1})} \leq C_{p,q}\|f\|_{L^p(\mathbb{R}^n)} \tag{8.29}$$

is true if and only if

$$1 \leq p < \frac{2n}{n + 1}, \quad \text{and} \quad p' \geq \frac{n + 1}{n - 1} q.$$

That p and q must be restricted to this range can be seen by taking $\hat{f}$ to be the characteristic function of a rectangle "adapted" to the sphere, that is, a rectangle with sides $\delta \times \delta^{1/2} \times \cdots \times \delta^{1/2}$ centered at $(1, 0, \ldots, 0)$. When $n = 2$ this conjecture was proved by C. Fefferman in the Acta paper cited above. Also see the paper by A. Zygmund (*On Fourier coefficients and transforms of functions of two variables*, Studia Math. **50** (1974), 189–201). It is also true when $q = 2$; this is shown by Theorem 8.34.

Theorem 8.34 was the best known result for $n \geq 3$ until it was improved by J. Bourgain (*Besicovitch type maximal operators and applications to Fourier analysis*, Geom. Funct. Anal. **1** (1991), 147–187). He showed that the restriction conjecture is true for $1 < p < p(n)$, where $p(n)$ is defined inductively and $(2n + 2)/(n + 3) < p(n) < 2n/(n + 1)$). (For instance, $p(3) = 31/23$.)

There is a close connection between the restriction problem, Bochner-Riesz multipliers, and the Kakeya maximal operator (see Chapter 2, Section 8.9). All the previously known results for these problems were improved in Bourgain's paper.

Further improvements for the Bochner-Riesz conjecture and the restriction problem are again due to J. Bourgain (*Some new estimates on oscillatory integrals*, Essays on Fourier Analysis in Honor of Elias M. Stein, C. Fefferman, R. Fefferman and S. Wainger, eds., pp. 83–112, Princeton Univ. Press, Princeton, 1995). In the case $n = 3$, these were in turn improved by T. Tao, A. Vargas, and L. Vega (*A bilinear approach to the restriction and Kakeya conjectures*, J. Amer. Math. Soc. **11** (1998), 967–1000). Very recently, T. Tao proved a kind of converse of Theorem 8.32 (*The Bochner-Riesz conjecture implies the restriction conjecture*, Duke Math. J. **96** (1999), 363–376).

8.5. Weighted norm inequalities for multipliers.

Given a multiplier m and the associated operator T_m, we can try to characterize, just as we did in Chapter 7 for singular integrals, the weights w such that T_m is a bounded operator on $L^p(w)$. The Marcinkiewicz multiplier theorem has a straightforward generalization to the weighted case.

Theorem 8.35. *Let m be a bounded function which has uniformly bounded variation on each dyadic interval in $\mathbb{R}$. Then if $w \in A_p$, T_m is a bounded operator on $L^p(\mathbb{R}, w)$, $1 < p < \infty$.*

This result was proved by D. Kurtz; see the paper cited in Section 8.2 above. In it he also proved a weighted analogue of Theorem 8.14.

For the multipliers in Hörmander's theorem (Corollary 8.11) the A_p condition is no longer sufficient; however, the following is true.

Theorem 8.36. *For $n \geq 2$, let $k = [n/2] + 1$. Suppose $n/k < p < \infty$ and $w \in A_{pk/n}$, or $1 < p < (n/k)'$ and $w^{1-p'} \in A_{p'k/n}$. Then, if m is a multiplier which satisfies (8.10), T_m is a bounded operator on $L^p(w)$. If $n > 2$ then we may extend the range of p's to include the endpoints $p = n/k$ and $p = (n/k)'$.*

Theorem 8.36 was proved by D. Kurtz and R. Wheeden (*Results on weighted norm inequalities for multipliers*, Trans. Amer. Math. Soc. **255** (1979), 343–362).

Much less is known about weighted norm inequalities for Bochner-Riesz multipliers. For $a \geq (n-1)/2$, it is known that T^a is bounded on $L^p(w)$, $1 < p < \infty$, when $w \in A_p$. When $a > (n-1)/2$ it can be shown that $|T^a f(x)| \leq CMf(x)$, where M is the Hardy-Littlewood maximal operator, so this follows at once from Theorem 7.3. For the critical index $a = (n-1)/2$, this is due to X. Shi and Q. Sun (*Weighted norm inequalities for Bochner-Riesz operators and singular integral operators*, Proc. Amer. Math. Soc. **116** (1992), 665–673). A different proof follows from results in the paper by Duoandikoetxea and Rubio de Francia cited above. In this case the operator is also weak $(1,1)$ with respect to A_1 weights. See the paper by A. Vargas (*Weighted weak type* $(1,1)$ *bounds for rough operators*, J. London Math. Soc. **54** (1996), 297–310). For some partial results in the general case, see the paper by K. Andersen (*Weighted norm inequalities for Bochner-Riesz spherical summation multipliers*, Proc. Amer. Math. Soc. **103** (1988), 165–171).

8.6. The spherical maximal function.

In Corollary 8.24 we proved that the dyadic spherical maximal function is bounded on L^p, $1 < p < \infty$, for $n \geq 2$. This was first proved independently by C. Calderón (*Lacunary spherical means*, Illinois J. Math. **23** (1979), 476–484) and R. Coifman and G. Weiss (Review of the book *Littlewood-Paley and multiplier theory* by R. E. Edwards and G. I. Gaudry, Bull. Amer. Math. Soc. **84** (1978), 242–250). When we consider the maximal function with continuous parameter,

$$\mathcal{M}f(x) = \sup_{t>0} \left| \int_{S^{n-1}} f(x - ty) \, d\sigma(y) \right|,$$

the following result is true.

Theorem 8.37. $\mathcal{M}$ *is bounded on* $L^p(\mathbb{R}^n)$ *if and only if* $p > n/(n-1)$.

For $n \geq 3$, Theorem 8.37 was proved by E. M. Stein (*Maximal functions: Spherical means*, Proc. Nat. Acad. Sci. U.S.A. **73** (1976), 2174–2175), and for $n = 2$ by J. Bourgain (*Averages in the plane over convex curves and maximal operators*, J. Analyse Math. **47** (1986), 69–85). Other proofs for $n \geq 3$ are due to M. Cowling and G. Mauceri (*On maximal functions*, Rend. Sem. Mat. Fis. Milano **49** (1979), 79–87) and J. L. Rubio de Francia (*Maximal functions and Fourier transforms*, Duke Math. J. **53** (1986), 395–404). This last proof is close in spirit to the method developed in Section 6: a decomposition of the multiplier into dyadic pieces, an L^2 estimate for each piece with exponential decay, and an L^1 estimate derived with vector-valued techniques.

In the case $n = 2$, new proofs were given by G. Mockenhaupt, A. Seeger and C. Sogge (*Wave front sets, local smoothing and Bourgain's circular maximal theorem*, Ann. of Math. **136** (1992), 207–218) and W. Schlag (*A geometric proof of the circular maximal theorem*, Duke Math. J. **93** (1998), 505–533).

Weighted norm inequalities for the spherical maximal operator (with both discrete and continuous parameters) are in J. Duoandikoetxea and L. Vega (*Spherical means and weighted inequalities*, J. London Math. Soc. **53** (1996), 343–353).

8.7. Further results for singular integrals.

The arguments in Section 7 readily extend to prove additional results about singular integrals which cannot be proved using the method of rotations. For example, define the operator T to be convolution with the kernel

$$K(x) = h(|x|)\frac{\Omega(x')}{|x|^n},$$

where $\Omega \in L^q(S^{n-1})$ for some $q > 1$ and has zero integral, and h satisfies the growth condition

$$\sup_{R>0} \frac{1}{R} \int_0^R |h(t)|^2 \, dt < \infty.$$

Then the proof of Theorem 8.19 can be readily adapted to show that T is bounded on L^p, $1 < p < \infty$. Singular integrals of this type were first considered by R. Fefferman (*A note on singular integrals*, Proc. Amer. Math. Soc. **74** (1979), 266–270), and J. Namazi (*A singular integral*, Proc. Amer. Math. Soc. **96** (1986), 421–424).

Similar techniques can also be used to prove weighted norm inequalities.

Theorem 8.38. *Given* $\Omega \in L^\infty(S^{n-1})$ *such that* $\int \Omega(u) \, d\sigma(u) = 0$, *define the singular integral*

$$Tf(x) = \mathrm{p.\,v.} \int_{\mathbb{R}^n} \frac{\Omega(y')}{|y|^n} f(x - y) \, dy.$$

If $w \in A_p$, $1 < p < \infty$, *then* T *is bounded on* $L^p(w)$.

The proof of this result can be found in the paper by Duoandikoetxea and Rubio de Francia cited above. The hypothesis that $\Omega \in L^\infty$ cannot be weakened to $\Omega \in L^q$, $q < \infty$; counter-examples were first given by B. Muckenhoupt and R. Wheeden (*Weighted norm inequalities for singular and fractional integrals*, Trans. Amer. Math. Soc. **161** (1971), 249–258). When $\Omega \in L^q$, $1 < q < \infty$, T is bounded on $L^p(w)$ if $q' \le p < \infty$ and $w \in A_{p/q'}$ or if $1 < p \le q$ and $w^{1-p'} \in A_{p'/q'}$. (Cf. Theorem 8.36 above.) This condition was discovered independently by J. Duoandikoetxea (*Weighted norm inequalities for homogeneous singular integrals*, Trans. Amer. Math. Soc. **336** (1993), 869–880) and D. Watson (*Weighted estimates for singular integrals via Fourier transform estimates*, Duke Math. J. **60** (1990), 389–399).

Additional weighted inequalities for these operators, together with structural properties of the weights, are given by D. Watson (*Vector-valued inequalities, factorization, and extrapolation for a family of rough operators*, J. Funct. Anal. **121** (1994), 389–415) and J. Duoandikoetxea (*Almost-orthogonality and weighted inequalities*, Contemp. Math. **189** (1995), 213–226). Weighted weak $(1, 1)$ inequalities were proved by Vargas in the paper cited in Section 8.5.

8.8. Operators on curves.

Besides the motivating example described in Section 7, singular integrals and maximal functions on curves have appeared in several different contexts and have been studied extensively. The first results were for homogeneous curves (curves of the type $(t^{a_1}, t^{a_2}, \ldots, t^{a_n})$ and some more general versions); these results were later extended to "well-curved" curves: curves Γ whose derivatives $\Gamma'(0), \Gamma''(0), \ldots$ span $\mathbb{R}^n$. The survey article by E. M. Stein and S. Wainger (*Problems in harmonic analysis related to curvature*, Bull. Amer. Math. Soc. **84** (1978), 1239–1295) contains the principal results and their proofs. Another good summary is in the article by Wainger (*Averages and singular integrals over lower dimensional sets*) in [**16**].

The next case considered was that of "flat" curves—that is, curves whose derivatives at the origin all vanish. These were first considered in $\mathbb{R}^2$; see (among others) the article by Duoandikoetxea and Rubio de Francia cited above, the articles by M. Christ (*Hilbert transforms along curves, II: A flat case*, Duke Math. J. **52** (1985), 887–894), A. Nagel, J. Vance, S. Wainger and D. Weinberg (*Hilbert transforms for convex curves*, Duke Math. J. **50** (1983), 735–744, and *Maximal function for convex curves*, Duke Math. J. **52** (1985), 715–722), H. Carlsson et al. (*L^p estimates for maximal functions and Hilbert transforms along flat convex curves in $\mathbb{R}^2$*, Bull. Amer. Math. Soc. **14** (1986), 263–267), A. Córdoba and J. L. Rubio de Francia (*Estimates for Wainger's singular integrals along curves*, Rev. Mat. Iberoamericana **2** (1986), 105–117), and A. Carbery, M. Christ, J. Vance, S. Wainger, and D. Watson (*Operators associated to flat plane curves: L^p estimates via dilation methods*, Duke Math. J. **59** (1989), 675–700).

The extension of the results on flat curves to higher dimensions has been more difficult. See the articles by A. Nagel, J. Vance, S. Wainger and D. Weinberg (*The Hilbert transform for convex curves in $\mathbb{R}^n$*, Amer. J. Math. **108** (1986), 485–504), A. Carbery, J. Vance, S. Wainger and D. Watson (*The Hilbert transform and maximal function along flat curves, dilations, and differential equations*, Amer. J. Math. **116** (1994), 1203–1239), A. Carbery, J. Vance, S. Wainger, D. Watson and J. Wright (*L^p estimates for operators associated to flat curves without the Fourier transform*, Pacific J. Math. **167** (1995), 243–262), and A. Carbery and S. Ziesler (*Hilbert transforms and maximal functions along rough flat curves*, Rev. Mat. Iberoamericana **10** (1994), 379–393). Also see the survey article by A. Carbery, J. Vance,

S. Wainger and D. Watson (*Dilations associated to flat curves in* $\mathbb{R}^n$, Essays on Fourier Analysis in Honor of Elias M. Stein, C. Fefferman, R. Fefferman and S. Wainger, eds., pp. 113–126, Princeton Univ. Press, Princeton, 1995).

In recent years non-convolution operators have also been studied. In this case the operators are defined on variable curves, that is, curves which also depend on the point x. In a similar fashion, curves have been replaced by surfaces, both in the convolution and the variable case. Some examples can be found in Stein [**17**, Chapter 11].

Chapter 9

The $T1$ Theorem

1. Cotlar's lemma

In this chapter we return to a question we first considered in Chapter 5: given a Calderón-Zygmund operator T with associated kernel K, when is T bounded on L^2? If T is a convolution operator, the problem reduces to showing that $\hat{K} \in L^\infty$. For operators which are not convolution operators the problem is much more difficult. In some cases, however, a result due to M. Cotlar is useful.

Lemma 9.1 (Cotlar's Lemma). *Let H be a Hilbert space, $\{T_j\}$ a sequence of bounded linear operators on H with adjoints $\{T_j^*\}$, and $\{a(j)\}$ a sequence of non-negative numbers such that*

$$\|T_i T_j^*\|_{\mathcal{L}(H)} + \|T_i^* T_j\|_{\mathcal{L}(H)} \le a(i-j).$$

Then for all integers n and m, $n \le m$,

$$\left\| \sum_{j=n}^{m} T_j \right\|_{\mathcal{L}(H)} \le \sum_{i=-\infty}^{\infty} a(i)^{1/2}.$$

Proof. Let

$$S = \sum_{j=n}^{m} T_j.$$

Then $\|S\| = \|SS^*\|^{1/2}$; in fact, for any integer $k > 0$, $\|S\| = \|(SS^*)^k\|^{1/2k}$. But

$$(SS^*)^k = \sum_{j_1,\ldots,j_{2k}=n}^{m} T_{j_1} T_{j_2}^* \cdots T_{j_{2k-1}} T_{j_{2k}}^*,$$

and the norm of each summand can be bounded in two ways:

$$\|T_{j_1} T_{j_2}^* \cdots T_{j_{2k-1}} T_{j_{2k}}^*\| \leq \|T_{j_1} T_{j_2}^*\| \cdots \|T_{j_{2k-1}} T_{j_{2k}}^*\|$$
$$\leq a(j_1 - j_2) \cdots a(j_{2k-1} - j_{2k}),$$

and

$$\|T_{j_1} T_{j_2}^* \cdots T_{j_{2k-1}} T_{j_{2k}}^*\| \leq \|T_{j_1}\| \|T_{j_2}^* T_{j_3}\| \cdots \|T_{j_{2k-2}}^* T_{j_{2k-1}}\| \|T_{j_{2k}}^*\|$$
$$\leq a(0)^{1/2} a(j_2 - j_3) \cdots a(j_{2k-2} - j_{2k-1}) a(0)^{1/2}.$$

If we take the geometric mean of both bounds and sum over all the j_i we get

$$\|(SS^*)^k\| \leq a(0)^{1/2} \sum_{j_1,\ldots,j_{2k}=n}^{m} a(j_1 - j_2)^{1/2} a(j_2 - j_3)^{1/2} \cdots a(j_{2k-1} - j_{2k})^{1/2}.$$

Fix $j_1, \ldots, j_{2k-1}$ and sum over j_{2k}; then sum over j_{2k-1} and so on down to j_1. Then

$$\|(SS^*)^k\| \leq a(0)^{1/2}(m - n + 1) \left(\sum_{i=-\infty}^{\infty} a(i)^{1/2} \right)^{2k-1},$$

where $m - n + 1$ is the number of terms which appear when we sum in j_1. Hence,

$$\|S\| = \|(SS^*)^k\|^{1/2k} \leq (m - n + 1)^{1/2k} \sum_{i=-\infty}^{\infty} a(i)^{1/2},$$

and if we let k tend to infinity we get the desired result. $\qquad\square$

If for all x in a dense subset of H the sum

$$\sum_{-\infty}^{\infty} T_j x$$

exists, we can extend it to an operator on all of H; the norm of this operator is bounded by $\sum a(i)^{1/2}$. In fact, it is not necessary to assume that $\sum T_j x$ exists on a dense subset because the hypotheses of Cotlar's lemma imply that the series converges for any $x \in H$.

Example 9.2 (An application to the Hilbert transform). Let $H = L^2(\mathbb{R})$ and for $f \in L^2(\mathbb{R})$ define

$$T_j f(x) = \int_{2^j < |t| \le 2^{j+1}} \frac{f(x-t)}{t} \, dt.$$

For each integer j, $|T_j f(x)| \le 4Mf(x)$ (where M is the Hardy-Littlewood maximal operator), so T_j is clearly bounded on $L^2(\mathbb{R})$. We will use Cotlar's lemma to prove that any finite sum of the T_j's is uniformly bounded, which in turn proves that the truncated integrals of the Hilbert transform are uniformly bounded. (Actually, we will show that only those integrals truncated at the dyadic numbers 2^j are bounded, but it is easy to pass to any other truncation.)

Since $T_j^* = -T_j$, we only need to estimate $\|T_i T_j\|$. If we let $K_j(x) = x^{-1}\chi_{\Delta_j}(x)$, where $\Delta_j = \{x \in \mathbb{R} : 2^j < |x| < 2^{j+1}\}$, then $T_j f(x) = K_j * f(x)$ and $T_i T_j f(x) = K_i * K_j * f(x)$. Hence,

$$\|T_i T_j\| \le \|K_i * K_j\|_1.$$

However,

$$K_i * K_j(x) = \int_{\mathbb{R}} \frac{1}{t} \chi_{\Delta_i}(t) \frac{1}{x-t} \chi_{\Delta_j}(x-t) \, dt.$$

Without loss of generality we may assume that $i < j$ and $x > 0$. Then $K_i * K_j(x) = 0$ if $x \notin (2^j - 2^{i+1}, 2^{j+1} + 2^{i+1})$, and on this interval, $|K_i * K_j(x)| \le 2 \cdot 2^{-j}$. We will use this estimate on the intervals $(2^j - 2^{i+1}, 2^j + 2^{i+1})$ and $(2^{j+1} - 2^{i+1}, 2^{j+1} + 2^{i+1})$.

On the rest of the interval, if $t \in \Delta_i$ then $x - t \in \Delta_j$, so that

$$K_i * K_j(x) = \int_{\mathbb{R}^n} \frac{1}{t} \chi_{\Delta_i}(t) \left(\frac{1}{x-t} - \frac{1}{x} \right) \chi_{\Delta_j}(x-t) \, dt;$$

hence, $|K_i * K_j(x)| \le 2 \cdot 2^{i-2j}$. Therefore,

$$\|K_i * K_j\|_1 \le C 2^{-|i-j|},$$

and this estimate allows us to apply Cotlar's lemma as desired.

2. Carleson measures

Definition 9.3. A positive measure ν on $\mathbb{R}^{n+1}_+$ is a Carleson measure if for every cube Q in $\mathbb{R}^n$

$$\nu(Q \times (0, l(Q))) \le C|Q|,$$

where $l(Q)$ is the side length of Q. The infimum of the possible values of the constant C is called the Carleson constant of ν and is denoted by $\|\nu\|$.

An example of a Carleson measure in the upper half-plane $\mathbb{R}^2_+$ is $dr\,d\theta$ (polar coordinates).

The property underlying the definition of Carleson measures is not limited to cubes but also extends to more general sets. Given an open set $E \subset \mathbb{R}^n$, let

$$\hat{E} = \{(x,t) \in \mathbb{R}^{n+1}_+ : B(x,t) \subset E\}.$$

Then the following is true.

Lemma 9.4. *If ν is a Carleson measure in $\mathbb{R}^{n+1}_+$ and $E \subset \mathbb{R}^n$ is open, then*

$$\nu(\hat{E}) \leq C\|\nu\||E|.$$

Proof. In $\mathbb{R}^n$, form the Calderón-Zygmund decomposition of the characteristic function of E at height $1/2$. This yields a collection of disjoint dyadic cubes $\{Q_j\}$ such that

$$E \subset \bigcup_j Q_j \quad \text{and} \quad |E| \leq \sum_j |Q_j| \leq 2|E|.$$

Let $(x,t) \in \hat{E}$; then $x \in Q_j$ for some j. If $\tilde{Q}_j$ is the dyadic cube containing Q_j whose sides are twice as long, then $\tilde{Q}_j$ contains points of E^c. Therefore, since $B(x,t) \subset E$, we must have that $t < \sqrt{n}\,l(\tilde{Q}_j) = 2\sqrt{n}\,l(Q_j)$. Hence,

$$\hat{E} \subset \bigcup_j Q_j \times (0, 2\sqrt{n}\,l(Q_j)),$$

and so

$$\nu(\hat{E}) \leq \sum_j \nu(Q_j \times (0, 2\sqrt{n}\,l(Q_j))) \leq \|\nu\|(2\sqrt{n})^n \sum_j |Q_j| \leq \|\nu\|2(2\sqrt{n})^n|E|.$$

$\square$

The converse of Lemma 9.4 is also true. It is straightforward to show that if for any ball $B \subset \mathbb{R}^n$, $\nu(\hat{B}) \leq C|B|$, then ν satisfies Definition 9.3, and $\|\nu\|$ is comparable with the constant in this inequality.

A Carleson measure can be characterized as a measure ν for which the Poisson integral defines a bounded operator from $L^p(\mathbb{R}^n, dx)$ to $L^p(\mathbb{R}^{n+1}_+, \nu)$. This is a consequence of a more general result.

Theorem 9.5. *Let ϕ be a bounded, integrable function which is positive, radial and decreasing. For $t > 0$, let $\phi_t(x) = t^{-n}\phi(t^{-1}x)$. Then a measure ν is a Carleson measure if and only if for every p, $1 < p < \infty$,*

$$(9.1) \qquad \int_{\mathbb{R}^{n+1}_+} |\phi_t * f(x)|^p \, d\nu(x,t) \leq C \int_{\mathbb{R}^n} |f(x)|^p \, dx.$$

The constant C is comparable with $\|\nu\|$.

Proof. First suppose that ν is a Carleson measure. Define the maximal operator
$$M_\phi f(x) = \sup\{|\phi_t * f(y)| : |x - y| < t\}.$$
It is easy to show (cf. Chapter 2, Section 8.7) that
$$M_\phi f(x) \le C M f(x),$$
where M is the Hardy-Littlewood maximal operator.

Now

(9.2) $$\int_{\mathbb{R}^{n+1}_+} |\phi_t * f(x)|^p \, d\nu(x,t)$$
$$= p \int_0^\infty \lambda^{p-1} \nu(\{(x,t) \in \mathbb{R}^{n+1}_+ : |\phi_t * f(x)| > \lambda\}) \, d\lambda.$$

Let $E_\lambda = \{x \in \mathbb{R}^n : M_\phi f(x) > \lambda\}$; then
$$\{(x,t) \in \mathbb{R}^{n+1}_+ : |\phi_t * f(x)| > \lambda\} \subset \hat{E}_\lambda.$$
Hence, by Lemma 9.4
$$\nu(\{(x,t) \in \mathbb{R}^{n+1}_+ : |\phi_t * f(x)| > \lambda\}) \le \nu(\hat{E}_\lambda) \le C\|\nu\| |E_\lambda|.$$
Therefore, the right-hand side of (9.2) is dominated by
$$pC\|\nu\| \int_0^\infty \lambda^{p-1} |E_\lambda| \, d\lambda = C\|\nu\| \int_{\mathbb{R}^n} M_\phi f(x)^p \, dx \le C\|\nu\| \int_{\mathbb{R}^n} |f(x)|^p \, dx,$$
which gives us inequality (9.1).

Now, conversely, suppose that (9.1) holds. Let $B \subset \mathbb{R}^n$ be the ball with center x_0 and radius r, and let $(x,t) \in \hat{B}$ (i.e. $B(x,t) \subset B$). Then
$$|\phi_t * \chi_B(x)| = \int_{B(x_0,r)} \phi_t(x-y) \, dy \ge \int_{B(0,t)} \phi_t(y) \, dy = \int_{B(0,1)} \phi(y) \, dy = A.$$
Hence,
$$\nu(\hat{B}) \le \frac{1}{A^p} \int_{\mathbb{R}^{n+1}_+} |\phi_t * \chi_B(x)|^p \, d\nu(x,t) \le C \int_{\mathbb{R}^n} |\chi_B(x)|^p \, dx = C|B|,$$
so by the remark following Lemma 9.4, ν is a Carleson measure. □

Carleson measures can also be characterized in terms of BMO functions.

Theorem 9.6. *Let $b \in BMO$ and let $\psi \in \mathcal{S}$ be such that $\int \psi = 0$. Then the measure ν defined by*
$$d\nu = |b * \psi_t(x)|^2 \frac{dx \, dt}{t}$$
is a Carleson measure such that $\|\nu\|$ is dominated by $\|b\|_*^2$.

Proof. Fix a cube Q in $\mathbb{R}^n$. Since the translate of a BMO function is again in BMO, we may assume without loss of generality that Q is centered at the origin. Let Q^* be the cube with the same center whose side length is $2\sqrt{n}$ times larger. Let b_{Q^*} be the average of b on Q^*. Then, since $\int \psi = 0$,

$$\nu(Q \times (0, l(Q))) = \int_Q \int_0^{l(Q)} |b * \psi_t(x)|^2 \frac{dx\,dt}{t}$$

$$\leq 2 \int_Q \int_0^{l(Q)} |(b - b_{Q^*})\chi_{Q^*} * \psi_t(x)|^2 \frac{dx\,dt}{t}$$

$$+ 2 \int_Q \int_0^{l(Q)} |(b - b_{Q^*})\chi_{\{\mathbb{R}^n \setminus Q^*\}} * \psi_t(x)|^2 \frac{dx\,dt}{t}$$

$$= I_1 + I_2.$$

(Recall that $l(Q)$ denotes the side length of Q.)

Now,

$$I_1 \leq 2 \int_{\mathbb{R}^n} \int_0^\infty |((b - b_{Q^*})\chi_{Q^*})\hat{}(\xi)|^2 |\hat{\psi}(t\xi)|^2 \frac{d\xi\,dt}{t};$$

since $\hat{\psi}(0) = 0$, $|\hat{\psi}(t\xi)| \leq C \min(|t\xi|, |t\xi|^{-1})$, and so

$$\int_0^\infty |\hat{\psi}(t\xi)|^2 \frac{dt}{t} \leq C \int_0^{1/|\xi|} |t\xi|^2 \frac{dt}{t} + C \int_{1/|\xi|}^\infty |t\xi|^{-2} \frac{dt}{t} \leq C.$$

Therefore, by this estimate and by Corollary 6.12,

$$I_1 \leq C \int_{Q^*} |b - b_{Q^*}|^2 \leq C|Q| \|b\|_*^2.$$

To estimate I_2, let Q_k^* denote the cube centered at the origin whose side length is 2^k times that of Q^*. Then

$$I_2 \leq \int_Q \int_0^{l(Q)} \left| \sum_{k=0}^\infty \int_{Q_{k+1}^* \setminus Q_k^*} (b(y) - b_{Q^*})\psi_t(x - y)\,dy \right|^2 \frac{dx\,dt}{t}.$$

Since $x \in Q$, if $y \notin Q_k^*$ then $|x - y| \geq 2^{k-1}l(Q)$. Therefore, because $\psi \in \mathcal{S}$,

$$|\psi_t(x - y)| \leq Ct^{-n}(t^{-1}2^k l(Q))^{-n-1}.$$

Hence,

$$I_2 \leq C \int_Q \int_0^{l(Q)} \left| \sum_{k=0}^\infty \int_{Q_{k+1}^*} |b(y) - b_{Q^*}|\,dy \frac{t}{(2^k l(Q))^{n+1}} \right|^2 \frac{dx\,dt}{t}$$

$$\leq C \int_Q \int_0^{l(Q)} \left(\sum_{k=0}^\infty \frac{t}{2^k l(Q)} \|b\|_* \right)^2 \frac{dx\,dt}{t}$$

$$\leq C|Q| \|b\|_*^2.$$

$\square$

The converse of Theorem 9.6 is also true, although we will not prove it here: if ψ and ν are as above and ν is a Carleson measure then $b \in BMO$. For a proof see Stein [**17**, Chapter 4].

Finally, if we combine Theorems 9.5 and 9.6 we get the following.

Corollary 9.7. *Let ϕ be as in Theorem 9.5, ψ as in Theorem 9.6 and let $b \in BMO$. Then*

$$\int_{\mathbb{R}^n} \int_0^\infty |\phi_t * f(x)|^p |\psi_t * b(x)|^2 \, \frac{dx\,dt}{t} \leq C\|b\|_*^2 \int_{\mathbb{R}^n} |f(x)|^p \, dx.$$

3. Statement and applications of the $T1$ theorem

In this section we state our main result, the $T1$ theorem, and give several applications. In the next section we will give its (lengthy) proof.

We will consider operators T which map the Schwartz class to the space of tempered distributions, $T : \mathcal{S}(\mathbb{R}^n) \to \mathcal{S}'(\mathbb{R}^n)$. In other words, given $f, g \in \mathcal{S}(\mathbb{R}^n)$, we know the value of $\langle Tf, g \rangle$. Recall that a function $K : \mathbb{R}^n \times \mathbb{R}^n \setminus \Delta \to \mathbb{C}$ (where Δ is the diagonal of $\mathbb{R}^n \times \mathbb{R}^n$) is said to be a standard kernel if it satisfies conditions (5.12), (5.13) and (5.14). We say that T is associated with a standard kernel K if for Schwartz functions f and g with disjoint, compact supports,

$$(9.3) \qquad \langle Tf, g \rangle = \int_{\mathbb{R}^n} \int_{\mathbb{R}^n} K(x, y) f(y) g(x) \, dx\, dy.$$

The adjoint operator T^* is defined by

$$\langle T^* f, g \rangle = \langle f, Tg \rangle, \quad f, g \in \mathcal{S}(\mathbb{R}^n).$$

It is associated with the standard kernel $\tilde{K}(x, y) = K(y, x)$.

When T is a bounded operator on L^2 we can define Tf for $f \in L^\infty$ as a function in BMO (see Chapter 6, Section 2). Now, however, if we want to define T on L^∞, we cannot use this approach since we do not know *a priori* that T is bounded on L^2. As a substitute we will define Tf for functions f which are bounded and in C^∞. In fact, Tf will be an element of the dual of $C_{c,0}^\infty$, the subspace of C_c^∞ functions with zero average.

Fix $g \in C_{c,0}^\infty$ with support in $B(0, R)$ and let $f \in L^\infty \cap C^\infty$. Fix $\psi_1, \psi_2 \in C^\infty(\mathbb{R}^n)$ such that $\mathrm{supp}(\psi_1) \subset B(0, 3R)$, $\psi_1 = 1$ on $B(0, 2R)$ and such that $\psi_1 + \psi_2 = 1$. Then $f\psi_1 \in \mathcal{S}(\mathbb{R}^n)$ and $\langle T(f\psi_1), g \rangle$ makes sense. If f were a function of compact support then by (9.3) we would have that

$$\langle T(f\psi_2), g \rangle = \int_{\mathbb{R}^n} \int_{\mathbb{R}^n} K(x, y) f(y) \psi_2(y) g(x) \, dx\, dy.$$

Since f need not have compact support, we instead define $\langle T(f\psi_2), g\rangle$ by

$$\int_{\mathbb{R}^n} \int_{\mathbb{R}^n} [K(x,y) - K(0,y)] f(y)\psi_2(y)g(x)\, dx\, dy.$$

Since g has zero average, this coincides with the previous definition when f has compact support; for arbitrary bounded, C^∞ functions f this expression makes sense because the integral in y is taken far from the origin (on $\mathrm{supp}(\psi_2)$), and (since K is a standard kernel)

$$|K(x,y) - K(0,y)| \leq \frac{C|x|^\delta}{|y|^{n+\delta}}.$$

We now define Tf by

$$(9.4) \qquad \langle Tf, g\rangle = \langle T(f\psi_1), g\rangle + \langle T(f\psi_2), g\rangle.$$

Since g has zero average, this definition is independent of the choice of ψ_1 and ψ_2.

Below we will use (9.4) to define $T1$ and T^*1.

Given $f \in C^\infty \cap L^\infty$, we say that $Tf \in BMO$ if there exists a function $b \in BMO$ such that

$$\langle Tf, g\rangle = \langle b, g\rangle$$

for all $g \in C^\infty_{c,0}$. Since $C^\infty_{c,0}$ is dense in H^1, by the duality of H^1 and BMO (Theorem 6.15) this is equivalent to saying that

$$|\langle Tf, g\rangle| \leq C\|g\|_{H^1}.$$

To state the $T1$ theorem we need one more definition.

Definition 9.8. The operator T has the weak boundedness property (customarily denoted WBP) if for every bounded subset B of $C^\infty_c(\mathbb{R}^n)$ there exists a constant C_B such that for any $\phi_1, \phi_2 \in B$, $x \in \mathbb{R}^n$ and $R > 0$,

$$|\langle T\phi_1^{x,R}, \phi_2^{x,R}\rangle| \leq C_B R^n,$$

where

$$\phi_i^{x,R}(y) = \phi_i\left(\frac{y-x}{R}\right), \quad i = 1, 2.$$

If an operator T is bounded on L^p for some p then it is easy to show that it satisfies the weak boundedness property.

Given a standard kernel K which is anti-symmetric (i.e. $K(x,y) = -K(y,x)$), we can associate it with an operator T by defining

$$(9.5) \qquad \langle Tf, g\rangle = \lim_{\epsilon \to 0} \int_{|x-y|>\epsilon} K(x,y)f(y)g(x)\, dy\, dx.$$

By the anti-symmetry of K this is equivalent to

$$\langle Tf, g \rangle = \frac{1}{2} \int_{\mathbb{R}^n} \int_{\mathbb{R}^n} K(x, y)[f(y)g(x) - f(x)g(y)] \, dy \, dx,$$

and this integral converges absolutely: by the mean value theorem (adding and subtracting $f(y)g(y)$) the term in square brackets yields a factor of $|y - x|$ which lets us integrate near the diagonal.

The operator defined by (9.5) has the WBP. In fact, it is enough to note that

$$\langle T\phi_1^{z,R}, \phi_2^{z,R} \rangle = R^n \langle T_{z,R}\phi_1, \phi_2 \rangle,$$

where $T_{z,R}$ is defined as in (9.5) but with the kernel $R^n K(Rx + z, Ry + z)$. This is a standard kernel with the same constants as the kernel K.

The importance of the WBP is shown by the one-dimensional operator of differentiation. It takes $\mathcal{S}(\mathbb{R})$ to $\mathcal{S}'(\mathbb{R})$ and is associated with the standard kernel zero, but is not bounded on L^2. It is straightforward to check that it does not have the weak boundedness property. Clearly, differentiation is not the operator associated by (9.5) with the kernel zero—that would be the zero operator which trivially has the WBP.

We can now state the $T1$ theorem.

Theorem 9.9. *An operator $T : \mathcal{S}(\mathbb{R}^n) \to \mathcal{S}'(\mathbb{R}^n)$, associated with a standard kernel K, extends to a bounded operator on $L^2(\mathbb{R}^n)$ if and only if the following conditions are true:*

(1) $T1 \in BMO$,

(2) $T^*1 \in BMO$,

(3) T has the WBP.

We have already seen the necessity of these three conditions: (1) and (2) follow from Theorem 6.6 and the remarks after it, and we noted the necessity of (3) immediately after Definition 9.8.

Corollary 9.10. *If K is a standard kernel which is anti-symmetric and T is the operator defined by (9.5), then T is bounded on $L^2(\mathbb{R}^n)$ if and only if $T1 \in BMO$.*

This follows immediately from Theorem 9.9 since T always has the WBP and $T^*1 = -T1$.

Example 9.11 (An application of the $T1$ theorem). Recall that in Chapter 5, Section 3, we defined the Calderón commutators,

$$T_k f(x) = \lim_{\epsilon \to 0} \int_{|x-y|>\epsilon} \left(\frac{A(x) - A(y)}{x - y} \right)^k \frac{f(y)}{x - y} \, dy,$$

where $A : \mathbb{R} \to \mathbb{R}$ is Lipschitz and $k \geq 0$ is an integer. These are operators defined as in (9.5) with anti-symmetric kernels

$$K_k(x, y) = \frac{(A(x) - A(y))^k}{(x - y)^{k+1}}.$$

Corollary 9.12. *The operators T_k are bounded on L^2 and there exists a positive constant C such that $\|T_k\| \leq C^k \|A'\|_\infty^k$.*

It follows from this result and Definition 5.11 that the T_k's are Calderón-Zygmund operators.

Proof. From the proof of Theorem 9.9 we will see that the norm of an operator T depends linearly on the constants involved in the hypotheses; in the special case of Corollary 9.10 these reduce to the constants of K as a standard kernel and the BMO norm of $T_k 1$.

Since a straightforward argument shows that the constants of K_k as a standard kernel are bounded by $C_1(k+1)\|A'\|_\infty^k$, it will suffice to show that for some $C > 0$ and all k,

$$(9.6) \qquad\qquad \|T_k 1\|_* \leq C^{k+1} \|A'\|_\infty^k.$$

For in this case, if $C \geq C_1$ then we have

$$\|T_k\| \leq C_2(C_1(k+1) + C^{k+1})\|A'\|_\infty^k \leq 2C_2 C^{k+1}\|A'\|_\infty^k.$$

We will prove (9.6) by induction. When $k = 0$, T_0 equals the Hilbert transform, and so $T_0 1 = 0$. Now suppose that (9.6) is true for some k. If we integrate by parts we see that

$$T_{k+1} 1 = T_k A'.$$

(Formally, this calculation is immediate; however, making it rigorous requires some care. The details are left to the reader.) Therefore,

$$\|T_{k+1} 1\|_* = \|T_k A'\|_* \leq \|T_k\|_{L^\infty, BMO}\|A'\|_\infty.$$

From the proof of Theorem 6.6 we have that

$$\|T_k\|_{L^\infty, BMO} \leq C_3(C_1(k+1)\|A'\|_\infty^k + \|T_k\|_{L^2, L^2})$$
$$\leq C_3(C_1(k+1) + 2C_2 C^{k+1})\|A'\|_\infty^k.$$

Since C_1, C_2, C_3 are all independent of k, if C is sufficiently large then

$$C_3(C_1(k+1) + 2C_2 C^{k+1}) \leq C^{k+2}.$$

This yields the desired inequality. $\square$

Another operator we considered in Chapter 5, Section 3, is associated with the anti-symmetric kernel

$$K(x,y) = \frac{1}{x - y + i(A(x) - A(y))},$$

and is related to the Cauchy integral along a Lipschitz curve. As we showed there, if $\|A'\|_\infty < 1$ then we can expand this kernel as

$$K(x,y) = \sum_{k=0}^{\infty} i^k K_k(x,y).$$

From this expansion and Corollary 9.12 we get the following.

Corollary 9.13. *There exists $\epsilon > 0$ such that if $\|A'\|_\infty \le \epsilon$ then the operator associated with the kernel K is a Calderón-Zygmund operator.*

For more on these operators see Section 5.2 below.

4. Proof of the $T1$ theorem

As we already noted, all that we have to prove is that the three conditions are sufficient for T to be bounded on L^2. We will consider two cases: first the case when $T1 = T^*1 = 0$, and then the general case which we will reduce to the first. Since the proof is rather long, we will try to clarify it by giving several intermediate results as lemmas.

Case 1: $T1 = T^*1 = 0$ *and T has the WBP*. Fix a radial function $\phi \in \mathcal{S}(\mathbb{R}^n)$ which is supported in $B(0,1)$ and has integral 1, and let $\phi_j(x) = 2^{-jn}\phi(2^{-j}x)$. Define the operators

$$S_j f = \phi_j * f \quad \text{and} \quad \Delta_j = S_j - S_{j-1}.$$

Then we can formally decompose T as

$$T = \sum_{j=-\infty}^{\infty} (S_j T \Delta_j + \Delta_j T S_j - \Delta_j T \Delta_j).$$

The following lemma makes this identity precise.

Lemma 9.14. *Let*

$$R_N = \sum_{j=-N}^{N} (S_j T \Delta_j + \Delta_j T S_j - \Delta_j T \Delta_j).$$

Then for $f, g \in C_c^\infty(\mathbb{R}^n)$,

$$\lim_{N \to \infty} \langle R_N f, g \rangle = \langle Tf, g \rangle.$$

Proof. If we expand the sum for R_N we get

$$R_N = S_{-N}TS_{-N} - S_{N+1}TS_{N+1}.$$

Since $S_{-N}f$ converges to f in $\mathcal{S}(\mathbb{R}^n)$, and since T is a continuous map from $\mathcal{S}(\mathbb{R}^n)$ to $\mathcal{S}'(\mathbb{R}^n)$,

$$\lim_{N\to\infty} \langle S_{-N}TS_{-N}f, g\rangle = \langle Tf, g\rangle.$$

Therefore, we need to show that

(9.7) $$\lim_{N\to\infty} \langle S_N TS_N f, g\rangle = 0.$$

We will prove this using the WBP for T. For $N \geq 1$ define the functions

$$f_N(x) = 2^{nN}(\phi * f(2^N \cdot))(x).$$

Then $\{f_N\}$ is a bounded subset of $C_c^\infty(\mathbb{R}^n)$ since the f_N's are supported in a fixed, compact subset of $\mathbb{R}^n$ and satisfy the uniform bound

$$\|D^\alpha f_N\|_\infty \leq \|f\|_1 \|D^\alpha \phi\|_\infty.$$

Define the sequence $\{g_N\}$ in the same way. Then by the WBP,

$$|\langle Tf_N(2^{-N}\cdot), g_N(2^{-N}\cdot)\rangle| \leq C2^{nN}.$$

Since $f_N(2^{-N}x) = 2^{nN}S_N f(x)$ and g satisfies the same identity, it follows that

$$|\langle TS_N f, S_N g\rangle| \leq C2^{-nN}.$$

If we let N tend to infinity we get (9.7). $\qquad\qquad\qquad\square$

By Lemma 9.14, to prove that T is bounded on L^2 it will suffice to prove that the R_N's are uniformly bounded on L^2. We will show this by applying Cotlar's lemma. For simplicity, we will only consider the operators $T_j = S_j T\Delta_j$ and show that $\|T_j T_k^*\|, \|T_j^* T_k\| \leq C2^{-\delta|j-k|}$, where δ comes from the standard estimates for K, the kernel of T. Similar estimates for the other two summands are gotten by analogous arguments. (Note that below we only use the hypothesis $T^*1 = 0$; in the arguments for these other operators we use the fact that $T1 = 0$.)

We begin by finding the kernel of T_j: let $\psi = \phi - \phi_1$ and define

$$\phi_j^x(u) = 2^{-jn}\phi\left(\frac{u-x}{2^j}\right) \quad \text{and} \quad \psi_j^y(u) = 2^{-jn}\psi\left(\frac{u-y}{2^j}\right).$$

Then for $f, g \in C_c^\infty(\mathbb{R}^n)$,

$$\langle T_j f, g\rangle = \langle T\Delta_j f, S_j g\rangle = \int_{\mathbb{R}^n}\int_{\mathbb{R}^n} \langle T\psi_j^y, \phi_j^x\rangle f(y)g(x)\, dy\, dx.$$

Hence, the kernel K_j of T_j is

$$K_j(x, y) = \langle T\psi_j^y, \phi_j^x\rangle.$$

Lemma 9.15. *Define $p(x) = (1+|x|)^{-n-\delta}$, where δ is the constant from the estimates for K as a standard kernel, and let $p_j(x) = 2^{-jn}p(2^{-j}x)$. Then*

(1) $|K_j(x,y)| \leq Cp_j(x-y)$;

(2) $|K_j(x,y) - K_j(w,y)| \leq C\min(1, 2^{-j}|x-w|)[p_j(x-y) + p_j(w-y)]$, *and the analogous inequality in the second variable;*

(3) *for all x,* $\displaystyle\int_{\mathbb{R}^n} K_j(x,y)\, dy = 0$;

(4) *for all y,* $\displaystyle\int_{\mathbb{R}^n} K_j(x,y)\, dx = 0$.

Proof. (1) First suppose that $|x-y| \leq 10 \cdot 2^j$. If we let $\tilde{\phi}(u) = \phi(u - 2^{-j}(x-y))$, then (as we vary x and y) $\tilde{\phi}$ runs over a bounded subset of $C_c^\infty(\mathbb{R}^n)$. Further, $\phi_j^x = \tilde{\phi}_j^y$, so by the WBP

$$|K_j(x,y)| = |\langle T\psi_j^y, \tilde{\phi}_j^y\rangle| \leq C2^{-nj} \leq Cp_j(x-y).$$

If $|x-y| \geq 10 \cdot 2^j$, then ϕ_j^x and ψ_j^y have disjoint supports, and so

$$K_j(x,y) = \int_{\mathbb{R}^n}\int_{\mathbb{R}^n} \phi_j(x-u)K(u,v)\psi_j(v-y)\, du\, dv.$$

Since ψ has zero integral, this can be rewritten as

$$K_j(x,y) = \int_{\mathbb{R}^n}\int_{\mathbb{R}^n} \phi_j(x-u)[K(u,v) - K(u,y)]\psi_j(v-y)\, du\, dv.$$

Because of the supports of ϕ_j and ψ_j, we must have that $|x-u|, |v-y| \leq 2^j$ and $|u-y| \approx |x-y|$. This, together with inequality (5.13), which holds since K is a standard kernel, gives us that

$$|K_j(x,y)| \leq \frac{C2^{j\delta}}{|x-y|^{n+\delta}} \leq Cp_j(x-y).$$

(2) If $|w-x| \geq 2^j$ then this inequality follows from (1). Therefore, we may assume that $|w-x| < 2^j$. If u is on the line segment between x and w then

$$p_j(u-y) \leq C[p_j(x-y) + p_j(w-y)].$$

Hence, (2) follows from the mean value theorem if

$$|\nabla_x K_j(x,y)| \leq C2^{-j}p_j(x-y).$$

To prove this it suffices to note that

$$\nabla_x K_j(x,y) = \langle T\psi_j^y, \nabla\phi_j^x\rangle = 2^j\langle T\psi_j^y, (\nabla\phi)_j^x\rangle$$

and then to argue as we did in (1).

The same argument with ∇_y gives us the analogous inequality in the second variable.

(3) Formally, this identity is equivalent to $T1 = 0$. To actually prove it, note that for $R > 2^{j+1}$ we have by Fubini's theorem that

$$\int_{|y|\leq R} K_j(x,y)\, dy = \langle Th, \phi_j^x \rangle,$$

where

$$h(u) = 2^{-jn} \int_{|y|\leq R} \psi\left(\frac{u-y}{2^j}\right) dy.$$

This is zero if $|u| \geq R + 2^{j+1}$ since supp$(\psi) \subset B(0,2)$, and it is zero if $|u| \leq R - 2^{j+1}$ since ψ has zero integral and compact support. If R is sufficiently large then h and ϕ_j^x have disjoint supports, so we can evaluate $\langle Th, \phi_j^x \rangle$ using (9.3). Therefore, by the standard estimates for K,

$$|\langle Th, \phi_j^x \rangle| \leq C \int_{R-2^{j+1}<|u|<R+2^{j+1}} \int_{\mathbb{R}^n} \frac{2^{-jn}}{|u-v|^n}\phi\left(\frac{v-x}{2^j}\right) dv\, du$$
$$\leq C 2^{-j} R^{n-1} R^{-n},$$

and this tends to zero as R tends to infinity.

(4) Formally, this identity is equivalent to $T^*1 = 0$; we will use this fact to prove it. Arguing as we did above, for $R > 2^j$ we have that

$$\int_{|x|\leq R} K_j(x,y)\, dx = \int_{|x|\leq R} K_j(x,y)\, dx - \langle T\psi_j^y, 1 \rangle = \langle \psi_j^y, T^*h \rangle,$$

where

$$h(u) = 2^{-jn} \int_{|x|\leq R} \phi\left(\frac{u-x}{2^j}\right) dx - 1.$$

Since ϕ has integral 1 and supp$(\phi) \subset B(0,1)$, $h(u) = 0$ if $|u| \leq R - 2^j$. For R sufficiently large, ψ_j^x and h have disjoint supports, so by (9.3), and again since ψ has zero integral and supp$(\psi) \subset B(0,2)$,

$$\langle \psi_j^y, T^*h \rangle$$
$$= \int_{|v-y|\leq 2^{j+1}} \int_{|u|>R-2^j} [K(u,v) - K(u,y)]h(u)2^{-jn}\psi\left(\frac{v-y}{2^j}\right) du\, dv.$$

Therefore, by the standard estimates for K,

$$|\langle \psi_j^y, T^*h \rangle| \leq C 2^{-jn} \int_{|v-y|\leq 2^{j+1}} \int_{|u|>R-2^j} \frac{|v-y|^\delta}{|u-y|^{n+\delta}} du\, dv$$
$$\leq C 2^{j\delta} \int_{|u|>R/2} \frac{du}{|u|^{n+\delta}},$$

and the last term tends to zero as R tends to infinity. $\qquad\square$

To complete the proof we need to estimate the norm of $T_j T_k^*$ as an operator on L^2. The kernel of this operator is

$$A_{j,k}(x,y) = \int_{\mathbb{R}^n} K_j(x,z) K_k(y,z)\, dz$$

and it satisfies two estimates.

Lemma 9.16.

(1) *For all* x, $\displaystyle\int_{\mathbb{R}^n} |A_{j,k}(x,y)|\, dy \le C 2^{-\delta|j-k|}$;

(2) *for all* y, $\displaystyle\int_{\mathbb{R}^n} |A_{j,k}(x,y)|\, dx \le C 2^{-\delta|j-k|}$.

Proof. By Lemma 9.15

$$|A_{j,k}(x,y)| = \left| \int_{\mathbb{R}^n} K_j(x,z)[K_k(y,z) - K_k(y,x)]\, dz \right|$$

$$(9.8) \qquad \le C \int_{\mathbb{R}^n} p_j(x-z) \min(1, 2^{-k}|x-z|)[p_k(z-y) + p_k(x-y)]\, dz.$$

It is easy to see that

$$\int_{\mathbb{R}^n} p_k(z-y)\, dy = C$$

and that

$$\int_{\mathbb{R}^n} p_j(x-z) \min(1, 2^{-k}|x-z|)\, dx \le C 2^{-\delta|k-j|}.$$

The desired inequalities now follow immediately: we get (1) if we write the integral of (9.8) as

$$C \int_{\mathbb{R}^n} p_j(x-z) \min(1, 2^{-k}|x-z|) \int_{\mathbb{R}^n} [p_k(z-y) + p_k(x-y)]\, dy\, dz,$$

and we get (2) if we write the integral of (9.8) as

$$C \int_{\mathbb{R}^n} p_k(z-y) \left(\int_{\mathbb{R}^n} p_j(x-z) \min(1, 2^{-k}|x-z|)\, dx \right) dz$$

$$+ C \int_{\mathbb{R}^n} p_k(x-y) \left(\int_{\mathbb{R}^n} p_j(x-z) \min(1, 2^{-k}|x-z|)\, dz \right) dx.$$

$\square$

Given Lemma 9.16, it is simple to show that

$$\|T_j T_k^*\|_{L^2, L^2} \le C 2^{-\delta|j-k|}.$$

By the Cauchy-Schwarz inequality, if $f \in \mathcal{S}(\mathbb{R}^n)$,

$$\|T_j T_k^* f\|_2^2 = \int_{\mathbb{R}^n} \left| \int_{\mathbb{R}^n} A_{j,k}(x,y) f(y)\, dy \right|^2 dx$$

$$\leq \int_{\mathbb{R}^n} \left(\int_{\mathbb{R}^n} |A_{j,k}(x,y)| \, dy \right) \left(\int_{\mathbb{R}^n} |A_{j,k}(x,y)| |f(y)|^2 \, dy \right) dx$$

$$\leq C 2^{-2\delta |j-k|} \|f\|_2^2.$$

Essentially the same argument gives the same bound on the norm of $T_j^* T_k$. Therefore, we can apply Cotlar's lemma to the R_N's, and this completes the proof of the case when $T1 = T^*1 = 0$.

Case 2: Arbitrary operators T.

Lemma 9.17. *Given any function $b \in BMO$, there exists a Calderón-Zygmund operator L such that $L1 = b$ and $L^*1 = 0$.*

Assume Lemma 9.17 for a moment. Given an operator T which satisfies the conditions of the $T1$ theorem, suppose $T1 = b_1$ and $T^*1 = b_2$. Then there exist Calderón-Zygmund operators L_1 and L_2 such that $L_1 1 = b_1$, $L_1^* 1 = 0$, $L_2 1 = b_2$ and $L_2^* 1 = 0$. Then the operator $\tilde{T} = T - L_1 - L_2^*$ has the WBP and satisfies $\tilde{T}1 = \tilde{T}^*1 = 0$. Therefore, by the previous argument $\tilde{T}$ is bounded on L^2 and so T is as well.

Proof of Lemma 9.17. Let ϕ and ψ be radial functions in $\mathcal{S}(\mathbb{R}^n)$ which are supported in the unit ball and such that ϕ is positive and has integral 1 and ψ has integral zero. Define the operator L by

$$Lf = c \int_0^\infty \psi_t * ((\psi_t * b)(\phi_t * f)) \, \frac{dt}{t},$$

where c is a constant which we will fix below. (The operator L is called a paraproduct.) We will show that the kernel of L satisfies the standard estimates, that L is bounded on L^2, and that $L1 = b$ and $L^*1 = 0$. In order to be rigorous in the following calculations we ought to integrate between ϵ and $1/\epsilon$ and then let ϵ tend to 0. However, we will omit these details.

(1) *The size of the kernel.* The kernel of L is

$$K(x,y) = c \int_0^\infty \int_{\mathbb{R}^n} \psi_t(x-z)(\psi_t * b)(z)\phi_t(z-y) \, dz \frac{dt}{t} = c \int_0^\infty K_t(x,y) \frac{dt}{t}.$$

Fix $z \in \mathbb{R}^n$ and let Q be a cube with center z and side length $2t$, and let b_Q be the average of b on Q. Then, since ψ has zero average,

$$|(\psi_t * b)(z)| = \left| \int_Q \psi_t(z-y)(b(y) - b_Q) \, dy \right| \leq 2^n \|\psi\|_\infty \|b\|_*.$$

Therefore,

$$|K_t(x,y)| \leq 2^n \|\psi\|_\infty \|b\|_* \|\psi_t\|_\infty \|\phi_t\|_1 \leq \frac{C}{t^n} \|b\|_*.$$

Since $K_t(x, y) = 0$ if $|x - y| > 2t$, we also have that

$$|K_t(x, y)| \leq C\|b\|_* t^{-n} \left(1 + \frac{|x - y|}{t}\right)^{-n-2}.$$

It follows from this that

$$|K(x, y)| \leq \frac{C\|b\|_*}{|x - y|^n}.$$

By analogous arguments we can also show that

$$|\nabla_x K_t(x, y)| + |\nabla_y K_t(x, y)| \leq C\|b\|_* t^{-n-1} \left(1 + \frac{|x - y|}{t}\right)^{-n-2},$$

and so we have that

$$|\nabla_x K(x, y)| + |\nabla_y K(x, y)| \leq \frac{C\|b\|_*}{|x - y|^{n+1}}.$$

From these inequalities it follows that K satisfies (5.12), (5.13) and (5.14) with $\delta = 1$ and constant $C\|b\|_*$.

(2) *Boundedness on L^2.* Let $g \in \mathcal{S}(\mathbb{R}^n)$ with $\|g\|_2 \leq 1$. Then

$$\langle Lf, g \rangle = c \int_{\mathbb{R}^n} \int_0^\infty (\psi_t * b)(x)(\phi_t * f(x))(\psi_t * g(x)) \frac{dt \, dx}{t}$$

$$\leq c \left(\int_{\mathbb{R}^n} \int_0^\infty |\psi_t * b(x)|^2 |\phi_t * f(x)|^2 \frac{dt \, dx}{t}\right)^{1/2}$$

$$\times \left(\int_{\mathbb{R}^n} \int_0^\infty |\psi_t * g(x)|^2 \frac{dx \, dt}{t}\right)^{1/2}.$$

By Corollary 9.7 the first term is bounded by $C\|b\|_*\|f\|_2$. In the second term, if we apply the Plancherel theorem to the inner integral and then exchange the order of integration and integrate in t, we get the bound $C\|g\|_2$. Hence, $\langle Lf, g \rangle \leq C\|b\|_*\|f\|_2\|g\|_2$, so L is bounded on L^2.

(3) *$L1 = b$ and $L^*1 = 0$.* For each $t > 0$ we have that

$$(\psi_t * ((\psi_t * b)\phi_t * \cdot))^* = \phi_t * ((\psi_t * b)\psi_t * \cdot).$$

Since ψ has zero integral, $\psi * 1 = 0$ and so it follows that $L^*1 = 0$.

Now let $g \in C_{c,0}^\infty$. Since for all x, $\phi_t * 1(x) = 1$, we have that

$$\langle L1, g \rangle = c \int_0^\infty \int_{\mathbb{R}^n} \psi_t * b(x)\phi_t * 1(x)\psi_t * g(x) \frac{dx \, dt}{t}$$

$$= c \int_0^\infty \int_{\mathbb{R}^n} b(x)\psi_t * \psi_t * g(x) \frac{dx \, dt}{t}.$$

For this integral to equal $\langle b, g \rangle$, as desired, we need

$$(9.9) \qquad c \int_0^\infty \psi_t * \psi_t * g \frac{dt}{t} = g,$$

where the integral is understood to converge in H^1. We omit the details. We note, however, that (9.9) determines the value of c which we left undefined above. If we take the Fourier transform we see that (9.9) holds in L^2 if and only if for any $\xi \neq 0$,

$$c \int_0^\infty |\psi(t\xi)|^2 \frac{dt}{t} = 1.$$

Since ψ is radial, the integral does not depend on ξ, and so this determines the value of c. $\qquad\square$

5. Notes and further results

5.1. References.

Cotlar's lemma appeared for the first time in an article by M. Cotlar (*A combinatorial inequality and its applications to L^2 spaces*, Rev. Mat. Cuyana **1** (1955), 41–55) for self-adjoint operators. The general case we give is due independently to M. Cotlar and E. M. Stein and appeared first in a paper by A. Knapp and E. M. Stein (*Intertwining operators for semi-simple groups*, Ann. of Math. **93** (1971), 489–578). Carleson measures and their characterization by Theorem 9.5 are due to L. Carleson (*An interpolation problem for bounded analytic functions*, Amer. J. Math. **80** (1958), 921–930; and *Interpolation by bounded analytic functions and the corona problem*, Ann. of Math. **76** (1962), 547–559). Their relationship to BMO is due to C. Fefferman and E. M. Stein (*H^p spaces of several variables*, Acta Math. **129** (1972), 137–193).

The $T1$ theorem is due to G. David and J. L. Journé (*A boundedness criterion for generalized Calderón-Zygmund operators*, Ann. of Math. **120** (1984), 371–397). There are a number of proofs of this theorem; we followed the original, as further expanded in the thesis of G. David (Univ. Paris Sud, 1986). A much shorter proof is due to R. Coifman and Y. Meyer (*A simple proof of a theorem by G. David and J.-L. Journé on singular integral operators*, Probability Theory and Harmonic Analysis, J. Chao and W. Woyczyński, eds., pp. 61–65, Marcel Dekker, New York, 1986); it also appeared in their article in Stein [**16**] and in the book by Torchinsky [**19**]. The original proof and yet another proof using wavelets appear in volume II of the book *Ondelettes et Opérateurs* by Y. Meyer (Hermann, Paris, 1990; English translation in Y. Meyer and R. Coifman, *Wavelets: Calderón-Zygmund and Multilinear Operators*, Cambridge Univ. Press, Cambridge, 1997). The operators in Lemma 9.17, the so-called paraproducts, were first introduced by R. Coifman and Y. Meyer [**2**]. For an overview including applications and their relation to the $T1$ theorem, see the monograph by M. Christ (*Lectures on Singular Integral Operators*, CBMS Regional Conference Series in Mathematics **77**, Amer. Math. Soc., Providence, 1990).

The version of the $T1$ theorem given by Stein [**17**] is very interesting. The WBP and the conditions on $T1$ and T^*1 in the statement of the theorem are replaced by a "restricted boundedness" condition for T and T^*: $\|T(\phi^{x,R})\|_2, \|T^*(\phi^{x,R})\|_2 \leq CR^{n/2}$. The role of BMO appears in the proof: restricted boundedness and the conditions on the kernel are enough to define the action of the operator on constant functions and to realize it as a BMO function. But BMO does not appear in the statement of the theorem, and it only involves the space L^2.

5.2. Calderón commutators and the Cauchy integral.

The operators given as applications of the $T1$ theorem in Section 3 were first studied by A. P. Calderón. He proved that the commutator T_1 is bounded on L^2 (*Commutators of singular integral operators*, Proc. Nat. Acad. Sci. U.S.A. **53** (1965), 1092–1099) and proved Corollary 9.13 (*Cauchy integrals on Lipschitz curves and related operators*, Proc. Nat. Acad. Sci. U.S.A. **74** (1977), 1324–1327). Also see his survey paper *Commutators, singular integrals on Lipschitz curves and applications* (Proceedings of the I.C.M. (Helsinki, 1978), pp. 85–96, Acad. Sci. Fennica, Helsinki, 1978). The boundedness on L^2 of the remaining commutators was proved by R. Coifman and Y. Meyer (*Commutateurs d'intégrales singulières et opérateurs multi-linéaires*, Ann. Inst. Fourier **28** (1978), 177–202) with bounds worse than those in Corollary 9.12 (on the order of $k!\|A'\|_\infty^k$). These do not allow the series in the proof of Corollary 9.13 to be summed. The restriction of this corollary that $\|A'\|_\infty \leq \epsilon$ is not necessary: the result is true for any A such that $A' \in L^\infty$. This was first proved by R. Coifman, A. McIntosh and Y. Meyer (*L'intégrale de Cauchy définit un opérateur borné sur L^2 pour les courbes lipschitziennes*, Ann. of Math **116** (1982), 361–387). G. David (*Opérateurs intégraux singuliers sur certaines courbes du plan complexe*, Ann. Sci. Ec. Norm. Sup. **17** (1984), 157–189) obtained the general result starting from Corollary 9.13 by proving that if it is true for $\|A'\|_\infty \leq \epsilon$ then it is true for $\|A'\|_\infty \leq \frac{10}{9}\epsilon$. A similar argument was developed independently by T. Murai (*Boundedness of singular integral operators of Calderón type*, Proc. Japan Acad. Ser. A Math. Sci. **59** (1983), 364–367; see also his book which is cited below. Further, David gave a characterization of those curves on which the Cauchy integral defines a bounded operator on L^2: they are precisely those curves such that any circle of radius r contains in its interior a piece of the curve of length at most Cr for C fixed. (These are usually referred to as Ahlfors-David curves.)

In the book by T. Murai (*A Real Variable Method for the Cauchy Transform and Analytic Capacity*, Lecture Notes in Math. **1307**, Springer-Verlag, Berlin, 1988) the first two chapters are devoted to the study of the L^2 boundedness of the commutator T_1 and the Cauchy integral. It contains several

proofs of these results; of interest is the short proof for the Cauchy integral
due to P. Jones and S. Semmes. This proof and a second one appear in
a paper by these authors and R. Coifman (*Two elementary proofs of the
L^2 boundedness of Cauchy integrals on Lipschitz curves*, J. Amer. Math.
Soc. **2** (1989), 553–564); see also P. Jones (*Square functions, Cauchy integrals, analytic capacity, and harmonic measure*, Harmonic Analysis and
Partial Differential Equations (El Escorial, 1987), pp. 24–68, Lecture Notes
in Math. **1384**, Springer-Verlag, Berlin, 1989) and S. Semmes (*Square function estimates and the $T(b)$ theorem*, Proc. Amer. Math. Soc. **110** (1990),
721–726). A very elementary geometric proof of the general result was found
by M. Melnikov and J. Verdera (*A geometric proof of the L^2 boundedness of
the Cauchy integral on Lipschitz graphs*, Internat. Math. Res. Notices **1995**,
no. 7, 325–331).

5.3. The bilinear Hilbert transform.

While studying the L^2 boundedness of the commutator T_1, Calderón
showed via an argument analogous to the method of rotations (see Chapter 4,
Section 3) that T_1 is bounded if the family of bilinear singular integral
operators

$$H_a(f,g)(x) = \lim_{\epsilon \to 0} \int_{|t| > \epsilon} f(x-t)g(x+at) \, \frac{dt}{t}$$

is a uniformly bounded map from $L^2(\mathbb{R}) \times L^\infty(\mathbb{R})$ to $L^2(\mathbb{R})$ for $-1 \leq a \leq 0$.
When $a = 0$ this operator reduces to $Hf \cdot g$ and when $a = -1$ to $H(f \cdot g)$,
where H is the Hilbert transform. Therefore, the problem is to show that
H_a is uniformly bounded for $-1 < a < 0$.

The operator H_1 is called the bilinear Hilbert transform. Calderón also
posed the simpler problem of proving that H_1 is a bounded operator from
$L^2 \times L^2$ into L^1.

For over thirty years no progress was made on these problems. Then
in a pair of remarkable papers, M. Lacey and C. Thiele (*L^p estimates on
the bilinear Hilbert transform for $2 < p < \infty$*, Ann. of Math. **146** (1997),
693–724, and *On Calderón's conjecture*, Ann. of Math. **149** (1999), 475–496)
proved the following result.

Theorem 9.18. *Given $a \in \mathbb{R}$ and exponents p_1, p_2 and p_3 such that $1 <
p_1, p_2 \leq \infty$, $p_3 > 2/3$ and $1/p_1 + 1/p_2 = 1/p_3$, then*

$$\|H_a(f,g)\|_{p_3} \leq C_{a,p_1,p_2} \|f\|_{p_1} \|g\|_{p_2}.$$

Theorem 9.18 establishes Calderón's conjecture for the bilinear Hilbert
transform and shows that the operators H_a, $-1 < a < 0$, are bounded.

However, the constant $C_{a,2,\infty}$ is unbounded as a tends to -1 and 0, so this result does not complete Calderón's proof of the L^2 boundedness of T_1. But as this book was going to press, L. Grafakos and X. Li announced a proof that the constant is independent of a when $2 < p_1, p_2 < \infty$ and $1 < p_3 < 2$, and in all the cases covered by Theorem 9.18 if a is bounded away from -1.

5.4. The Tb theorem.

The $T1$ theorem does not give a better result for the Cauchy integral than Corollary 9.13 because we cannot directly calculate the action of the operator on the function 1. However, A. McIntosh and Y. Meyer (*Algèbres d'opérateurs définis par des intégrales singulières*, C. R. Acad. Sci. Paris **301** (1985), 395–397) generalized the $T1$ theorem as follows. Let b be a function which is bounded below (more precisely, for some $\delta > 0$, $\operatorname{Re} b(y) > \delta$ for all y). If $Tb = T^*b = 0$ and $M_b T M_b$ has the WBP (where M_b is multiplication by b), then T is bounded on L^2. If we let $b(y) = 1 + iA'(y)$, then this is bounded below and one can show that the Cauchy integral of b is zero, so we can apply this result directly to the Cauchy integral.

With this result as their starting point, G. David, J. L. Journé and S. Semmes (*Opérateurs de Calderón-Zygmund, fonctions para-accrétives et interpolation*, Rev. Mat. Iberoamericana **1** (4) (1985), 1–56) found a significant generalization of the $T1$ theorem, the so-called Tb theorem. To state it, we need several definitions. Given μ, $0 < \mu < 1$, define $C_c^\mu(\mathbb{R}^n)$ to be the space of functions of compact support such that

$$\|f\|_\mu = \sup_{x \neq y} \frac{|f(x) - f(y)|}{|x - y|^\mu} < \infty.$$

Given a function b, let $bC_c^\mu = \{bf : f \in C_c^\mu\}$.

A bounded function $b : \mathbb{R}^n \to \mathbb{C}$ is para-accretive if there exists $\delta > 0$ such that for every $x \in \mathbb{R}^n$ and $r > 0$ there exists a ball $B = B(y, \rho) \subset B(x, r)$ with $\rho \geq \delta r$ which satisfies $|b_B| \geq \delta$.

Theorem 9.19. *Let b_1 and b_2 be two para-accretive functions on $\mathbb{R}^n$ and let*

$$T : b_1 C_c^\mu(\mathbb{R}^n) \to (b_2 C_c^\mu(\mathbb{R}^n))'$$

be an operator associated with a standard kernel $K(x, y)$. Then T has a continuous extension to L^2 if and only if $Tb_1 \in BMO$, $T^*b_2 \in BMO$ and $M_{b_2} T M_{b_1}$ has the WBP.

Because Theorem 9.19 is given in terms of the space C_c^μ instead of C_c^∞, it can be generalized to spaces of homogeneous type (see Chapter 5, Section 6.4). There are other variants of this result, including defining Tb for functions b not in C^∞ and a somewhat different version of the weak bound-edness property. For all of these results we refer to the articles cited above. See also M. Christ (*A T(b) theorem with remarks on analytic capacity and the Cauchy integral*, Colloq. Math. **60/61** (1990), 601–628), and the book by Meyer cited above.

Bibliography

[1] N. K. Bary, *A Treatise on Trigonometric Series*, translated by M. F. Mullins, Pergamon Press, New York, 1964.

[2] R. Coifman and Y. Meyer, *Au délà des opérateurs pseudo-différentiels*, Astérisque **57** (1979).

[3] K. M. Davis and Y. C. Chang, *Lectures on Bochner-Riesz Means*, London Math. Soc. Lecture Notes **114**, Cambridge Univ. Press, Cambridge, 1987.

[4] H. Dym and H. P. McKean, *Fourier Series and Integrals*, Academic Press, New York, 1972.

[5] R. E. Edwards, *Fourier Series: A Modern Introduction*, 2nd ed., Springer-Verlag, New York, 1979.

[6] J. García-Cuerva and J. L. Rubio de Francia, *Weighted Norm Inequalities and Related Topics*, North Holland Math. Studies 116, North Holland, Amsterdam, 1985.

[7] M. de Guzmán, *Real Variable Methods in Fourier Analysis*, North-Holland Math. Studies 46, North-Holland, Amsterdam, 1981.

[8] J. L. Journé, *Calderón-Zygmund Operators, Pseudo-Differential Operators and the Cauchy Integral of Calderón*, Lecture Notes in Math. **994**, Springer-Verlag, Berlin, 1983.

[9] J. P. Kahane and P. G. Lemarié-Rieusset, *Fourier Series and Wavelets*, Gordon and Breach, Amsterdam, 1995.

[10] Y. Katznelson, *An Introduction to Harmonic Analysis*, Dover, New York, 1976.

[11] P. Koosis, *Introduction to H_p Spaces*, 2nd ed., Cambridge Tracts in Mathematics, 115, Cambridge Univ. Press, Cambridge, 1998.

[12] T. W. Körner, *Fourier Analysis*, Cambridge Univ. Press, Cambridge, 1988.

[13] U. Neri, *Singular Integrals*, Lecture Notes in Math. **200**, Springer-Verlag, Berlin, 1971.

[14] W. Rudin, *Real and Complex Analysis,* 3rd ed., McGraw-Hill, New York, 1987.

[15] E. M. Stein, *Singular Integrals and Differentiability Properties of Functions*, Princeton Univ. Press, Princeton, 1970.

[16] _____, ed., *Beijing Lectures in Harmonic Analysis*, Princeton Univ. Press, Princeton, 1986.

[17] _____, *Harmonic Analysis: Real Variable Methods, Orthogonality, and Oscillatory Integrals*, Princeton Univ. Press, Princeton, 1993.

[18] _____ and G. Weiss, *Introduction to Fourier Analysis in Euclidean Spaces*, Princeton Univ. Press, Princeton, 1971.

[19] A. Torchinsky, *Real-Variable Methods in Harmonic Analysis*, Academic Press, New York, 1986.

[20] G. Weiss, "Harmonic Analysis," in *Studies in Mathematics*, vol. 3, I. I. Hirschman, Jr., ed., Math Assoc. of America, 1965, pp. 124–178.

[21] A. Zygmund, *Trigonometric Series*, vols. I and II, 2nd ed., Cambridge Univ. Press, London, 1959.

[22] _____, *Intégrales Singulières*, Lecture Notes in Math. **204**, Springer-Verlag, Berlin, 1971.

Index